D1105217

The Legend of MERCURY

THIRD EDITION

The Legend of MERCURY

Jeffrey L. Rodengen

Edited by Stanimira Stefanova and David Tumarkin
Design and layout by Jill Apolinario and Sandy Cruz

Dedicated to Norm DeRoche of Lake Ruth Marine,
a great marine dealer, and even greater friend.

Write Stuff
Since 1986

Write Stuff Enterprises, LLC
1001 South Andrews Avenue
Fort Lauderdale, FL 33316
1-800-900-Book (1-800-900-2665)
(954) 462-6657
www.writestuffbooks.com

Copyright © 2014 by Write Stuff Enterprises, LLC. All rights reserved. No part of this book may be reproduced or transmitted in any form by any means, electronic or mechanical, including photocopying and recording, or by any information storage or retrieval system, without permission in writing from the publisher.

The publisher has made every effort to identify and locate the source of the photographs included in this edition of *The Legend of Mercury Marine.* Grateful acknowledgment is made to those who have kindly granted permission for the use of their materials in this edition. If there are instances where proper credit was not given, the publisher will gladly make any necessary corrections in subsequent printings.

Publisher's Cataloging in Publication
(Prepared by The Donohue Group, Inc.)

Rodengen, Jeffrey L.
   The legend of Mercury / Jeffrey L. Rodengen ; edited by Stanimira Stefanova and David Tumarkin ; design and layout by Jill Apolinario and Sandy Cruz. — Third edition.

    pages : illustrations, maps ; cm

   Title supplied by publisher: Legend of Mercury Marine.
   Includes bibliographical references and index.
   ISBN: 978-1-932022-37-7

   1. Brunswick Corporation. Mercury Marine—History. 2. Outboard motors—United States—History. 3. Boating industry—United States—History. I. Stefanova, Stanimira. II. Tumarkin, David A. III. Apolinario, Jill. IV. Cruz, Sandy. V. Title. VI. Title: Legend of Mercury Marine

VM348 .R6323 2014
623.8/723   2014944425

Completely produced in the
United States of America
10 9 8 7 6 5 4 3 2 1

Also by Jeffrey L. Rodengen

The Legend of Chris-Craft

IRON FIST:
The Lives of Carl Kiekhaefer

Evinrude-Johnson and
The Legend of OMC

Serving the Silent Service:
The Legend of Electric Boat

The Legend of Dr Pepper/Seven-Up

The Legend of Honeywell

The Legend of Briggs & Stratton

The Legend of Ingersoll-Rand

The Legend of Stanley:
150 Years of The Stanley Works

The MicroAge Way

The Legend of Halliburton

The Legend of York International

The Legend of Nucor Corporation

The Legend of Goodyear:
The First 100 Years

The Legend of AMP

The Legend of Cessna

The Legend of VF Corporation

The Spirit of AMD

The Legend of Rowan

New Horizons:
The Story of Ashland Inc.

The History of American Standard

The Legend of Mercury Marine

The Legend of Federal-Mogul

Against the Odds:
Inter-Tel—The First 30 Years

The Legend of Pfizer

State of the Heart: The Practical Guide
to Your Heart and Heart Surgery
with Larry W. Stephenson, M.D.

The Legend of Worthington Industries

The Legend of IBP

The Legend of Trinity Industries, Inc.

The Legend of
Cornelius Vanderbilt Whitney

The Legend of Amdahl

The Legend of Litton Industries

The Legend of Gulfstream

The Legend of Bertram
with David A. Patten

The Legend of Ritchie Bros. Auctioneers

The Legend of ALLTEL
with David A. Patten

The Yes, you can of Invacare Corporation
with Anthony L. Wall

The Ship in the Balloon:
The Story of Boston Scientific and the
Development of Less-Invasive Medicine

The Legend of Day & Zimmermann

The Legend of Noble Drilling

Fifty Years of Innovation: Kulicke & Soffa

Biomet—From Warsaw to the World
with Richard F. Hubbard

NRA: An American Legend

The Heritage and Values of RPM, Inc.

The Marmon Group: The First Fifty Years

The Legend of Grainger

The Legend of The Titan Corporation
with Richard F. Hubbard

The Legend of Discount Tire Co.
with Richard F. Hubbard

The Legend of Polaris
with Richard F. Hubbard

The Legend of La-Z-Boy
with Richard F. Hubbard

The Legend of McCarthy
with Richard F. Hubbard

Intervoice: Twenty Years of Innovation
with Richard F. Hubbard

Jefferson-Pilot Financial:
A Century of Excellence
with Richard F. Hubbard

The Legend of HCA

The Legend of Werner Enterprises
with Richard F. Hubbard

The History of J. F. Shea Co.
with Richard F. Hubbard

True to Our Vision
with Richard F. Hubbard

The Legend of Albert Trostel & Sons
with Richard F. Hubbard

The Legend of Sovereign Bancorp
with Richard F. Hubbard

Innovation is the Best Medicine:
The extraordinary story of Datascope
with Richard F. Hubbard

The Legend of Guardian Industries

The Legend of
Universal Forest Products

Changing the World: Polytechnic
University—The First 150 Years

Nothing is Impossible: The Legend
of Joe Hardy and 84 Lumber

In it for the Long Haul:
The Story of CRST

The Story of Parsons Corporation

Cerner: From Vision to Value

New Horizons:
The Story of Federated Investors

Office Depot: Taking Care of Business—
The First 20 Years

The Legend of General Parts:
Proudly Serving a World in Motion

Bard: Power of the Past,
Force of the Future

Innovation & Integrity:
The Story of Hub Group

Amica: A Century of Service
1907–2007

A Passion for Service:
The Story of ARAMARK

The Legend of Con-way:
A History of Service, Reliability,
Innovation, and Growth

TABLE OF CONTENTS

INTRODUCTION

FOUR DECADES AFTER FOUNDER Carl Kiekhaefer left the company, employees still like to say they "bleed black." The phrase is a sort of verbal shorthand to describe a Mercury culture rooted in innovation, ambition, and loyalty. The energy and innovative spirit that drive workers to achieve prodigious feats in engineering and workmanship still permeate the company as it celebrates its 75th year in 2014. Today, Mercury is the most recognized name in the marine industry.

Mercury began its rise to the top in 1939, the year Carl Kiekhaefer took over a failing marine outboard engine plant that was crowded with faulty and rejected engines. With the zeal that would one day make him a legend, Kiekhaefer successfully redesigned the engines and put his small company on the path to become the world's leading marine propulsion manufacturer.

Through the years, the organization overcame wartime shortages, government restrictions, stockholder rebellions, and Kiekhaefer's own raging and well-publicized paranoia. In spite of his infamous temper, or maybe because of it, those he hired remained loyal, inheriting Kiekhaefer's grit and indomitable attitude. Working together, they managed to convert decrepit dairy barns in Fond du Lac, Wisconsin, into world-class outboard production plants; they built the famous Lake X proving ground out of a remote, alligator-infested lake; and most of all, Kiekhaefer and his team convinced the public that Mercury engines were the best power on the water.

The company introduced the first commercially viable sterndrive in 1961, a development as revolutionary as it was controversial, and the MerCruiser I quickly dominated the market. But 1961 was a turning point for another reason: Carl Kiekhaefer, in serious financial straits, agreed to sell his company to Brunswick Corporation, setting the stage for a challenging transition period between his mercurial nature and the parent company. Kiekhaefer struggled with relinquishing control of his organization to Brunswick. Even after his departure in 1970, it took years to heal the wounds. A gradual degree of trust was established, however, that grew each year as successive leaders of Mercury put their own mark on the company culture.

In the 1970s and early 1980s, Mercury Marine enjoyed unparalleled prosperity. New and valuable relationships were established with such organizations as Walt Disney World, to whom Mercury supplied engines, support staff, and eventually the boats themselves. Mercury also worked with fishermen and their organizations to support the needs of the fishing community. The company also moved aggressively into foreign markets in Europe, Latin America, and Asia with sales offices, distribution centers, and service organizations. The MerCruiser sterndrive became the industry standard during this period, prompting the construction of a plant dedicated to MerCruiser production in Stillwater, Oklahoma.

But toward the end of the 1980s, the company's mettle was sorely tested as the marine industry struggled to overcome the most severe recession in its history. Mercury and Brunswick officers worked together to pull the organization out of the slump by concentrating on employees and dealers with new incentives and programs to teach each how to better serve their customers.

Now in the new millennium, Mercury Marine is poised for even greater accomplishments, con-tinuing its role as an industry innovator with regards to product features and environmentally conscious technology. In 2011, the company introduced the OptiMax 150 Pro XS outboard motor, which improved performance and speed while still delivering a 3-Star emissions rating from the California Air Resources Board.

But moving in new and challenging directions is not new for the company. Although Carl Kiekhaefer's company has matured in its own direction, the spirit that is behind its success is intact and remains as an integral part of the Mercury mystique. The water calls!

ACKNOWLEDGMENTS

A GREAT MANY PEOPLE ASSISTED in the preparation and publication of *The Legend of Mercury Marine*. This book would not have been possible without their gracious cooperation.

I will always be indebted to the hundreds of people who helped me with the writing of *Iron Fist: The Lives of Carl Kiekhaefer*. I would also like to thank Michael Koretzky, who assisted in the development of historical timelines and editing of the prior edition, and Bob Carter, who assisted with the research on Mercury's last 30 years as well as the initial collection of images. For the third edition of *The Legend of Mercury Marine*, special thanks go to Write Stuff Enterprises, LLC Executive Editor Stanimira Stefanova and Senior Editor David Tumarkin, who managed the editorial content of the book.

I am also grateful to many people inside and outside Mercury Marine for their time, photographs, and guidance. I am indebted to Jim Hubbard, retired senior vice president and chief of staff, for his guidance and dedication. Jim's suggestions and patient counsel helped unfold the story of Mercury in the post-Kiekhaefer years. A special thank you to Brunswick President and Chief Operating Officer Mark Schwabero; Mercury President John Pfeifer; Mercury Marine President—Global Sales and Marketing Kevin Grodzki; and Kim Greene, assistant to the president and senior executives. I am also grateful to Tony Esposito, former public relations manager, for his assistance throughout the project. Jeff Isom, former manager of the photo department, was very dedicated and helpful in hunting down hard-to-find images to illustrate Mercury's history.

The candid insights of Mercury employees, past and present, were extremely vital to this edition of the book, including: Steve Cramer, vice president and chief financial officer; Ray Atchinson, vice president, global parts and accessories and business development; Marty Bass, vice president, global category management; Mark Biznek, director, manufacturing strategy; Randy Caruana, vice president, sales and marketing; Erik Christiansen, general manager, Mercury Racing; Stephan Cloutier, vice president, global procurement; Denise Devereaux, vice president, human resources; Chris Drees, vice president and general manager of Brunswick marine parts and accessories products; Ben Duke, vice president, marketing; David Foulkes, vice president, product development, engineering and racing; Bill Gress, president, South America region; Mike Gyorog, vice president, global service and marine parts and accessories; Stuart Halley, director, product planning and program management; Tom Herre, retired city manager; Georges Jalbert, general manager, Canada; Fred Kiekhaefer, retired president, Mercury Racing; Bill McEathron, general manager, Asia; Randy Poirier, Brunswick director of engineering—drive systems; Tim Reid, director, engine design and development; Wayne Rollin, director, community development; Tom Schuessler, vice president and general manager, Brunswick Marine parts and accessories distribution; Mike Shedivy, president, Europe, Africa, and Middle East region; Gary Smet, vice president and executive project manager; Jeff Stueven, director, electrical and electronics engineering; and John Temple, general manager, Australia, New Zealand, and Pacific region.

The following Mercury employees, past and present, made significant contributions to previous editions. Among the people involved, I would like to thank: Dennis Banks, senior vice president of engineering and technology; Fred Brightbill, senior vice president of the Outboard Business Unit; George Buckley, president of Mercury Marine; Gerry Celichowski, technical director in the Hi-Performance Business Unit; Lois Cutburth, administrative assistant to Barry Eller in Stillwater, Oklahoma; Rick Davis, vice president of outboard engineering; Fred Hauenstein, technical director in the Hi-Performance Business Unit; Bob Hetzel, research and development engineer in Hi-Performance; Clem Koehler, retired director of public relations for Mercury; Larry Lohse, director of engineering for Hi-Performance; Tom Mielke, director of marketing for Hi-Performance; Roger Miller, retired vice president of Mercury International; Gerald Neisen, retired director of engineering; Richard O'Brien, vice president and treasurer for Brunswick; Roger Patterson, vice president of finance for Mercury Marine; Jerry Perkins, executive vice president of sales and marketing for Mercury Marine; Adrian Sakowicz, director of public relations for Brunswick; Denny Sheller, vice president of sales, marketing, and services for MerCruiser; and Dick Snyder, director of product safety engineering.

I would also like to thank Joe Wisner, director of sports and recreation at Walt Disney World, for his insights into the relationship between Brunswick Corporation and Disney. Particular thanks goes to Jim Kalkofen, executive director of In-Fishing Professional Walleye Trail, and Earl Bentz, five-time national offshore racing champion, for their assistance, anecdotes, and photographs.

Finally, a very special word of thanks to all the individuals with Write Stuff Enterprises who worked closely with me in creating the earlier editions. With this third edition, special thanks are extended to the following: Kim Campbell, managing editor; Melinda Waldrop, Christian Ramirez, and Ryan Garner, senior editors; Sandy Cruz, senior vice president/creative services manager; Cristofer Valle, senior graphic designer and studio administrator; Darcey McNiff Thompson, graphic designer; Christine McIntire, Sannie Kirschner, and Nicole Sirdoreus, proofreaders; Barbara Martin and Erika Wallace, transcriptionists; Amy Major, executive assistant to Jeffrey L. Rodengen; Marianne Roberts, president, publisher, and chief financial officer; and Norma Wolpin, marketing manager.

This book is a project of Write Stuff Enterprises, LLC, and Jeffrey L. Rodengen, its chairman and CEO. It is not a publication of Mercury Marine or Brunswick Corporation. Neither Write Stuff personnel nor Jeffrey Rodengen are employees or agents of Mercury Marine or Brunswick Corporation, or are otherwise affiliated with Mercury Marine or Brunswick Corporation. The author wishes to thank Mercury and Brunswick for their cooperation throughout the project, and particularly for making their pictorial and editorial archives available for use in researching and art preparation for the book.

Thor motors were assembled at the Cedarburg Manufacturing Company in 1935, four years before Carl Kiekhaefer took over the failing business.

CHAPTER ONE

MAGNETIC ATTRACTION

*It must be awfully nice to be a writer and be privileged to point to any-
one from on high and never be pointed back at. How would you like to
compare notes, if it were possible, on respective accomplishments on our
day of reckoning—as well as our wrongs?*

—Carl Kiekhaefer, December 1964[1]

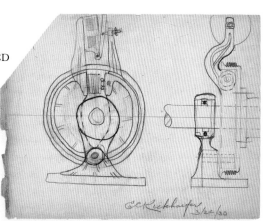

MERCURY MARINE TURNED 75 years old in 2014. The world leader in the marine industry, Mercury continues to embody the tenacity, endurance, and innovation of its founder, Carl Kiekhaefer. But in a sense, Mercury Marine has grown up since Kiekhaefer left the company in 1970. Its current leaders, workers, and retirees can point to many of the company's accomplishments with pride. It persevered through the cyclical downturns that have plagued the marine industry every 10 years, always emerging stronger than before.

Mercury Marine began its journey to the top of the marine industry as an afterthought. Though Kiekhaefer was hired as a draftsman at Evinrude Motors in Milwaukee in 1927, he was fired three months later. Twelve years would pass before Kiekhaefer began making outboards again to help finance his true interest: magnetic separators.

Kiekhaefer was fired from Evinrude for the same three traits that helped him to build an innovative competitor called Mercury. First, Kiekhaefer had a keen engineer's eye that allowed him to look at a machine and see its inherent flaws. Second, he often tinkered and toiled for weeks on end to fix those flaws, with time off only to eat and sleep. And third, he couldn't stand to work with anyone who didn't possess those first two qualities.

"When he was in a good mood and had faith in you as a person, he'd happily give you the shirt off his back," recalled Herman Stieg, Kiekhaefer's first right-hand man, in 1941. "But then if something wrong happened, he'd take that shirt back again—and he wouldn't bother opening the buttons."[2]

After his short stint at Evinrude, Kiekhaefer landed at Stearns Magnetic in Milwaukee, where he met Stieg in 1936. (Getting fired was a familiar ordeal for Kiekhaefer. Prior to working at Evinrude, he was a draftsman at Nash Motors, also in Milwaukee. After two dull years of drawing blueprints, "I took to wandering around the plant, getting to know the foremen, getting to know the executives, learning what machines did what," he said. "In short, satisfying my curiosity about what made things tick—until finally, I was fired for spending too much time talking to a foreman.")[3]

Despite a lack of formal education, Carl Kiekhaefer was an accomplished draftsman. Above is a 1930 sketch of a magnetic clutch.

Stieg worked for Kiekhaefer at Stearns, which built magnetic clutches and brakes, among other magnet-driven products. In fact, Kiekhaefer had avidly recruited Stieg, even insisting that Stearns hire the unproven 23-year-old. And when Stieg was offered a better job elsewhere, Kiekhaefer stormed into his boss' office to lobby for his man.

"I was going to quit because the wages weren't too high in those days," Stieg said. "So Carl went into the office, and he demanded they give me a 10-cent-an-hour raise, and by God, he got it! That was unheard of. You used to get a penny at a time. But he demanded it, and I got it, and I stayed."[4]

That fierce loyalty to his employees, even as he decreed they dedicate weekends and holidays to the job, was the foundation for the eventual ascendancy of Mercury Marine—and for the success of many Mercury competitors, because just as many workers fled from Kiekhaefer's frenzied work habits and eccentric personality. The company, in fact, trained more young leaders than it could retain. Mercury proved to be a spawning ground and training yard for its competitors. Charlie Strang, Kiekhaefer's right-hand man from 1951 to 1964, eventually became chairman and CEO of OMC. Years later, David Jones, president of Mercury from 1990 to 1997, also led OMC.

Learn by Doing ... and Doing and Doing

Kiekhaefer knew from the beginning that he would grow up a workaholic. "When the boys played cards and drank beer Sunday afternoons, I designed and invented, and did my college lessons till two or three o'clock in the morning," Kiekhaefer once wrote. "I worried about earning my future. ... I had ambitions for bigger things."[5]

Those ambitions weren't going to be fulfilled on the family farm in Ozaukee County in eastern Wisconsin, where he acquired valuable experience operating and repairing farm machinery but chafed under the strict upbringing of his German father, Arnold. "I, for one, would never want to relive my childhood in that old homestead," he once wrote to his mother.[6]

School wasn't the answer, either. He attended the Milwaukee School of Engineering for only one year after graduating from Cedarburg High School in 1924. While working at Stearns, he took night classes at the University of Wisconsin Extension Division, but he never graduated. He worked too much.

The lack of formal education didn't hurt his career. Hired by Stearns as a layout draftsman

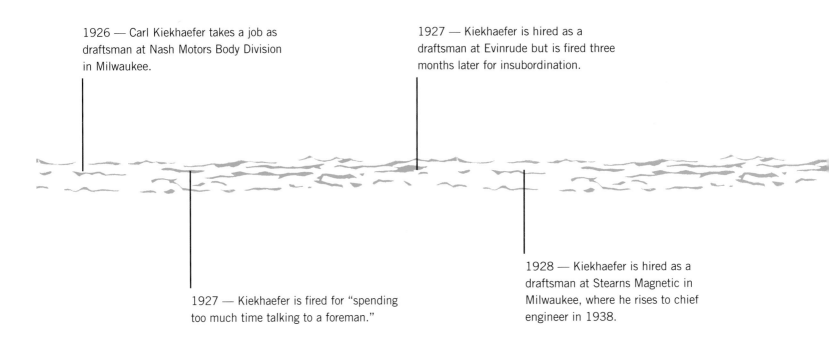

1926 — Carl Kiekhaefer takes a job as draftsman at Nash Motors Body Division in Milwaukee.

1927 — Kiekhaefer is hired as a draftsman at Evinrude but is fired three months later for insubordination.

1927 — Kiekhaefer is fired for "spending too much time talking to a foreman."

1928 — Kiekhaefer is hired as a draftsman at Stearns Magnetic in Milwaukee, where he rises to chief engineer in 1938.

in early 1928, Kiekhaefer was promoted to plant superintendent in 1933 and chief engineer in 1938. By the time he left to start his own company, Kiekhaefer was responsible for six patents, and during one year—1935—he calculated that he was responsible for 70 percent of Stearns' engineering designs.

"From the academic sense, I would not say Carl had much on the engineering line, but what he did have was a good solid design capability," Strang said. "He would never be able to stress-analyze something, or what have you. He would just look at something and say, 'Hey, it's not strong enough.' So he had an enhanced mechanical capability."[7]

Kiekhaefer thought his mechanical ability with magnetic equipment would guarantee his future. In 1938, when the business leaders of Cedarburg learned that an outboard motor plant on the outskirts of their small Wisconsin town was about to go bankrupt, they looked to Kiekhaefer and his father, Arnold, to save it—not by building outboard motors in the middle of the Great Depression, but by building the magnetic clutches and brakes that Kiekhaefer had worked on for more than a decade.

So Arnold mortgaged his farm and became president of the new enterprise. Everyone from the town's butcher to the dentist chipped in $1,000. Carl contributed the least, only $500, but became the vice president and general manager. The investors were depending on his expertise to keep the town's largest manufacturing plant humming. "What I didn't know then about running a business of my own would have filled many a volume," he admitted, but added, "Once you are an engineer, you're one of God's chosen people, and you can do no wrong."[8] What happened next proved Kiekhaefer could indeed be wrong, yet still make it turn out right.

Outboards as an Afterthought

Kiekhaefer believed that manufacturing magnetic separators was a surefire way to earn profit. While magnetic separators perform many tasks, one of the most popular in Kiekhaefer's home state at the time was the plucking of bolts, bailing wire, and other metal debris from animal feed. Livestock frequently died from ingesting these items, and granary explosions were often caused by stray metal producing sparks in the fine dust.

1939 — Kiekhaefer takes over the bankrupt Cedarburg Manufacturing Company and begins redesigning its Thor outboard engines.

1941 — Kiekhaefer announces the arrival of the "Mercury Mystery Motor," the Thunderbolt, at the New York Motor Boat Show.

1940 — Kiekhaefer introduces the name Mercury, assigning it to a line of new outboard motors.

When Cedarburg's leaders set out to save the town's largest employer, they viewed Kiekhaefer's experience at Stearns as their life preserver. The plant, built in the 1920s, had already seen the demise of the Schmidtdorf Electric Company, makers of spark plugs; the American Electric Motor Company, which produced induction motors; and finally the Cedarburg Manufacturing Company, which made outboard boat engines.

The last tenant, barely clinging to life, was going to leave behind an order from Montgomery Ward for 500 single-cylinder outboard engines, which the department store intended to sell under the name Sea King. The new investors wrote to Montgomery Ward's headquarters in Chicago and secured that order with a $6,000 check. Building and shipping those engines was supposed to buy Kiekhaefer time to set up his magnetic clutch, brake, and separator business, but he never got the time.

In January 1939, Montgomery Ward rejected 384 of the engines (called the Thor, after Thorwald Hansen, owner of the Cedarburg Manufacturing Company) from a previous order of 500. They simply didn't work. Hansen's son Royal had raced Evinrude outboards during the 1920s and had persuaded his father to design a cheaper engine.

The Hansens' idea was to build the engines not from aluminum, as their competitors did, but from steel stamping, which Thorwald had mastered during his many years of building automobile frames. But in their zeal to keep costs down, the Hansens went too far. They used the least costly metals and alloys for components, such as bronze connecting rods and bearings, nickel alloy gears, a low-grade steel drive shaft, and an aluminum propeller. The mild steel they had chosen rusted quickly in fresh water and corroded rapidly in salt water, and the grease in the nickel gears would run out, allowing water to seep in. Oddly enough, these engines weren't built to get wet. Montgomery Ward also canceled the pending order of 500 engines.

On Sunday, January 22, 1939, Kiekhaefer strode through the door and took possession of the plant. Legally, he had to wait until Wednesday, but the return of the 384 engines constituted an emergency. What he found inside the plant constituted a disaster:

There was no coal in the bins and no steam in the boiler. When I walked through that plant, I

Before Kiekhaefer took over the 1920s-era manufacturing plant in Cedarburg, Wisconsin, it had seen three businesses come and go.

THOR

Above: The Thor outboard was named after its designer, Thorwald Hansen. It was also supposed to evoke images of Thor, the Norse god of thunder, but the poorly designed engine often evoked images of boats stranded without power.

Below: The Thor Alternate 2 was redesigned by Kiekhaefer in 1939.

saw a bunch of broken-down lathes and other old-fashioned, broken-down machinery. It was proba-bly the most depressing day I have ever had in my life. I had no product. I had no employees and no money. But I did have resourcefulness.[9]

Kiekhaefer realized that the magnetic products would have to wait. Right then, he had to rebuild 384 out-board motors, and the only experience he had to draw on was a three-month stint at Evin-rude 12 years earlier.

A Man's Motor

The newly christened Kiek-haefer Corporation began with $25,000 from its new investors. But after the Thor engine debacle, the company's bank balance had plummeted to $5,146. It looked as if the Kiekhaefer Corporation had about 90 days to prove itself, or it would become the fourth casualty in the plant's 20-year existence.

On the day Kiekhaefer toured the plant, he saw tall stacks of wooden crates contain-ing the rejected engines and a row of partially assembled engines clamped to wooden sawhorses. He also saw the electrical tool-ing equipment that he believed would one day churn out the magnetic equipment he had learned to build at Stearns.

But 11 years at Stearns also taught him that it takes time to develop new products—certainly more than 90 days. Looking around, he reluctantly real-ized that his most liquid assets were those aban-doned engines that Montgomery Ward didn't want. And the Thor dealer network had dried up as quickly as the poorly designed engines had rusted out.

Then and there, Kiekhaefer decided the en-gines had to be rebuilt. So the 32-year-old farm boy from eastern Wisconsin, who had never even used an outboard before, retained some of the men who had worked for the Hansens and understood the Thor's assembly and testing process. He could pay them only 30 cents an hour during an era when Marvel and Cavalier cigarettes sold for a dime a pack. But two of those men, Ed Dehling and George Sekas, recalled Kiekhaefer brimming with confidence and repeating, "Stick with me, fellas."[10]

Within the first week, working shifts that began at dawn and ended around mid-night, the team had redesigned the carbure-tor of the single-cylinder Thor. It provided a better mixture to the cylinder and allowed the fitting of a streamlined cowling—good enough for Kiekhaefer to produce a new Thor brochure that stressed inland fishing and avoided any mention of salt-water boating.

The brochure called the Thor "a man's motor, built for fishermen." Beginning a tradition that would last throughout his career, Kiekhaefer tossed out the mis-leading copy prepared by an advertising

The first company portrait of Carl Kiekhaefer in 1940.
Kiekhaefer worked seven days a week to save the Thor engine.

agency: "The owner of a Thor always recommends it enthusiastically to his friends!" and "Thousands of fishermen enthusiastically recommend Thor Motors. Ask them why." Instead, Kiekhaefer himself wrote, "A motor heavy enough to drive your boat regardless of wind, weeds, waves, and weight."[11] His penchant for understatement first appeared in this brochure, when he explained why the Kiekhaefer Corporation would not make outrageous claims about his engine's speed, a common practice among his competitors.

So many things govern the speed of a boat, such as design, weight, load, head wind, rough water, skill of operation, that it is impossible to list accurately what your boat will do. Thor Motors will probably give you the same and probably more speed per H.P. than any other motor of similar rating.[12]

Redesigning a carburetor and rewriting a brochure were easy compared to the task now confronting Kiekhaefer. He had to face Montgomery Ward buyer Earnway Edwards, the director of purchases for the Sporting Goods Division.[13] Kiekhaefer drove to Chicago to see him and was "met with a cold reception from a very disinterested sporting goods buyer."[14]

Kiekhaefer recalled the nervous exchange nearly 20 years later and remembered it as a turning point in his career:

When I announced myself—after he finally did see me—as the new owner of the Thor outboard motor company, he never looked up from his desk but said, "Yes, what's that supposed to mean?"

I replied, "Frankly, we'd like to reinstate the order for Thor outboard motors that you canceled."

He countered by saying, "Pray tell me, what makes you think you could make this piece of junk run?" "Will you try them?" I questioned.

He looked up at me for a long time with a steady gaze. I could read his thoughts, and believe me, if I ever looked serious and intent, I did then. Something must have convinced him, because he said, "Well, all right. Send me a half-dozen that'll run."[15]

On his three-hour drive back to Cedarburg, Kiekhaefer's mind raced as fast as his car (he was a notorious lead foot, which would become significant a decade later). If he successfully modified the 384 engines and could sell them to Montgomery Ward, he would double his cash reserves in one transaction. All he had to do was redesign and rebuild the ignition, carburetion, timing, and crankshaft. And he'd have to do it quickly, before the Montgomery Ward buyer got suspicious.

Kiekhaefer was still thinking of this situation as a temporary nightmare. Once he reworked 384 outboards and reinstated the order for 500 more, he was sure he could return to retooling the plant for magnetic equipment.

His first solution was to use whatever was handy in the old plant to shore up the engines. Among the assets the Cedarburg Manufacturing Company left behind was a carload of nearly obsolete Bosch magnetos that Thor Hansen had used on an equally inept twin-cylinder engine version of his single-cylinder engine. It was aptly called the Pyramid 2, since it simply stacked a second cylinder on top of the first and added a piston, different crankshaft, and a few other component changes. It was not a big seller.

Thus, the leftover magnetos were still in their crates. These were of the opposed twin-cylinder engine variety, with two coils that were designed to fire two cylinders simultaneously.

One of the major problems with the Thor single-cylinder engine was its difficulty in starting and running smoothly once the wiring got wet. That was due to an insufficient spark being delivered to the cylinder. With his knowledge of magnetic equipment, Kiekhaefer knew he could rewire the magnetos to deliver the entire spark to one cylinder instead of two, doubling the strength of the spark. So he installed the twin magnetos in the six prototypes for Montgomery Ward.

The new, robust spark started the engine better, but it couldn't overcome the Thor's fickle gas and air mixture. The engine was designed without a traditional carburetor, which blends air and gas in just the right mixture to explode inside the cylinder. Instead, it had a mixing valve arrangement (another cost-saving move), which was nearly impossible to fine-tune.

On February 8, 1939, exactly two weeks after taking over the aging Cedarburg plant, Kiekhaefer drew his first sketch of an improvement for outboard motors. It was an enlarged intake manifold with a finely adjustable thumbscrew that allowed a better fuel mixture and took advantage of the hotter spark he had just created.

Then Kiekhaefer tore down the six engines and pulled out their crude and poorly balanced crankshafts. He replaced the Thor crankshafts with nicely forged versions from a 2-horsepower Elgin Waterwitch outboard, sold by Montgomery Ward's largest rival, Sears, Roebuck and Company.

With some minor alterations, the half-dozen Thors now started quickly (thanks to the hotter spark), idled pleasantly (the enlarged intake), and delivered smoother power (the pirated crankshaft). When Kiekhaefer boxed up the six Thors and sent them back to Chicago, the buyer called Cedarburg with the news: "All right. Fix up the rejects, and we'll see how they go."[16]

But Kiekhaefer's temporary foray into outboards wasn't over yet, because he couldn't very well install Sears-Waterwitch crankshafts in the remaining 378 Montgomery Ward–Sea King engines. Instead, he and his underpaid, overworked crew would have to rebuild the inventory of Thor crankshafts using the Waterwitch as a guide. The rebuilt engines were sent back to the same Montgomery Ward stores that had rejected them months before, and they sold well. Now that the Thor was no longer considered a pauper's engine and was deemed worthy of the Sea King name, Montgomery Ward reinstated the original order for 500 engines—and offered to throw in an order for 500 more if the first production run sold equally well.

The Kiekhaefer Corporation had gone from having no clients and no revenue to selling 884 outboards with the prospect of future orders.

Since Kiekhaefer and crew had invested their days, nights, and weekends to make a viable engine, there was no sense in stopping. Selling the rebuilt Thor engines under the Sea King name meant more profit for Montgomery Ward and less for the still-struggling Kiekhaefer Corporation. So with the Montgomery Ward order in his pocket, Kiekhaefer went to work strengthening the Thor's own anemic distribution network. He was now in the outboard motor business.

From Thor to Mercury

On Saturday, April 22, 1939, the Kiekhaefer Corporation displayed a brand-new line of Thor engines at the *Milwaukee Sentinel* Sportsman's Show, held in the Milwaukee Auditorium. Kiekhaefer had been in business only two months, but by working at the same pace he maintained to rebuild the original Thors, he was ready to introduce an "all-new" product.

The greatest improvement to the Thor single was the addition of a real carburetor, manufactured by Tillotson of Toledo. The Thor mixing valve, which would still be used on Kiekhaefer's Sea King models in 1939, had forced the engine to be regulated by the "spark lever," or magneto advance, which meant that even with reduced speed, the engine still had a full gas charge with a retarded magneto. This caused fouling of the spark plug, poor gas mileage, and rough performance.

The new carburetor allowed Kiekhaefer to boast that his "motor will accelerate smoothly, and without complaint, from idling to full throttle. Speed is controlled by throttle or 'Hand Accelerator' with a power response comparable to a fine automobile."[17]

Despite the amazing turnaround of the Thor engine, Kiekhaefer still wasn't thinking about a life-long career in the marine industry. He had just organized his young company into two divisions: automotive and electric. He envisioned the automotive division as a manufacturer of automotive brakes and super-chargers, along with the Thor outboard engine line. The electric division, still his lingering target for the business, would manufacture magnetic brakes, clutches, separators, electric motors, and any other custom electrical apparatus the market would bear.

Kiekhaefer insisted on being personally responsible for every facet of his new operation. From his many years as chief engineer at Stearns Magnetic, there wasn't a shop tool made that he couldn't operate. He would personally demonstrate drill press, lathe, grinder, and boring equipment to new employees until they could operate them to his high standards.

Wherever he went in the plant, he sped up assembly through some suggestion, usually accompanied by a demonstration. However, he rarely commented on good work and seldom praised excellent performance. His reward, rather, was to spare the worker his fury. A quiet glance without comment could be dividend enough to those who had experienced his wrath in the past.

As the quality of the Thor Single–Sea King engine steadily improved, Montgomery Ward awarded new production contracts. By the end of its first year in business, the Kiekhaefer Corporation had shipped more than 2,300 engines to Montgomery Ward stores. But the Thor Streamliner wasn't as successful, with only 473 engines shipped to Kiekhaefer's own dealers. Only 90 Thor Alternate 2 engines (the reconditioned Pyramid 2) were sold, and only 12 Thor Alternate 3 (the old Pyramid 3) engines were

Above: WISN radio announcer Tom Dolan was master of ceremonies at the *Milwaukee Sentinel* Sportsman's Show. Here he inspects the new Thor Streamliner, which was among the many attractions at the three-day event.

Right: A line of Montgomery Ward Sea Kings, circa 1939.

shipped during the entire year, sounding the death knell for these awkward versions.

But Montgomery Ward was impressed with Kiekhaefer for getting the Thor engines to run and for substantially increasing their performance without increasing their wholesale cost. Earnway Edwards, the Montgomery Ward buyer who gave Kiekhaefer one last chance, now called and offered Kiekhaefer the chance to design a new outboard.

No one at the plant had designed an entire engine before, but Kiekhaefer didn't let that stop him from accepting the challenge. Kiekhaefer and Montgomery Ward agreed on a set of design and cost specifications

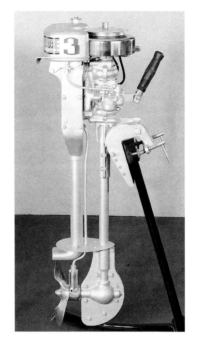

for a new three-horsepower, single-cylinder Sea King outboard, and when Kiekhaefer delivered the prototype to Chicago less than five weeks later, he walked away with an order for 20,000 engines.[18]

Soon, Western Auto Supply, a major chain of automotive parts and accessories, contacted the Kiekhaefer Corporation. Western Auto had been buying engines manufactured by Muncie Gear and selling them under Western's brand name of Wizard Outboard Motors. George W. Derse, the buyer for Western Auto, asked if Kiekhaefer could supply Western Auto its own style of outboard. After some negotiating (with Western Auto agreeing to pay for the tooling), Derse gave Kiekhaefer an order for 10,000 single-cylinder engines. Before the ink was dry on the order, Western Auto asked if Kiekhaefer would build a twin-cylinder model as well.[19]

Kiekhaefer swiftly returned to the plant and welded together two single-cylinder engines. Twenty-seven years later, he described what happened next:

The engine was finished and ready for testing just one day ahead of our appointment to demonstrate it to Western Auto. It was a bit of a mess because it was snowing that November day, and we were testing a new engine that was a hodgepodge of parts welded and brazed together.

Let me tell you that little old twin got the job done because we ended up with an order for 2,500 new Wizard twin outboard motors.

Along about this time, we remembered full well the fate of Thor—our predecessor—in dealing with one mail-order house. Here we were dealing with two. If one was bad, two could be worse. It was decided then and there that if these people

Above: Only a dozen Thor Alternate 3 engines were ever shipped, marking the beginning of the end for Thor—and the rise of Mercury.

could sell outboard motors, we could, too; and Mercury outboard motors were born that day.[20]

Rising Mercury

The Kiekhaefer Corporation had a head start in designing a new line of outboard engines, which was named after the Roman god of speed, Mercury. The combined contracts from Montgomery Ward and Western Auto Supply would total 32,000 engines by January 1940. Kiekhaefer could boast that Evinrude production was only slightly higher.

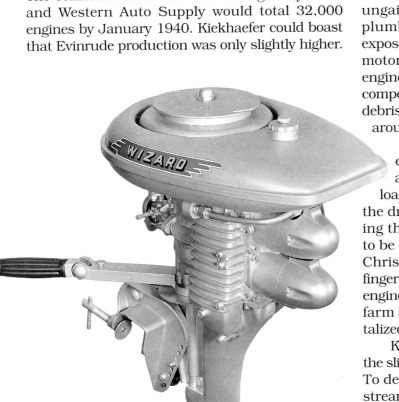

The Wizard was a private line commissioned by Western Auto Supply. Although identical to the models Kiekhaefer was selling on his own (for more profit), the Western Auto business staved off early financial ruin.

Aiming to introduce his new line at the January 1940 New York Motor Boat Show in Grand Central Palace, Kiekhaefer launched a feverish prototype development program in the last six weeks of 1939. Satisfied with the new single- and twin-cylinder engine designs he had finished for Montgomery Ward and Western Auto, he concentrated his design efforts on new lower units.

The lower unit of an outboard engine, with its ungainly and clumsy-looking combination of plumbing, bothered Kiekhaefer. This array of exposed tubing created a great deal of drag as the motor moved through the water, robbing the engine of efficiency and horsepower. The exposed components were easily bent or broken by floating debris and even the normal rattling and bumping around inside the trunk of a car.

Kiekhaefer had good instincts for practical engineering. He could tell at a glance whether a component or structure could handle the load for which it was designed. He would cruise the drafting tables of his designers, recommending that this "be beefed up here," or "this needs to be thicker there," and "make this stronger, for Chrissake. What are you guys, a bunch of lady-finger engineers, or what?" His rigid rules for over-engineering were carry-overs from his days on the farm and at Stearns, where equipment was brutalized by its users.

Kiekhaefer established a design goal of making the slimmest and most compact lower unit possible. To determine the right shape, he molded a thin, streamlined housing from clay to form the nearly knife-edged sections he desired. The results were dramatic, and all who saw the final result were amazed at both the beauty and the utility of the innovation. It looked almost like modern sculpture: a smooth, flowing shape of metal that made other outboard engines appear crude and outdated.

To cool most outboard motors in the 1930s, water had to be pumped through a water jacket surrounding the cylinders; the water was then exhausted. To accomplish this, manufacturers devised several varieties of mechanical pumps, including schemes that used a plunger pump, siphon-assisted pump, vacuum pressure pump, and centrifugal pumps. Each had advantages, but they shared a common fault: They operated just fine under ideal conditions but invariably failed when they swallowed sand, weeds, or other debris. If the engine was allowed to continue operating without water to cool the cylinders, the pistons seized up.

Kiekhaefer's small band of designers set out to develop a better pump. After experimenting with a number of circular impeller-style pumps, they combined the best features of a round, multi-bladed rubber impeller, turning inside a round housing with enough tolerance to admit some debris without plugging up the works. Even at idling speeds, the new Rotex Positive Water Pump could double the

water capacity of competitive engines. It was among the earliest innovations on Kiekhaefer's long list of industry firsts in marine propulsion.

Another significant Kiekhaefer innovation was the use of reed valves between the carburetor and the crankcase. Reed valves, like the little wafer reeds in a harmonica, flow outward against the pressure of air in one direction and lie flat against a seat in the other direction, preventing the return of air. In an outboard motor, a combination of air and gasoline is drawn into the crankcase of the engine before being compressed in the cylinder and ignited by the spark plug. The idea is to prevent this explosive mixture from being pushed back out of the crankcase, through the carburetor, and into the air, where it could explode in a backfire. The reed must be able to withstand millions of bends without cracking or

Below: Kiekhaefer made clay models of his new engines. On the left is a 1940 deluxe single clay model. The Thor Streamliner model is on the right.

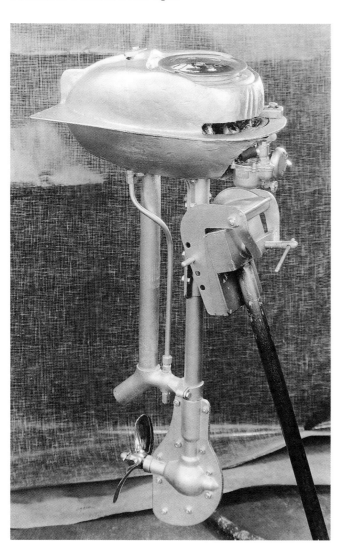
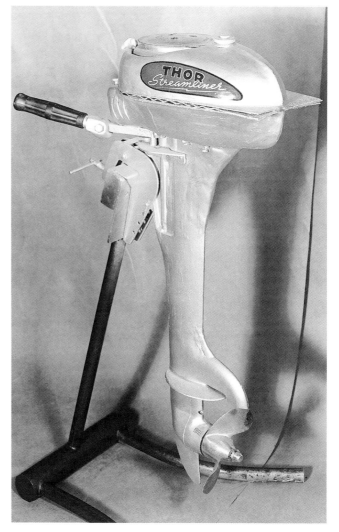

deforming. The idea wasn't new—Evinrude had used reed valves in four models as early as 1934. Evinrude called its design an "automatic air valve" and claimed it would help ensure fuel economy, avoid blow-back, and maintain the cleanliness of the boat.[21]

Envinrude's engine was considered too temperamental, however. It tended to flutter wildly, and pieces sometimes broke off and damaged the piston or cylinder, so the design was quickly abandoned. In fact, the "automatic air valves" worked so poorly that Evinrude had to repurchase many of the engines equipped with them that year. Kiekhaefer stubbornly appreciated the simple, self-adjusting, self-timing idea of reed valves. He experimented and finally discovered the right material, shape, thickness, pressure path, and seat combination to make them work properly.

Five models of Mercury were introduced in January 1940: three singles and two twins. Kiekhaefer simply named these the K1, K2, K3, K4, and K5. The Mercury K1 Special Single was identical to the new 2.5-horsepower Sea King designed for Montgomery Ward, while the K2 Standard Single and K3 Deluxe Single were the same 3-horsepower, single-cylinder engine designed for Western Auto Supply, with the K3 offering a more streamlined tank, lower unit, and mounting bracket. The twins (K4 Standard and K5 Deluxe) were the same alternate-firing twin Wizard that Western Auto Supply had commissioned, with the Deluxe version having a chrome tank and the throttle control located on the steering handle.

The retail prices for the first crop of Mercury engines ranged from $42.95 to $98.50. Among other innovations on these engines was the Twin-Flux magneto. True to Kiekhaefer's long career with electromagnets, the Twin-Flux was heavy-duty, generating a 20,000-volt spark that would snap over a

Thor motors, shown alongside competitive designs in 1939, show how Kiekhaefer's early designs were more streamlined.

In 1940, Kiekhaefer introduced the first line of Mercury engines, including the K3 (above and right). The 3-horsepower single-cylinder engine offered a more streamlined tank, lower unit, and mounting bracket.

quarter-inch, even at idling speeds. For these new engines, he also pioneered a multiple friction-disk steering system that allowed hands-free tracking while underway.

With these new features, plus five new models to prepare, Kiekhaefer mercilessly drove himself and his crew of 25 workers. They worked 18 hours a day, seven days a week. No one dared to leave while Kiekhaefer was still in the plant, for he made it clear that everybody would have to give 100 percent of their time and effort if they were going to be ready for the New York Motor Boat Show in early January. Weekends and holidays became meaningless to Kiekhaefer, as the steady stream of work continued through Thanksgiving, Christmas, and New Year's Day, with workers given barely enough time to have holiday dinner with their families.

Kiekhaefer himself spent precious little time at home with his wife, Freda, and two young daughters. Whenever he did go home, it was usually after midnight, his baggy clothes streaked with grease and sweat. Sometimes he'd bolt upright in the middle of the night, having dreamed a solution to some vexing problem. Even at home, work wasn't far away. In 1939, the Kiekhaefers lived in a miserable clapboard house next to a gravel pit not far from the factory.

While at the boat show, Kiekhaefer received a tip that somebody was trying to sell him out. He was in the middle of trying to establish the first of the new Mercury outboard dealer groups by persuading the old Thor dealers that this was a great opportunity. But back home, banker Edgar Roth had received an offer to sell the Kiekhaefer Corporation to the Flambeau outboard motor company for 50 percent more than the investors had originally advanced. So, for $37,500, Roth and the others were actively preparing to sell the company out from under Kiekhaefer while he was in New York and couldn't block the sale.

Kiekhaefer raced back to Cedarburg to save his company. The group of investors aligned with Roth, of Cedarburg Bank, had decided that "you

can never take a loss taking a profit,"[22] and here was a chance not only to get their money back, but to make $12,500 in the 11 months since they originally invested.

For two days, Kiekhaefer extolled the progress that the company had made in such a short time, describing the future that he envisioned and briefing the doubters on the great promise for the engines he had seen in New York. "The future of Kiekhaefer hung in the balance," Kiekhaefer would later write, "but believe me, I did a selling job to save our company."[23]

He reminded the investors that the company had managed to rack up $300,000 in sales in the first 11 months of 1939 and promised them that if they just held on tight, he could double it during 1940. One by one, he turned the investors around, and when they finally agreed to decline the Flambeau offer, he vowed to personally wrest controlling interest of the corporation.

With the attempted Flambeau takeover on his mind, Kiekhaefer made sure that the current stockholders, his father included, would be able to sell their stock back only to the company. He told his corporate and patent attorney, Guy Conrad, to prepare documents to that effect for every stockholder to sign. In one sweep of the pen,

Kiekhaefer's sales manager, Merlyn Culver, operating a Thor twin, which Kiekhaefer and his crew of 25 completely redesigned.

he had guaranteed that the company would never expand the current list of shareholders and never have to pay more than the book value to buy back any currently issued shares of stock. It was the first in a long and often vicious series of manipulations that would ultimately place 90 percent of the stock of the Kiekhaefer Corporation in his own pocket.

With control of the company now secure, Kiekhaefer inaugurated two assembly lines down the middle of the Cedarburg plant. One line alternated between Montgomery Ward–Sea King models and Western Auto Supply Wizards. The other line was dedicated to Mercury outboards. In this way, he could continue to meet the sporadic deadlines of the chain-store orders, and at the same time assure his new Mercury dealers and distributors that they would have enough product to satisfy their customers.

By September 1940, the end of the fiscal year, he had shipped 2,901 Mercury outboards, with singles outselling the twins by more than two to one. In addition, 4,000 Sea Kings, 2,000 Wizard singles, and 500 twins were built for a total of 6,500 private-label engines. All together, the dedicated crew had managed to build 9,401 engines by the end of the year.

In the frenzied rush to finish up Wizard orders for Western Auto Supply, Kiekhaefer had completely neglected to design a new line of engines for 1941. As late as December 19, 1940, the production department was still begging Kiekhaefer to develop new models to show at the 1941 New York Motor Boat Show, only a month away.

Kiekhaefer was determined to add new features to his 1941 models, even if he had only a few weeks to perform another miracle. The success of the Mercury line left little doubt that customers would respond to advanced features. But he knew that his engines were years behind the competition in many ways. So he made three basic improvements to his 1941 line, each of which had been standard features in the outboard industry for many years.

The first change was in the fuel tanks of his models. A lingering legacy from the days of Thorwald Hansen was his stamped steel gas tanks. They dented easily and rusted quickly, leaving engines that looked old before their time. Kiekhaefer designed a two-piece cast aluminum tank that looked almost identical to the steel

Kiekhaefer's skills as an engineer were matched by his skills in marketing, as demonstrated in this letter to Thor dealers about the 1939 line of new outboard motors.

tanks that adorned Mercurys in 1940. But these were, as the Kiekhaefer Corporation advertised, "rust-proof, leak-proof, and dent-proof."[24]

On two models for 1941, Kiekhaefer also introduced the Magnapull Starter, which eliminated the winding and pulling of a rope starter. This self-winding feature, introduced by Evinrude as the Simplex Starter six years earlier on two models, had been accepted quickly by consumers. But the combination of each of these improvements was sufficient to put Mercury outboards into the same performance league as Evinrude and Johnson and pull ahead of other competitors such as Elto, Champion, Waterwitch, Hiawatha Outboard, Lausen, and Muncie (Neptune).

When Kiekhaefer arrived at the 1941 New York Motor Boat Show, his new engines sported names such as Comet, Streamliner, Torpedo, and Rocket. The advertising slogan he chose for his new line was, "She's got no bad habits,"[25] and prices for his five models (from 2.9 horsepower to 6 horsepower) ranged from $47.95 to $114.50. On average, these were as much as 20 percent higher than comparable Evinrude models. And Evinrude could boast a line of nine engines, through four cylinders and over 33 horsepower, along with a 30-year advantage in market share and name recognition. Johnson displayed 10 engines for 1941, known as Johnson Streamliners, including twins to 22 horsepower, and Ready-starters on half its models.

Even with the evidence of his own scrambling to catch up with advancements made by others, Kiekhaefer mounted a loud and clamorous campaign to charge that the industry was busy copying his designs. He began by circulating the inaugural issue of *Mercury Outboard Motor News*, the company's first newsletter, to dealers in March 1941, reminding them of his 1940 prophecy about his new Mercury outboards, that they were "The 'Dream Motor' of Today That Others Will Seek to Imitate Tomorrow."[26]

Then, without actually naming the competition, he set out to prove that his lower unit housing, water pump, and even reed valve features had been blatantly copied by various leaders in the industry. The silhouettes and masked outboards shown in the newsletter were obviously those of Evinrude, Johnson, and Champion. But, fully aware of his own encroachments on the successful concepts pioneered by others, he graciously accepted their trespass and did not wish to risk the start of patent infringement actions—no doubt fearing retaliation in kind. He wrote:

We're not resentful nor alarmed that other manufacturers in our field have deemed it necessary to incorporate some of our last year's features into their 1941 models. ... Remember, "Imitation at its best is but imitation!"[27]

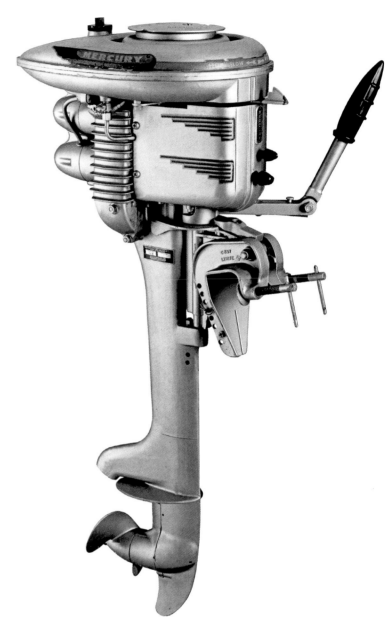

Mercury introduced the Rocket at the 1941 New York Motor Boat Show.

At the January 1941 New York Motor Boat Show and in letters to his dealers early in the year, Kiekhaefer took great delight in teasing prospective customers about the imminent arrival of the "Mercury Mystery Motor," called the Thunderbolt. Referring to an engine that should have been ready for the 1941 New York show, he couldn't resist the temptation to whet appetites for what he clearly considered to be a monumental engine. He wrote:

> *Yes, it's on the way! The THUNDERBOLT, the new super Deluxe Mercury Motor, will be ready soon. And, it sure IS going to be something "to write home about." Marvelous! Stupendous! Colossal! Superb! These are but a few of the adjectives that you will be looking for when the THUNDERBOLT arrives.*[28]

Actually, the "Mystery Motor" was a new four-cylinder engine that, with only a few exceptions, used most of the same components as the twin-cylinder models. It was designed to weigh a little over 60 pounds and have a firing impulse every 90 degrees, which enabled it to throttle down to low speeds smoothly. Kiekhaefer believed the unique "overlapping" firing order gave the engine the flexibility of four-cycle engines, but with two-cycle simplicity.

By the end of January 1941, Kiekhaefer had a near-operational prototype, but events that occurred a month earlier, many thousands of miles from Cedarburg, would soon alter his plans.

Kiekhaefer employees building Mercury engines for the Navy in 1943.

CHAPTER TWO

THE WAR YEARS

*Most of us engaged in business have plenty to think about these days.
... For the past several months, we have been hoping against hope that
the situation might improve. But today, we are faced with the inevitable.*

—Carl Kiekhaefer, July 1941[1]

BY THE SPRING OF 1940, WORLD WAR II was under way, and many of America's largest industries were switching to military production in preparation for possible US involvement. Kiekhaefer began seeking his corporation's share of military contracts even as his production department urged him to concentrate on designs for the 1941 Mercury line.

In the summer of 1940, he drove to the War Department offices at Fort Belvoir, Virginia, where he accepted the challenge to build a prototype of a 25-horsepower, four-cylinder engine to push a 25-ton pontoon boat. Although this assignment was within the Kiekhaefer Corporation's field, it was not within its grasp. The most powerful engine Kiekhaefer made was the 6-horsepower, twin-cylinder K5, and no amount of 18-hour work shifts and late-night engineering brainstorms could overcome the massive lead that Evinrude, Johnson, and Elto had in the big-engine market. After five months of production delays and engineering dead ends, Kiekhaefer wrote to the War Department asking for more time. He didn't get it.[2]

He then tried to convince the National Advisory Committee for Aeronautics at Langley Field, Virginia, that he was an active manufacturer of magnetic clutches. But the truth was, the Kiekhaefer Corporation had never built a magnetic clutch. Although the devices appeared in the original business plan, the company never had time to build anything but outboard motors, starting with the 384 rejected Thors. That didn't stop Kiekhaefer from drawing up blueprints of clutches ranging from 4 inches to 4 feet. He mailed these to Langley engineers with a note, calling them "our standard clutches."

Desperate Times

Meanwhile, the company's aluminum supplies for the Mercury line were being sucked away by military aircraft production. In February 1941, the government issued an order called M-1-a, which required special permission for the use and casting of aluminum.

Kiekhaefer was stunned. After persuading his stockholders not to sell their shares to Flambeau because he planned to double outboard sales in 1941, it was now very possible that the Kiekhaefer

---

The Share the Ride campaign encouraged commuters to carpool so more resources could be used for the war. A similar campaign wasn't needed for boating; restrictions on aluminum had shut down the outboard market.

Corporation would go bankrupt. In a desperate appeal for more aluminum, Kiekhaefer flew to Washington, DC, in early April 1941 to meet with Charles Hoge of the Priority Division. In a letter to Hoge, Kiekhaefer once again tried to work his magic:

It will mean that over 100 men, who cannot be absorbed locally, will be out of work. It will mean that we cannot continue with the special development work that is being carried on, at our expense, for a special motor for the US Army. ...

Since the outboard is strictly of portable application, heavy metals cannot be substituted successfully; in fact, our plant was formerly owned by the Cedarburg Mfg. Co., which got into financial difficulties through trying to market an outboard made of steel and cast iron. ...

The Mercury K5 motor, the most powerful of the Mercury line.

In behalf of employment for over 100 men, and in behalf of fine, local, civic-minded stockholders, we cannot face financial failure with a product that has, within two years, achieved such merit that the entire outboard industry has imitated its engineering design.[3]

Kiekhaefer didn't get the aluminum, but he did get a visit from Major C. Rodney Smith of the Army Corps of Engineers. Within days of his return from Washington, DC, Kiekhaefer gave Smith a tour of the Cedarburg plant. It was then that the major disclosed the government's need for "a lightweight gasoline motor of approximately 4 horsepower, suitable for powering a portable chain timber saw."[4]

Kiekhaefer jumped at the chance, but there were complications. First, such a saw had never been built in the United States before. Only Germany, the as-yet-undeclared enemy, had ever mass-produced one. Second, the new saw

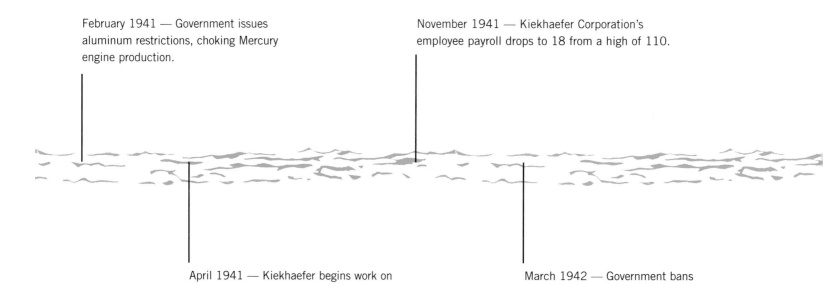

February 1941 — Government issues aluminum restrictions, choking Mercury engine production.

November 1941 — Kiekhaefer Corporation's employee payroll drops to 18 from a high of 110.

April 1941 — Kiekhaefer begins work on a prototype for a two-man chainsaw engine.

March 1942 — Government bans production of all leisure products made with aluminum.

In July 1941, the Kiekhaefer Corporation newsletter announced the difficult conversion from outboard motors to war production.

had to weigh less than 100 pounds, even though the German version weighed 105 pounds and was built using lightweight magnesium, a material scarce in the United States. So the new saw had to be lighter without using magnesium. Third, a prototype had to be ready for inspection in six weeks. Fourth—and most importantly—the War Department wanted a plain, unadorned machine that could be mastered by the rawest of recruits. "Above all, as I have stated to you repeatedly but cannot overemphasize, dependable starting by unskilled operators is an absolute essential," Smith wrote Kiekhaefer.[5]

Kiekhaefer learned that the Henry Disston & Sons company of Philadelphia was the leading candidate to make the guide bar and moving sawtooth portion of the new chainsaw. Disston employed 3,000 and was among the oldest saw firms in the world. Its first military contracts were from the War of 1812.

Disston was a household word in the US, and Mercury was not. Since Kiekhaefer was interested

May 1942 — Kiekhaefer finally receives orders for chainsaw engine production, staving off bankruptcy.

October 1943 — Kiekhaefer announces his company won the Army-Navy "E" Award.

1943 — Kiekhaefer Corporation ships more than 10,000 engines in six different configurations.

June 6, 1944 — Allies invade Europe two days after Kiekhaefer's birthday.

only in designing and producing the gasoline engine of the new chainsaw, and Disston was interested only in the guide bar and sawteeth, Kiekhaefer offered to join forces with the company, which already had government contracts to produce armor plate and machetes. That partnership, Kiekhaefer hoped, would discourage some of the competition. But just in case it didn't, Kiekhaefer traveled to Fort Belvoir, Virginia, to personally inspect the German Stihl engine, and persuaded the War Department to lend him the only saw in its possession. That effectively left any prospective competitors in the dark.

Two weeks later, Kiekhaefer delivered blueprints for a proposed Disston-Kiekhaefer two-man portable chainsaw that weighed less than 100 pounds and met the target performance of the German saw. The design revealed Kiekhaefer's years of practical experience on the farm, using equipment that would suffer heavy-duty cycles and dirty or wet operating conditions. The War Department was impressed with the saw. Officials said:

> *We are very pleased with the "clean lines" of your design, the location of the starter, the absence of exterior wires and cables, and the functional simplicity of the controls. ... Placing of control wires inside the tubing [handles] as you have shown is very desirable.*[6]

As Kiekhaefer began work on the prototype, he knew that the War Department would approve it only after the most comprehensive testing.

The Army needed a chainsaw that would operate in Arctic cold, tropical heat, and filthy conditions, with little or no maintenance and at altitudes ranging from the desert floor to mountain peaks. It would have to perform with contaminated fuel and improper lubrication—and still be easy to use.

Kiekhaefer's new twin-cylinder KB-6 chainsaw engine solved every problem the War Department threw at it. He had simplified the controls so much that all a soldier had to do was pull out the choke, snap out a clutch to disengage the saw chain, and pull up on the starter handle.

The final design—a full 5 horsepower and smaller than the German example—had much heavier bearings, could withstand the most arduous duty cycles, included a starter and a full-engine cowling, and still weighed less than 65 pounds. At the same time the Disston-Kiekhaefer machine was delivered to the War Department, a competitor emerged. Reed-Prentice of Worcester, Massachusetts, was a leading manufacturer of saw blades and also had a small, though largely unsuitable, line of portable gasoline engines. The two Reed-Prentice prototypes, powered by 4- and 8-horsepower engines, developed fractures in their crankshafts during testing.

The War Department was not enamored with the Reed-Prentice engines but did find merit in the saw mechanism. The department encouraged Reed-Prentice to contact Kiekhaefer to discuss a possible Reed-Prentice/Kiekhaefer team effort. So it began to look as if the Kiekhaefer Corporation was going to get the engine business no matter who was awarded the saw mechanism portion of the device. In a letter to Reed-Prentice, the War Department hinted that Kiekhaefer had just about wrapped up the engine contract:

The Kiekhaefer two-man chainsaw engine gave the War Department an edge over the chainsaw's original inventor, Stihl, of Germany.

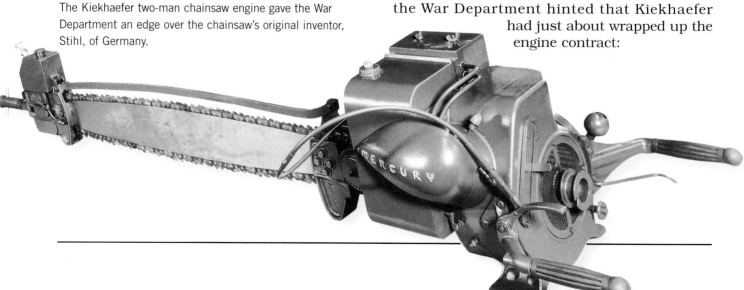

We ... hold no particular belief for the Kiekhaefer motor over any other gasoline drive but feel that it has shown sufficient promise over other types to make it a serious contender. ... Consequently, we believe that it would be well worth our while and your while to test the Kiekhaefer motor with your sawing device.[7]

Still, the War Department issued Kiekhaefer a list of changes it wanted: The engine should be even lighter and have a new transmission case, new set of gears, different cylinders, new fan housing, new magneto support bracket, new gas tank, and new controls. The changes were made in less than three weeks, and the improved model was resubmitted to the Army Corps of Engineers at Fort Belvoir. Among an ambitious list of 12 improvements was a remarkable 40 percent increase in displacement, giving the engine additional "lugging power" and power reserve. Kiekhaefer explained that the new model should eliminate all competition from the field:

This increase in displacement [doesn't] increase engine weight by more than one pound. Incidentally, this so-called improved engine, which we shall still call 5 horse, will greatly outperform anything the Engineer Board has had under test. ... The added power and performance should surprise them and should make all the competition appear ridiculous.[8]

The Noose Tightens

Kiekhaefer was running out of time. The casualties of the growing world crisis included the Comet, the Streamliner, the Rocket Deluxe, and his "Mercury Mystery Motor," the Thunderbolt. For seven months, he'd been waiting for a solid order from the War Department, and for seven months, he had experienced nothing but delays, changes, politics, more modifications, and more delays. From a high of 110 workers, temporary layoffs brought the working total down to only 18 by November 1941. Kiekhaefer was trapped between the prospect of

The 1941 Rocket Deluxe.

future defense contracts and the lack of aluminum to produce civilian outboard engines. He begged the government's Office of Production Management for aluminum to build more outboard engines to keep the company solvent. He wrote:

It is a cruel hard fact that our number of employees had dropped from 110 to 18. ... It is a fact also that we have developed a special device for the US Army on which contracts supposedly were to have been placed several months ago. ...

You can understand ... that all of the above development work takes money. It is a fact that we have built one device for the Engineer Board now that has cost us in the neighborhood of $50,000, without the benefit of a development order.[9]

The desperate appeals fell on deaf ears. Kiekhaefer was openly bitter about his rivals, Evinrude and Johnson, because of their relative ease in obtaining aluminum for outboard motor production. Fortunately, the Kiekhaefer Corporation wasn't alone in feeling that some sort of collusion among big businesses could mean the end for small companies. Even the US Senate was alarmed at the inequities that threatened small businesses. Senator Carl Hatch of New Mexico, who was head of a special committee to investigate defense program contracts, was "alarmed lest America have the experience of Britain, where 20,000 manufacturing plants were shut down almost overnight in the changeover from peace to a war economy."[10]

When President Franklin Roosevelt appointed Floyd Odlum as director of the Office of Production Management's division of contract distribution, Odlum quickly estimated that the release of just "2 percent of the supply of strategic materials would enable 30,000 to 45,000 small metal-working US plants to continue during the first half of 1942."[11]

Unfortunately for the Kiekhaefer Corporation, no relief was forthcoming. Though the corporation had shown a modest profit when it closed its books

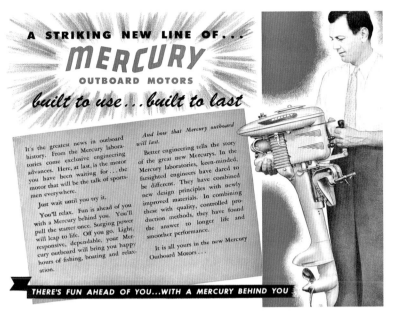

A STRIKING NEW LINE OF...

MERCURY

OUTBOARD MOTORS

built to use... built to last

It's the greatest news in outboard history. From the Mercury laboratories come exclusive engineering advances. Here, at last, is the motor you have been waiting for... the motor that will be the talk of sportsmen everywhere.

Just wait until you try it.

You'll relax. Fun is ahead of you with a Mercury behind you. You'll pull the starter once. Surging power will leap to life. Off you go. Light, responsive, dependable, your Mercury outboard will bring you happy hours of fishing, boating and relaxation.

And how that Mercury outboard will last.

Better engineering tells the story of the great new Mercurys. In the Mercury laboratories, keen-minded, farsighted engineers have dared to be different. They have combined new design principles with newly improved materials. In combining these with quality, controlled production methods, they have found the answer to longer life and smoother performance.

It is all yours in the new Mercury Outboard Motors...

THERE'S FUN AHEAD OF YOU...WITH A MERCURY BEHIND YOU

Mercury touted its engines' reliability in this "built to last" flyer from the early 1940s.

at the end of September, the company would be virtually shut down by November. The year 1941 had taken the Kiekhaefer Corporation on a roller coaster ride of financial promise and disaster. More than 15,000 engines left the plant before the company ran out of aluminum, representing more than $612,000 in sales. Because of the money poured back into the company for engine development work and new tooling, the Kiekhaefer Corporation would show only a $38,000 profit. It would seem like good news compared to the events that were to follow.

In late 1941, Kiekhaefer lost the man whom he later considered to be his closest friend and confidant, his uncle, John Blank. In his capacity as corporate secretary of the Cedarburg Mutual Fire Insurance Company, Blank was preparing to make a call on a client 10 miles west of Cedarburg and decided to take his wife, Flora, along for the ride. They headed west out of town, approaching the railroad tracks they had crossed hundreds of times before. They were struck by the full force of a fast-moving train and instantly killed.

Kiekhaefer had lost the one person in his life who truly believed in his abilities and who had nurtured his self-image and confidence since he was a young boy. It was Blank who had brought the opportunity of the Cedarburg Manufacturing Company to Kiekhaefer, had designed the plan to reduce the debts of the company, and had organized the investors to purchase the assets from

Thorwald Hansen. Blank's son, Willis, inherited most of his father's interest in the Kiekhaefer Corporation and was named secretary, the same position that his father had held. It is significant that of all the original stockholders in the Kiekhaefer Corporation, Willis eventually would be the only one outside of the immediate Kiekhaefer family allowed to retain a large block (10 percent) of stock.

War Overseas and at Home

As Kiekhaefer negotiated the mountains of Washington red tape and the many political obstacles related to defense contracting in peacetime, conditions around the world deteriorated. The United States was swept into the cauldron of conflict by the surprise attack on Pearl Harbor, and confusion reigned throughout the industrial/defense community. On December 7, 1941, more than 360 Japanese warplanes participated in the attack, sinking or seriously damaging five US battleships and 14 smaller ships. More than 2,000 Navy personnel perished. Within four days of the attack, the United States declared war on Japan and Axis partners Italy and Germany.

As the US ramped up its war production, Kiekhaefer's struggles continued in Cedarburg, Wisconsin. With constant pressure and stubborn determination, he managed to secure enough stray aluminum to embark on an on-again, off-again production of outboard engines. Actually, Kiekhaefer had been planning for an aggressive 1942 season, hoping to produce no fewer than 25,000 motors—a blend of Mercury, Sea King, and Wizard product lines. During the first three months of 1942, he was off to a great start, building more than 5,000 Mercury engines in 3-, 3.2-, and 6-horsepower models before what Kiekhaefer would later describe as his second great disaster in business occurred.

On March 27, 1942, the US government issued Limitation Order 80, or L-80, which prohibited the manufacture of leisure products from aluminum and ordered that all fabrication of leisure-industry aluminum be suspended indefinitely. The government classified slot-machine manufacturers and outboard motor builders in the same category, characterizing both products as unnecessary and wasteful of strategic materials. Two days later, government compliance officers entered the Kiekhaefer Corporation plant unannounced to ensure absolute submission. In the absence of any substantial, finalized defense contracts, the Kiekhaefer Corporation was effectively put out of business.[12]

Finally, on May 18, 1942, Kiekhaefer received a contract for 3,300 saw engines. Remarkably, the government had arbitrarily mandated a 20 percent price reduction because of the large quantity involved. Kiekhaefer had no choice but to accept the terms, for the contract was the only thing standing between the small Cedarburg

plant and certain bankruptcy. But having a contract in his hand for slightly over $1 million dollars was the emotional rescue that Kiekhaefer had been waiting for.

More than two months would drag by before Kiekhaefer saw a single dollar of government funds. He was forced to undergo an agonizing campaign to borrow money, which took him to 12 different banks and government agencies before he gave up in disgust. It seemed that no one—from banks in his own backyard to Federal Reserve banks to the government's own Reconstruction Finance Corporation and the War Department—would help. Kiekhaefer was struck by the demeaning experience of being rejected by so many institutions. He found it unbelievable that US banks, so carefully

Corporal K. Munch and Pfc. W. Hullinghorst of the 131st Engineer Regiment of the US Army cut logs into 10- and 18-foot lengths using the two-man chainsaw that Kiekhaefer's lighter, stronger engine made possible.

regulated by the government, would deny funds to a company manufacturing critical defense materials under signed contracts. He pleaded with the War Production Board for relief:

> *Our financial condition is, of course, the result of all of [these] difficulties, and the situation is getting very critical. Materials are pouring in here by the carloads, and if we are to avoid disaster, we feel that W.P.B. must give us assistance NOW. ... Many manufacturers have ridiculed us for the part we have played in this program. On the other hand, we felt that we have an organization and talent to offer, and that it was the thing to do to help win this War. ... So many obstacles have been encountered in our War Effort that it becomes almost unbelievable.*[13]

When an initial advance was received from Disston in mid-July for just less than $400,000, Kiekhaefer calculated that he was nearly $150,000 short of funds needed to produce and ship the engines on time. Again, Kiekhaefer appealed to the War Production Board, but help was again refused. Once more, Kiekhaefer's father Arnold came to the rescue. The younger Kiekhaefer tried to secure a V-Loan ("V" for victory) from the Federal Reserve Bank in Chicago. A V-Loan would have been 90 percent secured by the federal government, exposing the bank to only a 10 percent risk. The $100,000 loan was denied because of the $10,000 unsecured portion. Arnold promptly put up additional collateral of his homestead acreage to satisfy the bank. It was the second time that Arnold risked the family homestead for the company, having paid back the first mortgage within two years of the start of operations. Three other banks had to combine resources to loan the additional $50,000 to complete production of the order.

Labor Pains

The constant strain of an empty treasury and the insecurity of war contracts left the Kiekhaefer Corporation vulnerable to a labor union organizing effort. As early as the spring of 1940, elements of the Machinists Union, American Federation of Labor (AFL), began to muscle their way into the company rank and file. Kiekhaefer responded by forming the Mercury Independent Workers Union. A dispute over which of the two groups had the authority to negotiate with Kiekhaefer management resulted in the issue coming before the Milwaukee office of the National Labor Relations Board.

Though the Kiekhaefer Corporation employed little more than 100 workers, it was the largest industry in Cedarburg and received extra attention from the AFL. Kiekhaefer was confused by the vocal protests of the organizers because he had a solid reputation for paying above-average wages and was careful following layoffs to rehire on the basis of seniority. As the war removed men from industry, a growing number of women were hired at the plant, and Kiekhaefer offered quite an enticing array of benefits to lure applicants. A recruitment brochure read:

> *There is a tier of showers, with private lockers, for both men and women, where you can "fresh up." You can enjoy such group activities as tennis, softball, ice hockey, musical organizations, and bowling leagues. There are frequent employee parties and a large recreation room. You have music while you work. You will like the many other extras that make it a pleasure to work at Kiekhaefer.*[14]

Though the brochure made it sound as if the Kiekhaefer Corporation was the Kiekhaefer Country Club, in truth, Kiekhaefer always treated his employees more than fairly, both financially and administratively. Even so, Kiekhaefer finally gave in to the union's demand for representation in July 1942. He felt he had been unfairly coerced into a relationship with the union, however, and complained loudly to the War Production Board.[15]

Union or no union, the discipline and assignment of personnel remained Kiekhaefer's absolute

An early Mercury Outboard Motors logo.

Employee brochures such as this one told only half the story. A regular Kiekhaefer expression was, "I pay my men twice what they're worth, and then I make them earn it!"

KIEKHAEFER CORPORATION
CEDARBURG, WISCONSIN
HOME OF
MERCURY
OUTBOARD MOTORS • INDUSTRIAL ENGINES

Anyone Kiekhaefer perceived as insubordinate, however, never received a second chance.

His temper grew during the war years, along with an aura of indefatigability and mechanical genius. The temper would both flash and subside quickly, like a polished sword, brandished and then returned to the scabbard. Shoddy or thoughtless workmanship was never ignored, and he would loudly and brutally point out another's carelessness, bludgeoning the hapless employee with corrections and eleventh-hour warnings. He still rolled up his shirt sleeves to demonstrate production techniques, regardless of the device or conditions around the equipment. It was not uncommon to see his white shirt halfway out of his baggy trousers, smeared with blotches of shiny black grease.

As the company geared up for defense production in 1942, Kiekhaefer set up two 11-hour shifts, though many bleary-eyed employees worked 14 or more hours before leaving the plant. Kiekhaefer, though, worked harder than most, setting the example by arriving earlier and staying later than even the youngest, healthiest workers. Contracts dribbled in from various branches of the military throughout the balance of the year, ranging from an Army order for a solitary engine rigged to power a 2.5-kilowatt generator set to orders for thousands of gas tank caps or a few special generator sets for the Signal Corps. An order for nearly 1,000 KB-4 outboard motors was received from the Navy, and a few special engines were built to power grinders and other tools for field combat applications.

On Loan

Kiekhaefer's calls for operating capital were finally answered in the fall of 1942. He had lobbied long and hard for the advancement of funds against government defense contracts, rather than loan guarantees, and had argued that he could reduce the cost of his chainsaw engines up to $10 by eliminating the financial hardships imposed on a small

domain. Some employees wondered whether it was the urgency of wartime production or the uncertainty of government contracting that led to a tightening of Kiekhaefer's standards. It was increasingly apparent that he ruled his organization with an iron grip and that he insisted on levels of performance that most employees had never experienced elsewhere. When he suspected greater capabilities in his labor or management force, he turned up the heat, adding to job descriptions and responsibilities until he judged an individual saturated, or at optimum performance. He was very fast to size up potential workers, and if they passed his lightning-quick evaluation, he offered them jobs on the spot.

company by a large contract. But loan guarantees were better than not being able to perform the contracts at all, and on September 18, 1942, the War Department agreed to guarantee a loan in the amount of $525,000, issued through the Marshall & Ilsley Bank in Milwaukee. Though the government guaranteed the full amount, the terms of the loan were quite strict. Among the provisions of the note was the requirement that both Arnold and Carl Kiekhaefer also personally guarantee the loan; pledge the company's land, plant, and machinery; assign an existing $100,000 life insurance policy on Carl's life; pay no other loans with the proceeds; and pay "no dividends ... on the company's outstanding stock until the loan has been fully paid."[16]

The guarantee also contained a provision that angered Kiekhaefer in a most personal way. Along with the funds came a government-assigned "financial manager" from the Federal Reserve Bank who was given complete authority over all Kiekhaefer Corporation operations. The federal watchdog was to be the final authority in all critical decisions in the company but was only available for four hours a day. If this wasn't upsetting enough to Kiekhaefer, he was ordered to pay the watchdog, installed as executive vice president, the princely sum of $1,600 a month. Kiekhaefer himself made less than $1,200 a month for the average 16-hour days he worked. It took only one week for Kiekhaefer to blow his stack. In an angry and provocative letter to Colonel John Seyboldt, chief contracting officer of the Army Corps of Engineers, Kiekhaefer lashed out at the bureaucratic nonsense that endangered his company's survival:

> It is the opinion of the Kiekhaefer Corporation that any so-called financial manager cannot with four hours daily attendance at the plant manage a business that runs twenty-four hours for six days a week. Such management just is not workable [due to the] confliction of authority, responsibility, and its resulting confusion. Responsibility without authority is one of the most useless situations in the world.[7]

In a final effort to oust the government financial manager, Kiekhaefer offered to substitute a senior accountant from Arthur Andersen & Company, who had worked extensively with General Motors in industrial accounting and expense budgeting. Even though Kiekhaefer's substitute candidate, George Reynolds, was a graduate of the Harvard Business School and was auditor of record for the Kiekhaefer Corporation, the substitution was denied.

By the first anniversary of the United States' entry into the war, only 348 of the 3,300 air-cooled engines ordered by the government contracts had been delivered. Bureaucratic red tape, financial delays, and specification changes kept the small plant swimming in nearly constant confusion. The corporation's books showed that the company suffered a stinging loss of $56,000 during fiscal 1942, almost entirely due to burgeoning development costs for the chainsaw engine.

For all of his troubles, Kiekhaefer could still tell the Corps of Engineers that he was proud of his accomplishments and would do it all over again, no matter how vulnerable his situation had become. Patriotically, he said, "Such unbankable things we have done, we would probably do over, under the same circumstances."[18]

Turning the Corner

Kiekhaefer's patience finally paid off in 1943, as the Kiekhaefer Corporation boxed more than 10,000 engines in six configurations, and for the first time built 1,000 engines in a single month. New government contracts poured in for a total of more than $2.5 million, more than double the 1942 levels. Though the twin-cylinder chainsaw engines for Disston still dominated production, single-cylinder engines for portable grinders and twin-cylinder engines for field compressors and generators accounted for nearly a quarter of revenues.

On October 2, 1943, Kiekhaefer received a letter from Robert P. Patterson, undersecretary of war, informing him that the coveted Army-Navy "E," or Production Award, was being conferred on the men and women of the Kiekhaefer Corporation.[19] The "E" award originated in 1906 as a Navy commendation for excellence in gunnery. Later, the prestigious award was extended to include outstanding performance in engineering and communications. Following the US entry into the war, the Army and Navy

The coveted "E" award flag, which the Army and Navy gave to manufacturers who most aided the war effort. The Kiekhaefer Corporation was one such honored recipient.

combined to cite outstanding defense production plants contributing to the war effort. On Saturday afternoon, October 30, 1943, the Kiekhaefer Corporation was heralded as the first manufacturing facility in Ozaukee County to receive the "E" award and flag. More than this, it was a day to celebrate Kiekhaefer as a newly emerged industrial leader. The entire day was officially proclaimed "Kiekhaefer Corporation Day" by Mayor H.A. Zeurnert, who also decreed that every business in Cedarburg participate in the celebration by flying the American flag and join in applause for the city's largest employer.[20]

C. Rodney Smith, promoted to colonel, was especially pleased to be making the presentation. He had been responsible for getting Kiekhaefer started in the defense business with his visit and challenge regarding the German chainsaw engine.[21] In his address, he paid tribute to "the brilliant engineering and the tremendous gamble which you of the Kiekhaefer Corporation have put into the conversion of your plant for the production of a lightweight, portable, gasoline-driven chainsaw engine for the Corps of Engineers." He continued:

> *When it is considered that this engine was developed in an amazingly short time and without the use of magnesium or the primary grades of aluminum—that in 31 instances, steel or plastics have replaced critical aluminum—the feat becomes more outstanding, a real tribute to that American Production that Hitler once said could never match his 10-year head start but which, today, is producing three and four times the total amount of output of the Axis powers. Forced labor never could have accomplished the results you have obtained here under the American system.[22]*

Awards and Rebellions

The Kiekhaefer Corporation made banner headlines twice within a three-week period in the fall of 1943. The first was an honor, the second a humiliation. On October 27, the Ozaukee *Cedarburg News* dedicated an entire 12-page issue to the glory of the Kiekhaefer Corporation for winning the "E" award. The special issue contained dozens of advertising sections, all offering praise and congratulations to the Kiekhaefer Corporation by neighboring businesses and distant suppliers anxious to add their voices to the wave of tributes.

Three weeks later, on November 18, 1943, the following front-page headlines appeared: "Kiekhaefer Stockholders Demand Firm's High Salaries Be Lowered" and "Notice Served on Corporation to Cut Expenses."[23] A week before, Kiekhaefer had received a letter of demand drafted by the legal firm of Schanen & Schanen of nearby Port Washington, Wisconsin. Five of the minority stockholders objected to the planned construction of an administration and research addition to the crammed Kiekhaefer Corporation facilities. Kiekhaefer had broken ground for the two-story, $70,000 building on October 7 with the blessing of the War Production Board. The 14,000-square-foot, brick-and-concrete structure was designed to reduce the great burden of cramped factory quarters for research and office personnel, and also to add an environmental testing chamber for measuring engine performance against extremes of temperature and humidity. When the Kiekhaefer Corporation sent notice of the proposed building to the stockholders on November 2, 1943, work had been in progress for nearly a month.

The angry stockholders, fearful that Kiekhaefer was never going to issue a dividend to justify their initial investment, wanted to pressure Kiekhaefer into either buying their stock at inflated prices or paying the handsome dividends they were certain the company could afford. They attacked Kiekhaefer for what they assumed were exorbitant

A special issue of the *Cedarburg News* was published in 1943 to commemorate the "E" award ceremony. *(Reprinted by permission from News Graphic, Conley Media.)*

executive salaries and directors' fees. Their letter of demand was hand-delivered by Roland C. Schaefer, the Sheriff of Ozaukee County, on the morning of November 13, 1943. It read:

> On behalf of the Cedarburg Finance Co., E.H. Roth, Dr. William H. Wiesler, Palmer J. Wirth, and M.P. Becker, owners of 105 shares of the common capital stock of the Kiekhaefer Corporation, we are directed to notify your corporation that said stockholders are opposed and object to any expenditures of moneys of said corporation for the construction of buildings, or additions and contents. ... These stock-

holders maintain that such an expenditure is entirely unnecessary and unwise and is detrimental to the best interests of said corporation, and that the corporation is not in a financial position to make such expenditures. ... You are further advised that in due course proper action will be taken to compel repayment ... of the excessive sums of money paid for directors' fees and officials' salaries, and other illegal expenditures, and to restrain you in the future from paying such enormous, illegal, and excessive sums of money for directors' fees and officials' salaries, and similar expenditures.[24]

Kiekhaefer responded swiftly to the renegade stockholders, the same group that had tried to sell him out to the Flambeau outboard group while he was at the 1940 New York Motor Boat Show. His reply, dated three days later on November 16, 1943, baited the investors into bringing their charges out in the open through the newspaper. Kiekhaefer's response, penned by corporate attorney and full-time employee Guy S. Conrad, left little doubt what Kiekhaefer thought of the attempted raid on his authority and treasury. It read:

> The Kiekhaefer Corporation asserts that the sole reason for the service of said notice resides in the preconceived plan of the named stockholders to force the purchase of their stockholdings in the Kiekhaefer Corporation at an exorbitant and unwarranted price. ... The stockholders ... are at liberty to take any legal action provided by law ... within their discretion, and at such time as they desire. The Kiekhaefer Corporation will welcome any such action by the ... minority stockholders.[25]

In their reply, the attorneys for the five shareholders disclosed a glimpse of the true reason for the rebellion: "The Cedarburg Finance Co. owns 50 shares of the common capital stock of the Kiekhaefer Corporation. The Cedarburg Finance Co. at present is contemplating the building of houses in Cedarburg and will have to raise about $100,000. In order to do this, it will have to pledge some of its assets for that purpose."[26] The stockholders' reply was received the same day that the headlines appeared in the Ozaukee newspaper on November 18, 1943. For these accusations to be made in his hometown newspaper was a huge affront to Kiekhaefer, who with 250 employees, was the community's largest employer and benefactor. He wrote a letter to the editor of the *Cedarburg News* in an appeal to every family in town:

When the writer assumed his position of General Manager, he never dreamed there was any other policy to follow than to build a solid, thriving concern in the community of Cedarburg. Our directors' policies have not changed in this respect, and we do not believe our employees or any man or woman in Cedarburg would like to see us stop expanding or stop creating new jobs or stop creating new opportunities for Cedarburg residents. ... We do not believe these are the times to pay tremendous dividends even if it were possible. With the war casualties coming so close to home, how can anyone in this community think about dividends and place them ahead of the war effort, particularly, bankers who have sons and daughters in the armed forces. Men and women of the Kiekhaefer Corporation, what do you think? Write what you think ... and ask them to publish it.[27]

Business eventually returned to normal, but within a few years, when Kiekhaefer would consider either a dramatic expansion of his Cedarburg facilities or moving the heart of his growing operation elsewhere, he would remember well the double banner headlines and the stinging reprisals in the autumn of 1943.

On Target

On January 1, 1944, work began on a new project under the direction of the Army Air Corps. A new engine was needed to power small radio-controlled target aircraft drones for air-combat gunnery practice. Since the delivery of the very first air-cooled chainsaw prototype, the Kiekhaefer Corporation had earned a reputation for fast, flexible, and innovative engineering. The first contract, for $40,000, was for two prototype engines named the Y-40, which would eventually become a twin-cylinder, horizontally opposed, two-cycle engine of 35 horsepower. The War Department's largest budget was reserved for aircraft production, and when the opportunity to get in on the deal came along, the Kiekhaefer Corporation eagerly accepted it.

The target drone engine project presented unique challenges because the target aircraft were small, measuring only 10 feet, 2 inches from wingtip to wingtip, and only 8 feet, 6 inches from propeller to tail, with a 13.5-inch-deep fuselage. The entire aircraft weighed less than 138 pounds, including engine and propeller. A catapult launched the drone, which was controlled in flight by a radio-control panel on the ground or from pursuit aircraft.

Once launched from ground or ship deck, the aircraft typically flew between 4,000 and 5,000 feet before leveling off, and accelerated to its maximum speed of 175 to 200 mph. If it survived the hail of .30- and .45-caliber bullets fired by student gunners, the drone would fly to a recovery area, deploy a parachute stored in the tail section, and descend back to earth at the relatively safe rate of 16 feet per second. It was hardly the typical mission for an outboard or chainsaw engine.

The drone engine developed by Kiekhaefer and his designers ultimately weighed 34 pounds and developed 35 horsepower at 4,200 to 4,400 rpm. It was considered a great technical achievement to produce an engine that weighed less than a pound per horsepower. The engine was equipped with a float-type carburetor and used a battery ignition system. To start the engine, the nearly three-foot-long wooden propeller was spun either by hand or by an electric spinner that turned the propeller until the engine fired. Once the engine reached launch rpm, a release pin was electrically retracted on the catapult, and the whole works was flung into the air, most likely to be blown to smithereens.

One of the obstacles to overcome was one first thought to be the easiest: engine cooling. Since the aircraft was moving through the air at nearly 200 mph, engineers initially thought that the engine would be cooled easily. Actually, because the aerodynamics of the small target drone were so critical, the engine had to be almost completely enclosed by a tight-fitting cowling, with outside air ducted to the cylinder cooling fins. Early tests revealed piston seizing, poor fuel distribution, incorrect clearances, and sticking piston rings. Once these problems were overcome by providing more cylinder fin area and greater piston-cylinder clearances, the Kiekhaefer engine passed flight tests with flying colors.[28] Again, the company had demonstrated its ingenuity and flexibility by having a prototype in the air in a little over three months' time. It would be nearly a year, however, until the engine, then known as the 0-45-1 and 0-45-35, was perfected and volume deliveries made.

Kiekhaefer's government contracts continued to grow from nearly $4 million in 1944 to about $5 million in 1945. Mandatory government contract renegotiation would reduce the spoils of war starting with the 1944 production year, although more than $800,000 was trimmed from profits. Kiekhaefer did not object, however, for he had anticipated making a rebate of more than $1.2 million, which meant that his heart-wrenching letters to the War Production Board had managed to save the company nearly $400,000 that year alone. Evinrude reported that OMC, by contrast, had sales of nearly $33 million in 1944, and had paid out nearly $2 million in contract rebates.[29] But while the Kiekhaefer Corporation's sales volume grew more than 80 percent, sales at OMC tumbled by nearly 80 percent during the same period.

Though the manufacture of the chainsaw engine for Disston was the backbone of all Kiekhaefer Corporation war efforts, the sales of compressor, generator, and water pump engines were nearly as large for 1944, a year when only one solitary outboard engine was manufactured, a KB-4 twin-cylinder engine that sold for $55.70. The following year, no outboard engines would be manufactured whatsoever, and sales of the new target drone engine would compete equally with chainsaw engine revenues.

The End in Sight

Two days after Kiekhaefer's 38th birthday, on June 6, 1944, the long-awaited Allied invasion of Europe commenced on the beaches of Normandy. Within months, Paris was liberated by French and American forces, and the German armies were in

full retreat. In April 1945, President Franklin Roosevelt succumbed to a cerebral hemorrhage, cheating him of the chance to see the conclusion of the great struggle. Within two hours, Harry S Truman was sworn in as the nation's new president. In the same month, Adolf Hitler committed suicide in an underground bunker in Berlin, and the body of executed Italian leader Benito Mussolini was hung by his heels to the cheers of crowds in Milan. On

The target drone engine seemed an easy engineering task but was fraught with maddening problems.

May 7, 1945, the war in Europe officially ended, as Germany surrendered unconditionally to the victorious Allied nations. Almost exactly three months later, atomic bombs devastated the Japanese cities of Hiroshima and Nagasaki, hastening the surrender of the Japanese empire and bringing World War II to a long-awaited end.

The Kiekhaefer Corporation had designed no less than 51 special applications of air-cooled engines for the military services and had endured the hardships of bureaucracy and competitive political muscle. Kiekhaefer products had performed in every major theater of the war and had

From left to right: A compressor, Navy pump, and chainsaw sharpener were among the other innovations that kept the Kiekhaefer Corporation going during the tough war years.

earned the highest marks for performance, reliability, and simple operation.

But a whole new war was just beginning for the Kiekhaefer Corporation, with stakes larger than even Kiekhaefer could imagine. The first shots in the postwar battle for control of the marine industry market were about to be fired.

KIEKHAEFER

MERCURY

1st...*in* **SPEED**

1st...*in* **STAMINA**

1st...*in* **STYLING**

1st...*in* **VALUE**

FIRST *in the hearts of sportsmen!*

Regardless of the model you select, your Mercury Outboard Motor is made up of specially engineered components . . . each part the product of an engineering project, developed, proved, and produced for the sole purpose of making your Mercury Outboard all you have desired . . . the most outboard per dollar.

You must drive a Mercury and see for yourself just what it will do . . . you will be happy with the ease of starting . . . astonished by its power and speed . . . comfortable at its controls . . . pleased with its rugged durability.

Mercury has pioneered and brought to you the "outboard of all time". . . it is conservative in its horsepower rating, but still provides the greatest performance per pound of weight. Consider just a few of the most outstanding features built into your Mercury, "full jeweled power"* . . . full-feathered safety steering . . . proper cooling at any speed . . . truly waterproof magneto . . . duo-flex propeller drive, and dozens of others. Yes, try a Mercury for size and select your favorite; then you are set to enjoy the ultimate in outboard performance.

★ SEE THE MERCURY LINE AT THE SHOWS

* *BALL AND ROLLER BEARINGS throughout*

**KIEKHAEFER CORPORATION
CEDARBURG, WISCONSIN**

Lightning DE LUXE

A 10 hp. twin, with flashing power that will plane a light runabout mere seconds away from the dock . . . give boat speeds never before dreamed of with a 10 hp. outboard . . . yet so smooth and flexible that it will throttle down, it will troll.

Rocket DE LUXE

— The truly all purpose outboard . . . a 7½ hp. twin with speed and endurance for the most rugged going . . . still capable of the smoothest, slow-motion trolling pace. An ideal family boat motor.

Comet DE LUXE

— A light, lively 3.6 hp. outboard that's right at home on the average fishing boat or the light craft carried on top of your car.

MATCHLESS IN OUTBOARD EXCELLENCE

Ads such as this one in 1948 sometimes seemed unnecessary, since the postwar boom nearly stripped outboard manufacturers' production capacity.

CHAPTER THREE

THE POSTWAR YEARS

*As you know, one of the rules of the Kiekhaefer Corporation is that no exec-
utive or office employee leave the plant during working hours without dis-
closing details to the operator. Failure to do so in the future will definitely
result in dismissal of the offender as well as the operator if not reported.*

—Carl Kiekhaefer, Christmas Day, 1944[1]

O N FEBRUARY 18, 1944,
the Kiekhaefer Corpora-
tion received its first postwar order for outboard engines from
Western Auto Supply. Though work
on the requested 15,000 engines could
not begin until the factory was released
from war production, it was a most welcome
development. Western Auto's order represented the first of such "postwar" orders, though
the war still had more than a year of fighting to go.

Kiekhaefer was impatient to begin working on
outboards again and sent an angry letter to the War
Department. Short of naming OMC, his letter complained bitterly that "some of our competitors are in
civilian outboard production—simply because they
chose not to take on certain war contracts." The letter fretted that Kiekhaefer Corporation's larger rivals
could hold onto engineers and manpower because
they were able to offer higher pay and shorter hours
and had better access to scarce raw materials. Kiekhaefer's letter questioned the adverse effects that the
war contracts would have if the company could not
begin working on outboards again—if they would
be drained of working capital due to their loyalty and
patriotism to the country.[2]

A few weeks later, Kiekhaefer received a letter
from the War Production Board indicating its willingness to rewrite Limitation Order 80, which had
prohibited the use of aluminum for recreational
products, with respect to outboard motors and

parts. Having learned through
experience that the company
would receive only a small percentage of anything he asked for
from the government, he replied that
he would build 78,000 outboards in
1945 if allowed the critical materials to
produce them. In his answer, he also estimated the man-hour requirements for building his single-cylinder engines "at three-quarters
of a motor being built per man in an eight-hour
day," and for his larger twin-cylinder models, "one-
half and one-quarter motor being built per man,
per eight-hour day."[3]

Company engineers had been working on
postwar designs, though in most cases only minor improvements to prewar designs had been
made. By July 1945, Limitation Order 80 was
lifted. Restrictions were still strictly enforced, however, which severely limited the practical ability to
produce outboards.[4]

But after the restrictions were lifted, Western
Auto Supply more than doubled its postwar order
from 15,000 to 33,000 engines, in three new models
ranging from 3 to 12 horsepower—with delivery
by Christmas 1945, if possible, but no later than
January 1946.[5] The Kiekhaefer Corporation began

The new Mercury Outboard Motors logo, with the prominent "K."

to feel the effects of what was known as "post-war fever."

The war had taught lessons to Kiekhaefer and his organization that might have been impossible to learn in the calm of peacetime. The quick reaction to engineering challenges was often prompted by a feeling of life-and-death struggle, and the wide array of products and assignments put flexibility into every job description. But the pace of war production put a tremendous strain on the organization, its employees, and their families. In February 1945, Kiekhaefer had ordered a mandatory seven-day workweek. Monday through Friday, employees worked from 8 a.m. to 9 p.m., with an hour off for lunch and for supper—an 11-hour day. On Saturday, hours ran from 8 a.m. to 5:30 p.m., with a half-hour for lunch, a slightly less brutal eight-hour day. On Sunday, workers toiled from 8 a.m. to noon. Kiekhaefer knew the schedule

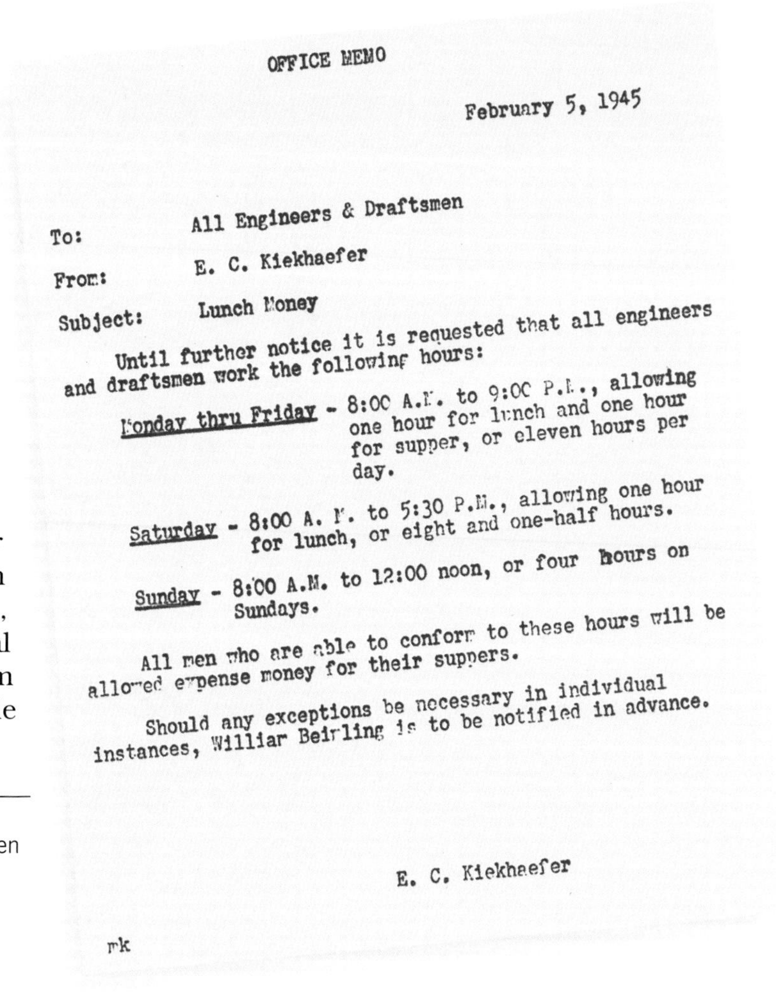

When Kiekhaefer sent a memo to his engineers and draftsmen announcing a seven-day workweek, they weren't happy. But they weren't surprised, either.

OFFICE MEMO

February 5, 1945

To: All Engineers & Draftsmen

From: E. C. Kiekhaefer

Subject: Lunch Money

Until further notice it is requested that all engineers and draftsmen work the following hours:

Monday thru Friday - 8:00 A.M. to 9:00 P.M., allowing one hour for lunch and one hour for supper, or eleven hours per day.

Saturday - 8:00 A.M. to 5:30 P.M., allowing one hour for lunch, or eight and one-half hours.

Sunday - 8:00 A.M. to 12:00 noon, or four hours on Sundays.

All men who are able to conform to these hours will be allowed expense money for their suppers.

Should any exceptions be necessary in individual instances, William Beirling is to be notified in advance.

E. C. Kiekhaefer

rk

1944 — Western Auto requests 15,000 outboards.

1946 — The old Corium Farms becomes the new Fond du Lac production plant.

1945 — Kiekhaefer orders a mandatory seven-day workweek.

was unpopular with most men and their families, so he softened the blow by allowing expense money for supper for all workers on the rough schedule.

At Home "at the Foot of the Lake"

The moment the war ended, Kiekhaefer was faced with a major dilemma. The Army Corps of Engineers told him to continue production of chain saw engines under his existing contracts, and the company even accepted additional contracts, with more target drone aircraft engine orders from the Army Air Corps. Though he finally had the opportunity to build outboard motors again, he had no room to assemble them. The entire facility at Cedarburg was jammed with chainsaw and aircraft engine production lines, with hardly enough room for employees and machinery. Still stinging with embarrassment over the accounts of his stockholder rebellion the year before, Kiekhaefer resolved to look elsewhere rather than expand his plant in Cedarburg. His odyssey to a dozen nearby Wisconsin cities turned up a number of potential sites, ranging from Wausau to Beaver Dam to Fond du Lac. High on his list of priorities were existing facilities with room to grow and a community that would bend over backward to keep his growing business.

He found the unique combination he was searching for in Fond du Lac, 40 miles to the northwest of Cedarburg. According to local folklore, by the middle of the 17th century, French explorers crossed the Great Lakes into Michigan and Wisconsin and made their way down the Fox River from Green Bay into Lake Winnebago. Named for the Indian tribe that first settled the region, Wisconsin's largest inland lake was measured as early as 1670 by grizzled trappers eager to establish a foothold in the lucrative beaver- and otter-saturated wilderness. The French named the southernmost point of Lake Winnebago Fond du Lac, which, loosely translated, means "at the foot" or "bottom" of the lake.

The thermometer dangled somewhere between 20 and 25 degrees below zero that January morning in 1946, as Kiekhaefer drove Herman Stieg southwest of town. Kiekhaefer was eager to show Stieg what the aggressive Fond du Lac Industrial Development Corporation had offered to sell him at a most attractive price. Kiekhaefer pulled up beside the largest barn Stieg had ever seen, nearly 300 feet long and almost five stories high, topped by

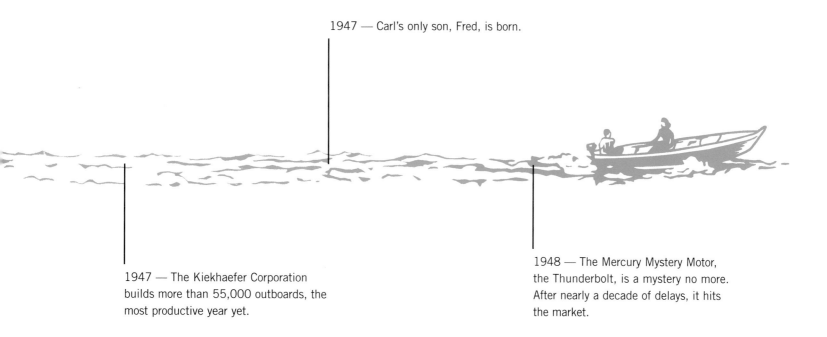

1947 — Carl's only son, Fred, is born.

1947 — The Kiekhaefer Corporation builds more than 55,000 outboards, the most productive year yet.

1948 — The Mercury Mystery Motor, the Thunderbolt, is a mystery no more. After nearly a decade of delays, it hits the market.

11 giant ventilators and surrounded by four towering grain silos.

"Much to my surprise," Stieg remembered, "he turned around to me, and he said, 'Well, how would you like the task of making a factory out of this barn here?' I thought, 'My God! What do you think I can do? This is so way beyond me.'"

But, observing Kiekhaefer, with his hands on his hips, head tilted back to take in the whole gigantic structure and a big cigar jutting nearly straight up from one side of a broad smile, Stieg knew anything was possible. "Sure," he said, "Why not?"[6]

The Corium Farms barn had been built in 1917 by Fred Rueping, owner of the Rueping Leather Company that had flourished in Fond du Lac since 1854. Corium, which means "leather" in Latin, grew to be the largest and most successful dairy farm in the region, with 500 acres and a herd of 300 thoroughbred cows descended from lines from the island of Guernsey off the coast of France. One of the first inhabitants of the barn was Imported Prospects Rose de Hords, the record-breaking milk and butterfat bovine bought for nearly $18,000 in 1919. For many years, Corium Farms was considered the very model of modern milking operations and swept blue-ribbon honors at a succession of Wisconsin state fairs.[7] When the dairy interests were sold

off in 1945, the mammoth structure was ultimately acquired by a consortium of civic-minded Fond du Lac boosters, much as the Cedarburg plant had been.

That persuaded Carl Kiekhaefer to take advantage of the unique situation, and the Kiekhaefer Corporation took possession of the Corium Farms barn and surrounding 38 acres on February 1, 1946. Kiekhaefer had managed to acquire the land and buildings for only $25,000, which worked out to roughly $2,250 for the land at $59 an acre, plus an additional $22,750 for the buildings. Now it was a race against the clock to transform the barn into a modern engine manufacturing plant.

Herman Stieg quickly hired a large crew of men to clear out the hundreds of bull and cow stanchions and stalls that made the interior of the cavernous building appear like a medieval maze of pipes, corrals, gutters, and troughs. Kiekhaefer rolled up his sleeves to join the crew in removing more than 200 tons of stacked hay that lay in the loft, 25 feet above the floor. They drove a hay baler underneath the loft, and with a small army of pitchforks, tossed the loose hay into the machine. Neatly tied bales were trucked away for sale to surrounding farms. "And he was right with us," Stieg remembered of Kiekhaefer, "pitching hay down into the baler.

The Fond du Lac plant, even following expansion, still used converted grain elevators for engine test cells.

HERMAN STIEG

ERMAN STIEG WAS 23 IN 1936, WHEN HE started work for Carl Kiekhaefer at Stearns Magnetic in Milwaukee. Even then, Kiekhaefer depended on Stieg's help with special projects, such as working on weekends at Stearns, greasy elbow to greasy elbow, helping Kiekhaefer pull the engine out of his car.

After Kiekhaefer started the Kiekhaefer Corporation, he called for his old friend to join him in Cedarburg. Beginning in early 1941, Stieg was going to be Kiekhaefer's point man in developing the magnetic separator business. When it became clear that outboard and air-cooled engines would dominate the future of the company, Kiekhaefer kept Herman moving around the plant, doing everything from subassembly to fixture layout to toolmaking to machine shop superintendent. He was put in charge of the plant's entire night shift in November 1942.

It was Stieg's habit of volunteering to go the extra mile whenever the occasion arose that cemented Kiekhaefer's confidence in him. Typical of his enthusiasm was the time on Easter Sunday in 1945, after the plant crew had been working all day Saturday and through the long night, preparing the first 50 aircraft target engines. The men could hardly stand up. "Carl got his father's farm truck in there and loaded [the engines] into it by about 10:00 on Sunday," Stieg remembered. "He looked around and said 'Well, who's going to drive this thing to Chicago now?' "

The silence of the exhausted crew made it clear that nobody was interested in putting in another eight or nine hours after working 27 straight hours. "I'll do it," Stieg answered, and grabbed the keys from Kiekhaefer.

In fact, he even went down and ran the baler for a while."[8]

Once the interior of the barn had been stripped, Stieg poured a new concrete floor to fill the gutters and holes that made the remaining slab look like a cratered mine field. At one end of the structure, he partitioned off areas for a machine shop and tool crib, leaving the bulk of the cavernous structure for assembly operations. Each special attribute of the building was put to good use. One of the four huge silos was used to house a large cylinder-honing machine that had to be skidded sideways into the opening and then set upright. Another silo became home to the air compressors needed for factory operations, while yet another became the motor spray-painting department. The last silo became a test cell for the target aircraft drone engines. Since these engines were tested with actual flight propellers, the giant silo worked perfectly to provide large volumes of air for both intake and exhaust. Offices for Kiekhaefer and other administrators were built in the loft, overlooking one end of the plant floor.

Meanwhile, Kiekhaefer realized that the narrow window for seasonal outboard motor production couldn't wait for conversion of the Corium Farms barn, so he began limited production in Cedarburg. The demanding conditions of wartime resulted in many lessons learned about engine durability and performance. Kiekhaefer was beginning to make major changes to his outboard engines for the first time since he reconditioned Thor engines for Montgomery Ward. As he coaxed higher and higher performance out of his prewar designs, flaws appeared. He replaced aluminum connecting rods with drop-forged, hardened, and precision-ground alloy steel, the same type used for drive shafts. The dynamometer readings for the Rocket continued to rise with each improvement, until the motor advertised as a 6-horsepower engine was roaring well past 7.5. These improvements were then incorporated in the single-cylinder, 3.2-horsepower Comet. Kiekhaefer capitalized on his new roller, ball, and needle bearing-equipped engines by calling them full-jeweled power heads. Watchmakers had for some time referred to their precision movements as "fully

Mercury made good use of the term "full jeweled" in all of its advertising, including this 1946 brochure.

jeweled" when gear bearings had been bored from semiprecious stones, which is undoubtedly where Kiekhaefer appropriated the friction-free slogan.

As a result of continuing aluminum shortages, only the two-cylinder Rocket was built in 1946, but between those labeled Mercury and those labeled Wizard for Western Auto Supply, the Kiekhaefer Corporation managed to ship nearly $1.5 million worth of outboards by the end of September. In addition, over $3.1 million in chainsaw, generator, and other industrial engines was built in the same period. The company was back in the outboard business with both feet.

The Mercury Lightning

The lessons learned from building thousands of chainsaw and other engines for the government, and the improved performance of the modified Rocket, were enough to convince Kiekhaefer to make a complete break with the Thor-based models and design a new engine from scratch. Work began almost immediately on the new 10-horsepower engine that was destined to propel the Kiekhaefer Corporation to prominence in the marine industry and send competitors scrambling to their drawing boards. Kiekhaefer wanted an engine to compete head to head with the best engines in the industry and to firmly establish Mercury's presence in the postwar marketplace. As the engine design lab worked on the essential components of the two-cylinder, alternate-firing engine, Kiekhaefer directed the sculpting of clay models to achieve the most modern appearance and distinctive markings possible to set the engine apart from the pack. He requested a fully enclosed or "hooded" engine, a cosmetic concept started by Evinrude in 1929, and one which Kiekhaefer had emulated with his own 1940 Thor Streamliner.

The cowling design that emerged from the lab was meticulously shaved and molded from clay, painted green, and supported by a two-by-four. Looking somewhat like an elongated sphere or plump football, it was proudly paraded into

Kiekhaefer's office for his inspection. It was this somewhat chubby profile that would finally emerge from the Kiekhaefer production lines as the Mercury Lightning.

Among the more distinctive visual features of the bright pea-green engine was an oversized letter "K" that doubled as the throttle lever handle. The 10-horsepower engine was blowing the dynamometer past the 16-horsepower mark, but Kiekhaefer insisted on calling it a 10-horse so that no other 10-horse in the water could possibly touch it. More than modesty, the underrating of horsepower remained a strategic marketing weapon for Kiekhaefer through the years. He carefully positioned his products so they would be known as the fastest in their advertised horsepower class. Along with the provocative slogan "Full Jeweled Power," the first totally new engine from Kiekhaefer was quick to gain a reputation for both speed and precision engineering, and it swamped the growing company with an avalanche of new orders. Kiekhaefer discussed his reasoning for underrating his engines in an interview years later, and admitted the deliberate step to establish Mercury products as high-performance. He said:

First of all, we found out when we got into the military, the 16-horsepower Evinrude was rated at 9-horse by the Army Engineers, and so down the line. They really de-rated the motors, and I know that ... the military was only trying to get a realistic horsepower rating, so we thought about that too, and we said, "Well, what the hell is the cost difference? We might as well go the other way."

Instead of building a 10-horse motor, we'll put out a 14-horse motor. And we were already beyond the 16-horsepower rating that Evinrude had. Consequently, we were able to outrun them. With our Mercury 10, we outran not only all their 10s but their 16s and in some cases even their 22s. ...

So we rated our engines very conservatively. Subsequently, they got the reputation of being high-performance. And it's just giving the customer a little more for his dollar. That was the principle of the thing, and we didn't have to be so darned exact. If we rated an engine 10-horse and some of them pulled 13 and some of them pulled 15, we weren't too worried about it."[9]

The Mercury Lightning was a legendary accomplishment in outboard motor history, consistently outperforming outboards rated at more than twice its horsepower.

Thirty years after the 10-horsepower Lightning was introduced, Kiekhaefer was presented with a beautifully framed, chronological montage of his accomplishments, but he complained that the Mercury Lightning wasn't depicted. "Without trying to be critical of a nice piece of art, I am sorry only that the Mercury Lightning did not appear," he said. "This was the most important engine Mercury ever built and also what put Mercury into orbit." He continued:

So many advancements were incorporated into this engine that it went clean over the tops of the heads of some of the competition. ... Features included ... the most horsepower per pound, the most horsepower per cubic inch, and the most horsepower per dollar of any outboard motor before or since 1947. The advent of the Mercury Lightning set Mercury aside into something separate and apart from the rest of the mob.[10]

By July 1946, Stieg had performed the near-miracle of transforming the giant Corium Farms dairy barn into a full-time engine manufacturing facility. While the production lines of Cedarburg were still churning out the Thor-based 6-horsepower Rocket, Kiekhaefer transferred most chainsaw engine production to Fond du Lac to make room for outboard production. While the new 10-horsepower Lightning was prepared for production, Kiekhaefer ordered the preparation of a new 6-horsepower, twin-cylinder Rocket and single-cylinder 3.2-horsepower Comet, modeled after the Lightning's fully shrouded Green Pumpkin design to round out a new trio of 1947 offerings. Just when both factories had begun to settle down, Kiekhaefer sent notice to Stieg that the new Lightning would be the first outboard motor built in the new Fond du Lac facility.

When the Lightning hit the water following its introduction at the New York Motor Boat Show in January 1947, it caused shock waves in the outboard industry. It ran away from everything even remotely close to its size and advertised horsepower. It beat nearly every popular motor on the market, including the 16-horsepower and even 22-horsepower Johnsons. One afternoon, when the first Lightning prototypes were still being tested, Kiekhaefer asked Bob Stuth, among the most versatile of Kiekhaefer's employees, to get his boat and 33.4-horsepower Evinrude Speedifour and bring them to the company's new outboard motor proving grounds on the Milwaukee River, just north of Thiensville, Wisconsin. Kiekhaefer wanted to prove that his new 10-horsepower engine could whip even the massive four-cylinder Evinrude. As the carefully staged race began, the lower unit of the Lightning prototype blew apart. Red-faced, Kiekhaefer "reeled into the lab about screwing up his day and embarrassing him," according to Stuth.[11]

The year 1947 was the fastest-growing in the company's history. From building 16,908 Rocket outboards in 1946, the company built more than 55,000 outboards during 1947, more than tripling production. Sales skyrocketed, doubling from $5.2 million to more than $10 million as a direct result of the Lightning.

Everything grew for Kiekhaefer that year, even his family. On August 23, 1947, a son was born to Freda and Carl. In the Teutonic Kiekhaefer family tradition, he was named Frederick Carl Kiekhaefer. "Freddie," as he would be known throughout his formative years, was a clever, restless child who, as the last of Carl and Freda's children, was destined to play an important and strategic role in Kiekhaefer's life. The two daughters, Helen and Anita, then 14 and 8 years old, respectively, were growing up without benefit of their father's attention. Though Kiekhaefer was clearly proud of his family, he spent infinitely more time preoccupied with his factories than he did at home.

Consolidating Control

Kiekhaefer had formed a new corporation in 1946 when he purchased the Corium Farms property, Kiekhaefer Aeromarine Motors, which was placed on the books as an affiliate. The formation of the new corporation allowed some advantages in monitoring the productivity of each plant independently and allowed Kiekhaefer a way to purchase shares in the Kiekhaefer

Background: The 3.2-horsepower Comet.

Corporation before the new engine designs could drive prices out of reach. Using corporate secretary Willis Blank as a shield, Kiekhaefer managed to trap the stock owned by the unfriendly shareholders. On December 25, 1946, just as the new Lightning was put into production, Kiekhaefer and Willis Blank signed an agreement that was the beginning of an ingenious plan to eventually consolidate all but 10 percent of shares into Kiekhaefer ownership.

First, Blank obtained an option to purchase the 85 shares of Kiekhaefer Corporation stock owned by Edgar Roth, Palmer Wirth, Matthew Becker, and the Cedarburg Finance Company—the conspiratorial stockholder group that had embarrassed Kiekhaefer in the headlines and tried to sell him out to Flambeau when he was out of town in 1940. Next, Kiekhaefer executed an option to buy any shares that Blank would acquire, along with an additional 60 shares from the Blank family under the control of Willis, including some shares owned by Willis alone. Willis Blank had received

300 shares of the new corporation, Kiekhaefer Aeromarine Motors, which would also be transferred to Kiekhaefer under the terms of the agreement. The complicated plan called for Kiekhaefer to pay Willis $25,000 to secure the options, place an additional $25,000 of security in escrow as a guarantee of good faith, and then pay for blocks of shares at regular intervals until 1950, when all the options would be exercised or expire. Total payments would add up to $215,000. In the presence of Kiekhaefer's corporate attorney and confidant, Guy Conrad, the papers were signed. Along with the stock options, the document provided Kiekhaefer with the immediate voting proxies, which remained his unless he suspended payments for the stock. For the first time since the attempted Flambeau sellout, Kiekhaefer could breathe easier, knowing that no one could wrestle control of the company away from him and his father or sell existing stock to anyone but himself.

Industry predictions of a postwar recreational boom underestimated the enthusiasm with which

Parts lists for Lightning, Comet, and Rocket engines.

The Thunderbolt, the original Kiekhaefer "Mystery Motor."

Bantam, Brooklure (Spiegel), Buccaneer (Gale), Chris-Craft, Chrysler, Corsair, Elgin (Sears Roebuck), Saber (Fedway), Firestone (Firestone Tire & Rubber), Flambeau, Hiawatha (Gamble-Skogmo), LeJay, Majestic, Martin (National Pressure Cooker), Milburn Cub, Motor Troller, Sea-Bee (Goodyear Tire & Rubber by Gale Products, OMC), Sea-Flyer (B.F. Goodrich), Silvertrol, Voyager, and West Bend outboards. Add to these the already established outboard manufacturers that began production before the war, such as Waterwitch (Sears Roebuck), Elto (Evinrude), Evinrude (OMC), Flambeau, Johnson (OMC), Lausen (Hart-Carter), and Muncie. Then throw in Sea King (Montgomery Ward by OMC) and Kiekhaefer's own Wizard for Western Auto Supply, and the competition had become a very real nightmare, producing a sea of confusing brand names and alliances within a short time.

As consumers became more acquainted with the new features offered on outboard motors, manufacturers flooded newspapers and magazines with boastful and often misleading advertisements. Speed and dependability were the most sought-after virtues in new engines, and the design teams at Kiekhaefer Corporation worked at a feverish pace to prepare the new 25-horsepower Thunderbolt, which had been promised as the "Mercury Mystery Motor" even before aluminum restrictions stopped development in 1941.

The Corium Farms facility was barely open for production when Stieg was ordered to expand it. A 25,000-square-foot addition was followed by another 40,000-square-foot annex the following year. With the market filling up rapidly with competition, the name of the game quickly became production.

When all of the normal startup flaws had been ironed out, Stieg left Fond du Lac to scour the country to buy as much machinery as he could. The government's war asset warehouses bulged with surplus machine tools, and the company needed to expand as quickly as possible to keep ahead of competition. Fortunately, surplus machinery could be bought for less than 25 cents on the dollar, so when Kiekhaefer gave Stieg a blank check to spend up to $600,000 on machinery,

returning war veterans would embrace outboarding. As the market grew, Kiekhaefer began to compete against a rash of new companies. "By the time the war was over, we hoped to get some rest," Kiekhaefer said, "but by that time there were some 60 outboard manufacturers in the business. Everybody that made pots and pans wanted to get in the outboard business."[12] Although Kiekhaefer exaggerated the number of companies involved, the threat was real enough. Within a four-year period, production started on Atco, Atlas (distributed by Standard Oil),

Stieg was able to secure nearly $3 million of prime production hardware. Much of the equipment was brand new, still in the original shipping cases, loaded with accessories, and still covered by warranty. "I just went out and, on my own, I'd say, 'I'll take these three machines,'" Stieg recalled, "and they'd write up the paperwork and send the bill to the company."[13]

The Kiekhaefer Corporation was tooling up to take on the entire industry. In less than a year, the company was able to quadruple production capacity and was prepared to take on all comers in a race for market share. Kiekhaefer patrolled his plants like General George Patton, barking orders and changes with every turn of the aisle. His reputation for toughness, tenacity, and engineering intuition was spreading far outside the confines of his factories. The market was ready, his facilities were ready, his products were ready, and the Kiekhaefer Corporation was ready to explode.

Mystery Revealed

The spectacular success of the 10-horsepower Mercury Lightning continued to propel the Kiekhaefer Corporation into high gear. During 1948, Kiekhaefer was finally able to build the prototype of the engine he had been promising since before World War II, the Thunderbolt. Once known as the "Mercury Mystery Motor," the Thunderbolt underwent major design changes once the Lightning was proven in the marketplace. Because the Thunderbolt had been on and off the drawing boards for so long, the engine

The Thunderbolt's compact and sleek design was just as much a selling point as its power.

that ultimately emerged from the engineering laboratory was the product of the widest design swings in Kiekhaefer history. Eventually, Kiekhaefer decided to base the new engine almost totally on the Lightning design. The new Thunderbolt prototype basically became two Lightning power heads welded together and joined by an elongated crankshaft. The world's first in-line four-cylinder outboard engine delivered well in excess of the advertised 25 horsepower, true to Kiekhaefer's penchant for underrating his motors. Kiekhaefer would later admit that the Thunderbolt actually developed a whopping 40 horsepower, making it the "first line of outboards to produce 1 horsepower per cubic inch."[14]

Using the same pistons, connecting rods, and reed valves as the Lightning resulted in an engine with exactly twice the displacement at 39.6 cubic inches, which weighed in at almost twice the Lightning at 115 pounds. With a unique squeeze-grip throttle, the bright green power head was notable for its lack of a rewind starter. With characteristic aplomb, Kiekhaefer ventured a number of comparisons about the long-awaited offspring from his lab:

As quiet as a 3.5, as easy to control as a 5, as easy to crank as a 10, weighing about that of a 16, having the performance more than a 33, and the feel and response of the finest V8 automotive engine or inboard engine—that's the Mercury 25 with the Magnificent Thunderbolt Engine. Not only the first powerful outboard in more than a decade, but the greatest news and the finest contribution to outboards in 40 years.[15]

Unfortunately, Kiekhaefer's plans for market dominance were once again interrupted by a war overseas—and a crisis at home.

Carl Kiekhaefer's glare could be as frightening as his outbursts. In the early 1950s, he had reasons for both.

CHAPTER FOUR

THE FIFTIES

At this time in particular, with the government restrictions of material, and no military demands to replace loss of production, complete disorganization in the various government offices, reorganization of sales technique and policies, engineering talent and policies, development engineering and financing, I have been rather busy. ... If you should find someone who would be willing to buy a couple of outboard plants, please get in touch. ..."

—Carl Kiekhaefer, January 1951[1]

LESS THAN FIVE YEARS AFTER THE German and Japanese surrender that promised a generation of peace throughout the world, North Korean forces stormed across the 38th parallel separating North and South Korea in June 1950, and raced to overrun South Korea's capital city of Seoul. President Harry Truman sent American armed forces to repel the invasion, in association with other United Nations member forces.

After months of seesaw battles, President Truman declared a state of emergency in the United States on December 16, 1950, imploring all citizens to unite their efforts to combat "Communist imperialism." Truman also called for "a mighty production effort" for the burgeoning military activity, and declared his intention to safeguard democracy with an "arsenal of freedom." For Carl Kiekhaefer, the meaning of the message was a familiar and frustrating one: the return of restrictions on the use of aluminum for outboard motors.

In Washington, DC, the National Production Authority (NPA) was established. The agency was a direct descendant of the War Production Board that had nettled the growth of the Kiekhaefer Corporation during World War II. The NPA had determined, as it had during the previous war, that aluminum should be diverted from outboard manufacturers because the products were clearly recreational in nature.

But OMC, Kiekhaefer's number one competitor," decided to take the NPA to task over its appraisal of outboard use, dispatching Joseph G. Rayniak to Washington to carry the standard of the marine industry. As the only outboard industry representative to appear at the NPA hearings, Rayniak prepared his case carefully and conclusively. The NPA had served notice that it intended to curb aluminum use to the outboard industry by an incredible 90 percent, allowing only 10 percent of forecasted outboards to be built during the national emergency. With the aid of a specially prepared pamphlet, "Outboards at Work," Rayniak explained to the government that more than 700,000 outboards were being used for vital commercial purposes such as fishing, logging, conservation, disaster relief, offshore oil operations, water taxis, and waterfront construction. Outboard motors were just as crucial to American industry as the many other products left unregulated. Based on Rayniak's testimony, it seemed to the NPA that Johnson and Evinrude products were the only outboards being used for industry.

In a surprising decision, the NPA not only canceled its planned restrictions at OMC but actually

The Mercury logo in the 1950s.

offered to assist the firm in obtaining additional aluminum for future production. Worse still, the hearings failed to lift restrictions for the Kiekhaefer Corporation or other manufacturers in the industry. Thanks to Rayniak, who would be rewarded three years later with the presidency of the corporation, OMC would coast through the Korean War, devoting only about 10 percent of its production capacity to defense, while the Kiekhaefer Corporation, for the second time in less than a decade, was nearly pushed out of the outboard business altogether.

Kiekhaefer became thoroughly disgusted with the need once again to transition from peacetime to wartime operations, as he stated in a letter to J. Paxton Hill, the utility racing secretary of the American Power Boat Association:

This is the second wartime operation that I am organizing within a 10-year period, and we never completely recovered from the first. Believe me, it would be much easier to carry a rifle. ... Wars always serve as a catching-up period for the weaker and more selfish competitors, who, instead of contributing in like measure on the new designs and production of military needs, are content to turn their vast plants over into machine shops to make nuts and bolts for the military while they and their engineering group are planning postwar-wise not only on engineering but organization-wise."[2]

For almost a year, Kiekhaefer had been thinking about selling the business. The advent of aluminum restrictions stiffened his resolve to join forces with a larger company to relieve himself of his growing administrative burden and allow himself more time for research and engineering. At least that's what he led his inside circle of executives to believe. Actually, Kiekhaefer was alarmed at the sharp leveling off of sales in the outboard and marine industries and was tired of struggling, like David, against the giant of OMC.

He began corresponding first with Walter F. Rockwell, president of the Timken-Detroit Axle Company, and uncle to W.F. "Al" Rockwell Jr., president of the substantial Rockwell Manufacturing Company of Pittsburgh. He also discussed a merger with Disston as well as Food Machinery and Chemical Corporation (FMC), which had acquired the Propulsion Engine Corporation of Kansas City, manufacturers of lawn mowers and

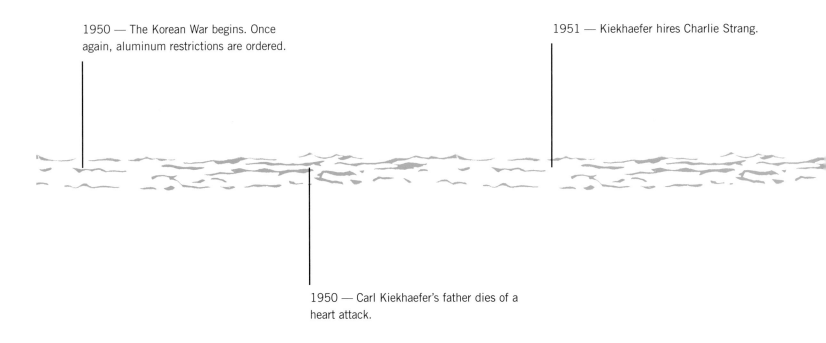

1950 — The Korean War begins. Once again, aluminum restrictions are ordered.

1951 — Kiekhaefer hires Charlie Strang.

1950 — Carl Kiekhaefer's father dies of a heart attack.

two-cycle engines. Kiekhaefer flew to San Jose, California, in November 1950, with the intention of selling the Kiekhaefer Corporation to FMC. But the deal was never consummated.

Finally, the merger madness passed over Kiekhaefer, and he began to concentrate on the growth of the business once again. In a period of less than 24 months, he had come within a few documents of selling his company to Rockwell Manufacturing, Disston, and FMC. The receipt of a contract of more than $3 million from Disston for saw engines, combined with a renewed interest by the government in having the Kiekhaefer Corporation build a new, more powerful target drone engine, were the major factors that ultimately convinced Kiekhaefer to hang on and build for the future.

Endings and Beginnings

On Saturday, October 7, 1950, Kiekhaefer's father, Arnold, suffered a heart attack and died.

The Disston chainsaw with the Mercury engine. Kiekhaefer nearly sold his company to Disston.

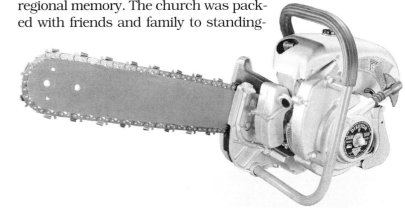

In his memory, the plants in Cedarburg and Fond du Lac closed for two days as funeral services were held at St. John's Lutheran Church in Mequon, followed by a burial in the parish cemetery. The Common Council of Cedarburg issued a proclamation, saying in part, "... through his initiative and ability he succeeded in establishing the Kiekhaefer Corporation, one of the leading industries in the City of Cedarburg, thereby directly and indirectly contributing to the prosperity, growth, and expansion of this City and bringing it national recognition."[3]

The funeral for Arnold was one of the largest in regional memory. The church was packed with friends and family to standing-

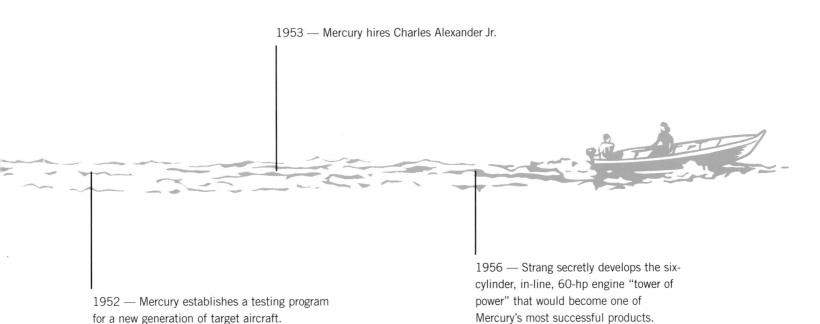

1953 — Mercury hires Charles Alexander Jr.

1952 — Mercury establishes a testing program for a new generation of target aircraft.

1956 — Strang secretly develops the six-cylinder, in-line, 60-hp engine "tower of power" that would become one of Mercury's most successful products.

room-only capacity. An overflow crowd spilled out into the crisp autumn morning, spreading over the lawns of St. John's in tribute to one of the community's most respected and beloved friends.

When Kiekhaefer first heard about his father's death, he was at the National Hydroplane "Free-For-All" Championships on Lake Alfred, near Winter Haven, Florida. Kiekhaefer had entered a number of new 25-horsepower Mercury Thunderbolt engines. One of the Mercurys that had performed brilliantly in one of the heats was driven by Kiekhaefer's close friend and Mercury dealer Jack Maypole. Citing a long-forgotten technicality, referee Dick "Coop" McFadden disqualified Maypole and unceremoniously moved his number from first to last on the tally board.

Though Maypole would later that day establish a new class speed record of around 70 mph, a young man named Charles Strang was angry at what he considered to be an unfair call. The 29-year-old M.I.T. faculty member, boat racer, and boating journalist stormed up to the judges' stand and began a loud exchange with McFadden, defending Kiekhaefer's driver. During Strang's technical explanation, McFadden signaled with his eyes and hands and discreetly said, "Shhhhhhh ... behind you." Kiekhaefer had wandered up behind Strang and said, "Thanks for sticking up for my driver. I want you to know I appreciate it."

It was the first exchange in what would become a long, close, and tumultuous friendship.

Strang had never met Kiekhaefer before, though as an avid outboard racer and boating journalist, he was aware of Kiekhaefer's growing reputation and of the powerful Mercury engines from Cedarburg and Fond du Lac. In fact, only the week before, Strang had written his first letter to Kiekhaefer, asking for photographs taken at races during the year for an article Strang was preparing

The Mercury 25 motor set a new speed record of 70 mph in 1950.

on outboard racing highlights of 1950. Later that day, at Lake Alfred, Armand Hauser, who, in 1950, was Kiekhaefer's sales manager and perpetual booster, introduced himself to Strang, telling him that Kiekhaefer wanted to speak with him in his suite at the Winter Haven Hotel.

The timing for their meeting was unfortunate, for Kiekhaefer had just received word about his father. When Strang reached the suite, Kiekhaefer thanked Strang again for his defense of Maypole and let him know that he would be happy to assist him with any photographs or information to support his articles. In even the briefest conversations with Strang, those who met him were struck with his honesty and his lightning-quick ease with technical subjects.

Strang followed up his short meeting with Kiekhaefer a few weeks later. It was a carefully detailed letter with a proposal to combine a souped-up 75-horsepower Evinrude power head, a Johnson drive shaft, and one of Kiekhaefer's new Quicksilver racing lower units in an attempt to set a new hydroplane "X" class record at over 85 mph. Attached to his letter was a sketch of how his "Mercrude" would be assembled.[4]

In the following weeks, the American Power Boat Association held its annual meeting in Chicago, which both Strang and Kiekhaefer attended. When Kiekhaefer spotted Strang at the gathering, he invited him to dinner along with McFadden, the referee that sparked their initial meeting in Florida. Kiekhaefer ushered them down to Chicago's famed Rush Street and, once seated, asked Strang what he thought of his new Thunderbolt engine. Strang replied quickly, "Great, but why didn't you build a bigger one?" referring to the horsepower edge that OMC still enjoyed over Mercury products in 1950. "Could we sell it if we did?" Kiekhaefer asked. "You bet," Strang snapped back. "Well, if you're so damn smart, why don't you come out and build it for us?" Kiekhaefer challenged.[5]

Strang thought Kiekhaefer was only joking and never gave the comment another thought—until Christmas Eve of 1950. Strang was visiting his aunt at Long Beach, New York, when the phone rang. Strang never discovered how Kiekhaefer found him, but it was a Christmas present that he would never forget. Kiekhaefer offered to give Strang complete control of a new research department, an atmosphere of unrestrained engineering creativity, and $7,500 a year to start. As if that weren't enough for a young outboard racing enthusiast who hadn't left the hallowed halls of M.I.T. for four years, Kiekhaefer told him that he wanted him to go to Europe first. Following the end of the school year at M.I.T., Strang would spend several months making a complete survey of two-cycle engine manufacturers in Europe, and then return to Wisconsin to take over his new department.

Strang agreed and traveled through Europe from July to August 1951, visiting virtually every notable engine-maker he could. He wrote dozens of letters to Kiekhaefer about his subjects, from Vespa, Lambretta, and Iso motor scooters in Italy, to ball bearing factories in Germany and England. Wherever he roamed, he made note of refinements to combustion chamber scavenging techniques, fuel-injection innovations, metallurgical advances, production capabilities, and opportunities for European distribution. He also developed a list of the top engineering and design talent working throughout the continent.[6] By August 1951, Strang had finally exhausted his list of manufacturers to investigate and returned to the United States to his new job.[7]

A Bumper Crop of Talent

By the time Strang got a desk job in Fond du Lac during the summer of 1951, the company had already assembled a formidable team of engineers that included a man named Ted Jones, the world's fastest man on water. Jones had pushed owner Stan Sayres' *Slo-Mo-Shun IV* three-point hydroplane of his own design to an unprecedented speed of over 160 mph. The following year, Jones won the American Power Boat Association Gold Cup, and his Unlimited Class Hydroplane design captured the International Harmsworth Trophy. That's

when Kiekhaefer showed up at his shop on Lake Washington, near Seattle. Jones said:

I was in the boat house on the lake getting the Slo-Mo-Shun ready for a test run. I felt someone was watching me, and yet I was supposed to be alone in the shop, and I looked around, and there's a fat man with a hat and an unlit cigar in his mouth just standing there watching me. I had a guard on the gate, a Pinkerton man. He'd keep people out 'cause ... everybody wanted to get in and see the boat, and I hadn't time to put up with it. "So," I said, "how did you get in?" He said, "Your guard likes money." He gave him a hundred dollar bill or something; there was nothing that would stop Carl, ever. Nothing.[8]

Jones became curious and learned more about the mysterious Kiekhaefer from his friends

Ted O. Jones, right, then the fastest man on the water, dominated the unlimited hydroplane record books for decades. Here, with Kiekhaefer, he was head of the company's target drone engine projects for the Navy at Point Mugu, California.

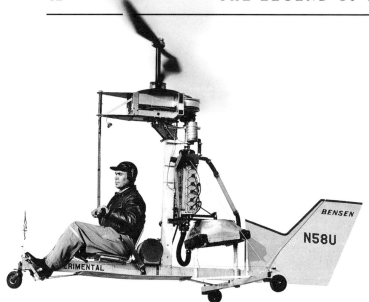

BENSEN

N58U

RIMENTAL

In the 1950s, a new one-man helicopter, designed especially for civilian use, was the futuristic answer to a commuter's dream—powered by a 60-horsepower Mercury outboard engine.

around the racing community. "I heard that he had the biggest temper of any man in the world," Jones said. When Kiekhaefer returned a few days later with an offer for Jones to design record-setting boats in the outboard class, Jones turned him down flat.[9]

Kiekhaefer didn't give up. He began to phone and correspond with Jones, slowly wearing him down. "Finally, he sent me $800 and an airline ticket and said, 'Come back and visit my plants,'" said Jones, who had relented and flew to Fond du Lac. In Kiekhaefer's office, Jones again told him that he had too much of a temper. Kiekhaefer pulled out a pad of paper and quickly hand-wrote a contract offer to Jones, including $10,000 a year for record-breaking boat designs, a bonus of $1,000 for each hull when the design was frozen, and an additional bonus of $7,500 for a Gold Cup design that would establish new records in 1952. Kiekhaefer also wanted Jones available for "special assignments."

A contract worth more than $21,000 in 1951 was impressive. When Jones finished reading, Kiekhaefer stood up, raised his right hand and with a sober poker face recited, "I, Carl Kiekhaefer, do solemnly swear to never display my temper to one Ted Jones." Kiekhaefer's unusual pledge and the plump contract were enough to persuade Jones to join the team.

As aluminum restrictions imposed by the Korean conflict began to choke off outboard engine production lines, the company once again focused on government contracts. By early 1952, the Kiekhaefer Corporation had established a testing program on a new generation of target aircraft

engines. The new engines, including a V4 inverted cylinder 90-horsepower model, were having technical problems. Jones was pulled away from boat design projects and sent to the Navy air base at Point Mugu near Oxnard in Southern California, where testing had nearly come to a standstill. Jones had never seen a target plane before. As he looked at the strange machines, a captain entered the hangar and said, "You'd better have one of those on the line ready to fly in the morning, and it's not good to defer in the Navy, so get with it."[10] In the dim light, Jones went to work, bolting together the useful pieces of smashed aircraft. He had never even seen the new Kiekhaefer Aeromarine engine before, but he managed to dissect and reassemble one before the scheduled test time in the morning. Jones stood back as naval personnel loaded the little target aircraft onto the catapult and prepared to launch. The catapult released, and the little craft went screaming into the air, only to lose power and auger into the ground a hundred yards away. The Navy personnel shook their heads and walked away. Jones knew that Kiekhaefer's new target aircraft engine program was in serious trouble.

One of the conditions for releasing the prototype engines for testing on aircraft was that they run 50 hours at high speed without a shutdown. Jones spent the entire night in the hangar preparing a new "bird" for flight test.

Once the engine began to perform well, the Navy placed orders for production models. Jones continued work on the target drone engine project at Point Mugu, and on March 11, 1952, he finally had the first 100 percent successful flight. Three months later, after a perfect "out of fuel" flight, Jones was asked by the Navy brass to refuel and prepare the target drone for another flight. Take-off and climb-out proceeded without a hitch, but then the radio-control servo units in the aircraft's elevator stuck in an absolute, vertical down position, and "the poor little bird hit the ground at 350 miles per hour." It would take another of Kiekhaefer's young geniuses to help solve the problem.

Of all the newly arrived talent in the 1950s, Jim Wynne was destined to have the most emotional impact on Kiekhaefer. Born in 1929, Wynne graduated from the University of Florida in 1951 with a bachelor's degree in mechanical engineering and entered the graduate school at M.I.T. only three months after Strang had left to join Kiekhaefer. *The New York Times* published an article advocating the re-emergence of the inter-collegiate boat racing association that was abandoned during World War II, leaving Strang as its reigning champion. Wynne then took the opportunity to write Strang, lending his support to the cause. Strang wrote back to thank him and asked if Wynne would be in a position to help Kiekhaefer Aeromarine with the new target drone engine the company was developing for the Navy.

Strang needed information on performance of the engine at various altitudes and knew that Wynne would have access to the Sloan Automotive Laboratory at M.I.T. (named after Alfred P. Sloan Jr., the brilliant executive and philanthropist who guided General Motors as president and chairman for more than a quarter-century, and who graduated from M.I.T. in 1895). Though Wynne was retained by Strang and Kiekhaefer for the token sum of $125 a month, the true value of the project to Wynne was the ability to use this practical research for his master's thesis.

In the fall of 1952, Wynne made a trip to Wisconsin to meet both Kiekhaefer and Strang for the first time. In February 1953, as Wynne was concluding his studies, Strang surprised him by offering him a job with Mercury. "I had been aiming for a career in the aircraft industry, primarily in aircraft engines," Wynne recalled, "and I really didn't see where I could

Another 1950s invention that literally didn't fly: the de Lackner DH-4 Heli-Vector, which was powered by a Mercury Mark 55.

get an engine-oriented career outside the aircraft field."[11] Wynne considered the opportunity most unique but was reluctant to relocate to the north. "I wanted to get back to Florida, or at least somewhere warm, and the thought of going to Oshkosh, Wisconsin, was not very enticing," he said. He was, however, genuinely impressed with both Kiekhaefer and Strang, and in March 1953 reported for work as the assistant director of research assigned to Edgar Rose, the new director of research who had been recruited only a month earlier.

Wynne had barely unpacked his bags in Wisconsin when he was dispatched to Point Mugu, California, to work on the target drone engine program for just "a couple of weeks." It didn't turn out that way. He said:

To make a long story short, I was there a year and a half. And this was just typical. Carl decided he wanted me out there. The fact that I had an apartment and a car parked in the driveway of the apartment [in Oshkosh] doesn't enter into it.[12]

Wynne was bounced around between California, Texas, the White Sands Proving Grounds, and Fort Bliss, tidying up loose ends of the drone engine project and trouble-shooting new outboard engine designs in Washington and Alaska. When he finally returned to Wisconsin in the fall of 1954, he was assigned the task of heading up Mercury's proving grounds. In Oshkosh, the company had expanded testing operations to include boat transom and clamped down static testing of outboards in the river running through town. When the river froze in the winter, testing operations continued near Sarasota, Florida, at Mercury's Midnight Pass facility on Siesta Key.[13]

In the spring of 1953, another strategic recruit arrived in Fond du Lac in the form of Charles Freeman Alexander Jr. "Alex," as he was informally known, worked for the Navy at Point Mugu with Wynne and Strang. Raised in Kansas City, Alexander graduated from the University of

Michigan with bachelor's degrees in mechanical engineering, marine engineering, and naval architecture. Within weeks of the surprise attack by the Japanese on Pearl Harbor, Alexander signed up for the Navy's Midshipman School at Columbia University, becoming a 90-day wonder Navy ensign. Out of 300 engineers in Alexander's class at Columbia, he grabbed top honors in the engine course, prompting the Navy to retain him to instruct future officers in the mysteries of internal combustion. After 16 months, he shipped out on a small aircraft carrier in the Pacific theater but hurried back to the West Coast at the end of hostilities. He worked for a year at the Atlas Diesel Engine Company in Oakland, California, before he landed a job as a civilian engineer in the Navy propulsion laboratory at Point Mugu in 1947.

At the US Naval Air Missile Test Center at Point Mugu, Alexander assisted in the construction of a large, five-foot-three-inch wind tunnel for "testing things like target drone engines, sub-sonic ram jets, and things that operated below the speed of sound."[14] When the Kiekhaefer target drone engine arrived at Point Mugu for evaluation, Alexander represented the Navy in the evaluation of the design. When Wynne, who Kiekhaefer had appointed assistant director of research, arrived at Point Mugu from Fond du Lac in April 1953, Wynne and Alexander began to work together, becoming friends.

Alexander let Wynne know he was looking for something with more possibilities than the civil service program and government wage scales, and Wynne passed the word along to Strang in Fond du Lac. Strang invited him to tour the Kiekhaefer facilities in Wisconsin and took him for a whirlwind tour in Strang's new blood-red Jaguar XK-140, which Kiekhaefer had given him. "I tore around the roads of Wisconsin that whole day," Alexander remembered, and by the end of the day he was hooked on the great future that seemed to be in store for Mercury. Two months later, in the spring of 1953, Kiekhaefer's new aircraft chief engineer was driving his family and worldly possessions across the Great Plains toward Wisconsin when he realized, "Boy, this is kind of wild, because I don't even have a letter from Strang telling me what the deal is."[15]

Alexander worked his way up through the Kiekhaefer Mercury organization and was assigned to special engineering projects suggested by Kiekhaefer himself. He thought of Kiekhaefer as a unique type of engineer. "His big talent, besides being very energetic and competitive," Alexander said, "wasn't engineering in the detail sense. His talent was sensing what the market would go for and what was also technically possible."[16]

The Jet Prop

Kiekhaefer's talent (one that had become embedded in the culture of the company) manifested itself in two important inventions: the tilt-up shock absorber and the Jet Prop underwater exhaust. These improvements would quickly become industry standards.

Boat operators and passengers occasionally suffered injuries when an outboard motor struck a solid object, like a big log, and flipped up into the boat with the propeller still spinning.[17] The shock absorber prevented this from happening.

The Jet Prop exhaust was an innovation that routed engine exhaust through the propeller hub far below the surface of the water. "Until Mercury perfected the through-hub exhaust," Alexander said, "if you raised the engine a little bit too high on the transom, or if the boat hopped a little bit in turning, it would lift the exhaust free of the water and the thing would howl as it would go around the corner." Before the Jet Prop, most outboard engines had a small tube or opening just above the propeller that "kind of plowed a hole in the water and laid the exhaust in it."[18]

Actually, and unknown to Kiekhaefer at the time, Evinrude had experimented with a form of through-hub exhaust and secured a patent. "The problem was," Alexander said, "it didn't work. The exhaust would get back into the propeller blades, and the propeller would just turn loose and bore a hole in the water and would not push the boat." But again, Kiekhaefer understood the practical engineering and marketing potential of a successful design, and put Alexander to work once again, telling him, "I want you to work up a design routing the exhaust through the prop."

Alexander discovered that by bringing the hub straight back behind the blades and cutting it off abruptly, he could stop the exhaust flow back into the blades. Alexander's innovation was successful,

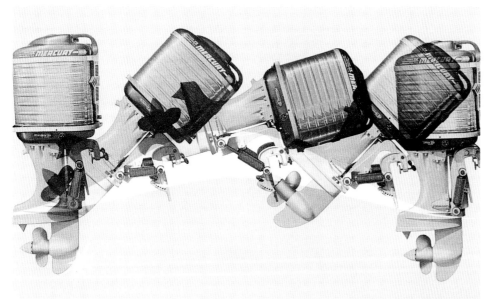

Above: The hydraulic dyna-shock absorbers saved many engines from destructive collisions with submerged obstacles.

Right: The Jet Prop wasn't a new idea, but Mercury was the first to make it work.

ing 1956. Surreptitiously, Strang conducted a secret development program that was to result in one of the most successful products in Mercury history: the six-cylinder in-line "tower of power" 60-horsepower outboard engine. Strang explained:

When he got off on something, boy, nothing else mattered but what he was doing. You were virtually forbidden to work on outboard motors during that period. ... He was on the day shift on the race cars, I worked on the night shift on the race cars. But I nutted up a six-cylinder outboard [by taking] some blueprints, and I cut three cylinders off one four-cylinder engine, and three off another and glued the blueprints together to make a drawing. Then we went out and got a couple of four-cylinder raw castings and sawed them off the same way the blueprints were cut.

and is responsible for the look of most outboard propellers with hub exhaust today—sort of a large round cylinder with blades attached to the sides.[19]

Tower of Power

In the mid-1950s, Carl Kiekhaefer's obsession with automobile racing nearly decimated his outboard business. The combination of heavy expenditures and reduced product research had been devastating in ways that were known to only a few insiders. Kiekhaefer spent well in excess of $1 million in pursuit of his stock car championships at a time when the funds were desperately needed for facilities improvement, promotion, and new product development.

But Kiekhaefer marched to his own drumbeat. He was pushing the company full speed ahead, believing that somehow, some way, the money would catch up as he began to scramble again for new products. Fortunately, Strang had ignored Kiekhaefer's orders to pay 100 percent attention to the auto racing program dur-

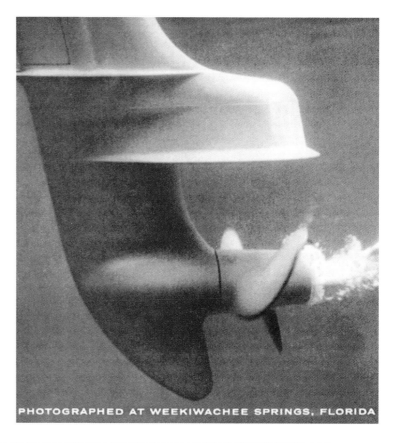

PHOTOGRAPHED AT WEEKIWACHEE SPRINGS, FLORIDA

CARL'S OBSESSION

STOCK CAR RACING DRIVERS AND SPECTATORS ALIKE laughed until their sides ached when they caught a glimpse of Carl Kiekhaefer at Daytona Beach, Florida, on February 27, 1955. Kiekhaefer, 48 years old and nearly bald, stepped onto the sandy beach wearing a freshly pressed long-sleeved white shirt, rimless spectacles, and bow tie, with a giant hand-rolled Cuban cigar clenched between his teeth. His crew, attired in matching white uniform overalls, slowly opened the doors to the white truck, emblazoned with the legend: "Kiekhaefer's Mercury Outboard Motors, The Most Powerful Name in Outboards." Kiekhaefer's crew contrasted sharply with the Daytona faithful—country boys and Dixie moonshine runners, smeared head to toe with oil from their filthy and dented entries—who put their wrenches down to gawk and laugh at the spectacle.

Then down the ramp came a gleaming platinum white 1955 Chrysler C300, all 4,005 pounds of it. It looked to most like a luxury touring car, as out of place as, in the words of one journalist, "an Egyptian pharaoh arriving by barge."[1]

They didn't laugh for long. Within two remarkable years, Kiekhaefer's team of drivers, race crews, mechanics, and engineers won 80 percent of all the races they entered. A string of defeats at the hands of Detroit's deep-pocketed (and embarrassed) Big Three automakers eventually persuaded Kiekhaefer to pull out of serious stock car racing, but

not before the Kiekhaefer team had captured three national championships.

The outboard manufacturer's lust to conquer NASCAR began in 1951 with a road race in Mexico, known formally as the Carrera Panamericana and informally as simply the Mexican Road Race. The race was a staggering 1,933 miles long, zigzagging along the most desolate, dusty, and hazardous roads of old Mexico. Kiekhaefer's introduction to auto racing left him with bad memories of a 4,000-mile arduous, sometimes adventurous, road trip south from Wisconsin. Kiekhaefer, his drivers, and the crews drove the entire distance, arriving hot, tired, and worn out. To top it all off, his team took third place behind a team of Ferraris.

The poor showing (in his view at least; it was, after all, Kiekhaefer's first race) only whet his appetite. Kiekhaefer and his team returned (by airplane this time, while the cars were

Above: Kiekhaefer's racing caravan leaves Fond du Lac for the 1953 Carrera Panamericana. The arduous drive resulted in Kiekhaefer trucking his cars to race sites during his NASCAR and AAA days.

Left: With the Mercury name splashed on his cars and trucks, Kiekhaefer justified his heavy investment in stock cars as a marketing expense. In reality, he spent heavily because he craved the competition.

transported by truck) the following year. Again, Kiekhaefer's cars failed to take first place. Cars built by Ford Motor Company took the race, and although post-race inspections turned up illegal modifications to supposedly "stock" engines, the power of the giant automaker prevailed. The Fords held onto their first- and second-place wins. And Kiekhaefer vowed never to return to the Mexican road race.

But the thrill of this new type of competition left its mark on Kiekhaefer. The rush he experienced in pursuit of the checkered flag was so well-suited to his obsessively competitive spirit that he laid plans to shift his focus to the American track. That February day at Daytona, his driver, Tim Flock, finished just behind Glen "Fireball" Roberts. But Roberts was disqualified for illegally modifying his car, and Flock was declared the winner.

From 1955 to 1957, not one violation of the rules was ever attributed to a Kiekhaefer car, pit crew, or driver, and none of his drivers received a scratch from driving a Kiekhaefer Mercury team car. In 1980, Kiekhaefer was inducted into the National Motorsports Press Association Stock Car Hall of Fame, long after many other participants from the same era had been installed. The induction honored his lasting contributions to the race. The professionalism he brought to the sport, from crew uniforms to technical innovations, was recognized by his

peers. In three short sentences, Kiekhaefer summed up this remarkable phase of his career and of the company: "Make no mistake, we have no regrets. We entered and we left when we wanted to. NASCAR stock racing was one thing when we entered, but it was something entirely different when we left."[2]

Above: A Mercury stock car winning yet another race. Kiekhaefer's single-mindedness resulted in the top winning percentage in stock car racing at that time.

Below: Kiekhaefer, flanked by Tim Flock and Frank "Rebel" Mundy, and the trophies they won.

Left: The Mercury Mark 55.

Below right: The Mercury Mark 75.

I got one of the race car guys ... to weld these things together to make a single six-cylinder block. Then we welded three two-cylinder crankshafts together and bootlegged them through the shop because [Carl] wasn't around. ... We finally put it on a boat and took him down to see it. It was pretty tall. He looked at it, and we pulled the cover off, and he started to laugh. He got in the boat and took one run up and down the river, he came back and said, "It speaks with authority; let's build it." That was the decision process. Nine months later we delivered the first one.[20]

The Mercury Mark 75 was the industry's first six-cylinder outboard engine, and at 60 horsepower, it was the most powerful production outboard motor ever manufactured up to that time. Kiekhaefer best expressed the technical achievements embodied in the design: "An interesting fact is that, although the 60-horsepower six-cylinder motor is the largest production outboard in the industry, it produces the most horsepower per pound, the most horsepower per cubic inch of displacement, the most horsepower per dollar of cost, and the most miles per gallon."[21]

In 1957, the closest thing any other manufacturer had was 40 horsepower, represented by Evinrude, Johnson, and Scott-Atwater. Johnson and Evinrude soon attempted to counter the Kiekhaefer development by announcing new 50-horsepower, V4 models. The OMC engines were so much more wide and stodgy compared with the tall, sleek-looking Mercury that throughout the industry, they attracted the unfortunate moniker of "Fat Fifty," while the largest Scott-Atwater engine, the 40-horsepower Royal

Scott, was a more conventional-looking, two-cylinder design.

Kiekhaefer committed perhaps his most inaccurate assessment when it came to the method of shifting the new 60-horsepower engine. Large outboard motors of the period, including Kiekhaefer's own four-cylinder, in-line, 40-horsepower Mercury Mark 55 engine, had a standard shifting configuration of forward, neutral, and reverse. The shifting gears in the lower unit of the 40-horsepower engine weren't strong enough, however, to handle the increased torque and power of the new 60-horsepower engine. Kiekhaefer decided to make the engine direct-reversing instead of designing and tooling a new gear case for the Mark 75.

He was aware that some of the very large marine diesel engines used in ships had what was known as a silent neutral. That is, instead of a transmission that would select neutral, the engine was shut down completely. When the helm required reverse, the rotation of the engine itself was reversed, and the engine restarted in the opposite direction. Kiekhaefer also knew that it was possible to run a two-cycle outboard engine in either right-hand or left-hand rotation, and that it would be theoretically possible to eliminate a transmission altogether if the various modifications associated with a change in running direction could be worked out.

From the start, however, his three top engineers, Strang, Alexander, and Rose—each as diplomatically as possible—hinted that the marketplace wouldn't accept the unusual scheme. Kiekhaefer was adamant about the clean, engineering simplicity of the concept, and word was passed along that the new engine was to be direct reversing. Kiekhaefer reasoned that it would be faster and easier to perfect the direct reversing principle in the engine than it would be to design, tool, and produce a stronger-shifting lower unit.

When the unit was introduced to the public, problems began to show up. The new motor was supplied with a special control

The Mercury "silent neutral" shift was one of Kiekhaefer's few failures. Fortunately, his engineers worked behind his back to fix the problem.

mark 75

NEW SINGLE-LEVER ONE HAND CONTROL

press

Press the button—
your Mercury six-in-line
starts electrically!

push

Push the lever forward—
away you go! Push it
farther, you go faster!

pull

Pull the lever back,
press the button, you reverse
smoothly. Direct reverse
changes crankshaft rotation
without gear shifting!

quadrant containing a single lever with a start button on top. When the operator wanted to start the engine, he had to first choose either forward or reverse because the engine had no neutral—except the silent neutral of a stopped engine. Starting the engine in either direction, of course, depended on the strength of the battery in the boat. If the battery was weak or discharged, when the operator shifted from forward into reverse, as in docking, the engine wouldn't start up in the opposite direction to brake the boat in time. "We called it the Dock Buster," Strang remembered.

Another problem was related to starting the engine in gear. Boat operators were quite spoiled by the ability to start an engine at the dock in neutral, let it warm up for a while, and then shift into forward to take off. But Kiekhaefer's direct-reversing engine had no neutral, so in whatever direction the engine was being started, the big propeller began to turn, slowing the cranking speed and making it harder to start. Once it did start, the boat was off and running.

Consumer resistance mounted, even as Kiekhaefer tried to convince the public that his way was better by claiming, "Eliminate the noise of resting at the dock with our exclusive 'silent neutral.'" The trouble was, all too often a slight irregularity in carburetor adjustments or a weak battery also gave the operator "silent forward" and "silent reverse."

Wynne, as chief of Mercury's proving grounds, had to test the units once they came from either the research lab or, eventually, the production lines. He said:

I thought it was the most stupid, idiotic, ridiculous idea I'd ever heard of in my life. ... But, I think Carl really thought that this was going to replace the gear shift lower unit. It was lighter and simpler, and I'm sure it was cheaper, but anybody that had any practical experience with operating boats just knew darn well that this wasn't going to be feasible over a period of time in the field. That didn't bother Carl. He went ahead and did it anyway. [He] forced that thing down everybody's throat.[22]

Engineers knew that eventually Kiekhaefer would request a traditional shifting mechanism for the new motor, so they secretly worked on a design. Alexander dreaded the clandestine engineering, even though it was in Kiekhaefer's best interests. Eventually, the traditional design won out, to the relief of the company's engineers, and the direct-reverse mechanism has become part of history.[23]

It was during this period that even Strang was getting frustrated in his role of chief "Kiekhaefer-handler." Strang was in the often-tricky position of buffer between Kiekhaefer and the top engineering and administrative personnel, all of whom trusted Strang's judgment and had grown accustomed to having Strang shield them from Kiekhaefer's explosive outbursts. Evidently out of respect for Strang's unique abilities, Kiekhaefer never once fired him, while any number of Kiekhaefer's top echelon would actually count with pride the number of times the boss had "fired" them only to bring them back on the job within hours or days. Strang, however, actually quit a number of times, and each time his resignation was totally ignored by Kiekhaefer. Strang said:

I quit a lot, but he never fired me. He didn't pay any attention to me at all. He just called me and expected me to be there in the morning.

My most memorable quitting I think was, we were having an argument outside of the plant on Murdock Street in Oshkosh. I don't really remember what it was all about, but I know I had a key ring, one of these ball chain key rings, and there were somewhere between 25

and 35 keys on it. I got so damn mad I fired the key ring into the ground, and Carl got in his car and drove away. It was dusk, and when I fired the damn key ring on the ground, the chain broke, and I spent the rest of the night with a flashlight crawling around on the grass looking for my damn keys.[24]

Kiekhaefer was plagued by his own key chain. Even though a standardized master key system was in place for the majority of plant entrances, Kiekhaefer carried a key ring that was larger than the custodial staff's. He constantly misplaced his ring or took off certain keys and lost them. "Door-kicking was his favorite hobby," his assistant Fritz Shoenfeldt recalled. "He had a ring of keys that weighed about 10 pounds." When he became

In 1958, a pair of Mercury 75s set a record by pulling 20 water skiers.

frustrated fumbling for the right key, he'd quickly lose his patience, step back a couple of paces, and let fly with all 240 pounds focused on the sole of his size 11 shoe. Doors exploded open amidst flying wood chips throughout his facilities at one time or another. Sometimes it seemed like the maintenance staff followed him around just to fix the broken doors and jambs. "He hurt his foot once on the Cedarburg door," Shoenfeldt remembered.

"[He] sprained it pretty bad and limped around for a week."[25]

Kiekhaefer was more than impatient with just locked doors; he became increasingly frustrated with both secrecy and publicity. He wanted to find a place to test new outboards, and at the same time dispel rumors that his engines both ran and burned out fast. He would find a place in Florida to satisfy both.

A rare withdrawal for Carl Kiekhaefer as he lets an alligator have its way in Florida.

CHAPTER FIVE

LAKE X

*Ran over alligator which surfaced just in front of boat! Engine kicked up.
No damage to boat or engine. Damage to alligator unknown.*

—Entry in Jim Wynne's log for the Operation Atlas
endurance run, September 21, 1957[1]

As CARL KIEKHAEFER CONTINUED TO STEP UP outboard motor design, he became increasingly frustrated with efforts to test his new motors in secrecy. He was so paranoid of OMC observation of his testing and production methods that he once denied a troop of Boy Scouts a tour of his Fond du Lac assembly plant, fearing that among them might be a planted OMC spy.[2] Testing on nearby Lake Winnebago left his new products exposed to the competition, and pleasure boat traffic on the lake made it next to impossible to conduct testing in peace.

At Kiekhaefer's Siesta Key proving grounds south of Sarasota, Florida, endurance testing of outboards in the coastal waters also became more and more difficult due to interference from both commercial and pleasure boat traffic. Jim Wynne, in charge of all Mercury proving grounds in the spring of 1957, shared Kiekhaefer's growing frustration with the lack of privacy and open water to complete even the most rudimentary testing. "We were having more and more problems with interference with other boats ruining our endurance tests," Wynne said. "Carl wanted a place that he could operate 24 hours a day, seven days a week, and not have anybody around him. So we got in the company plane and scoured the state of Florida looking for a lake."[3]

Among the spotters aboard the many Beech-18 flights that crisscrossed the state were Wynne, Rose Smiljanic, Kiekhaefer's assistant for 33 years,

and Charlie Strang. Promising sites were identified. Malcolm Pope, brother of Dick Pope, proprietors of Cypress Gardens, where Kiekhaefer had for years photographed and demonstrated his engines, knew the owners of one of the sites. Annie and C.B. "Charlie" Smith of Fort Lauderdale had recently purchased the land that completely surrounded Lake Conlin, near St. Cloud, Florida, and agreed to take Kiekhaefer and Smiljanic for a close inspection.

There was no real road to get to the lake, only a five-mile remnant of a brick trail laid in the sand that formed a segment of the old Dixie Trail, which had been built before the turn of the century by prison labor. The 8-foot-wide trail is considered one of Florida's first thruways and had been abandoned many years before. Where the bricks ended at the turn to the lake, only a winding dirt road remained to access the remote site. It seemed to Kiekhaefer and Smiljanic that they were driving through the set of an Amazon jungle film, for the tropical swamps and enormous stands of cypress trees surrounding the lake gave the property a distinct feeling of isolation—just what Kiekhaefer was looking for.

"X" marks the spot in St. Cloud, Florida, home of "Lake X."

When the lake finally came into view at a clearing on the northern shore, the sheer size of the body of water and property was impressive. The area of the lake was over 1,400 acres, surrounded by property that made a square (with one corner missing) of five miles by four miles, with a net area of roughly 17 square miles or 10,462 acres. The shoreline of the lake was about seven miles, with a potentially navigable course for boats of more than six miles. The deepest sections of the lake were 30 feet, and here and there the surface was broken by a towering cypress tree, seemingly growing right out of the water.

It was completely cut off from civilization, without power, telephone, water, or utility services. The lake waters and the surrounding lands were teeming with wildlife, including alligators, snakes, bass, catfish, eagles, hawks, herons, wild boars, turkeys, raccoons, armadillos, and Florida deer. The lake had no tributaries or inlets and not a single residence around its rugged perimeter. The swamps surrounding much of the lake created a natural barrier to keep out the curious.

Kiekhaefer was ecstatic. The problem was, he couldn't afford it. He had spent so much money on his three championship stock car titles that the company was, according to Kiekhaefer Mercury Controller Don Castle, "skating on thin ice." Kiekhaefer decided that the opportunity to obtain this unique and massive property was too good to pass up, regardless of the current state of the Mercury treasury. He successfully negotiated a two-year lease with a renewal option for two additional years, with clauses that would give him the first chance at purchasing when the lease expired.

Kiekhaefer wanted the location of the lake to remain a secret, so he referred to it as "Lake X" when speaking with outsiders, and the name stuck.

From that day on, Lake Conlin was never mentioned again, and the lake is still known throughout the world of high-performance marine products only as Lake X.

As news of Kiekhaefer's latest gamble spread throughout the organization, Thomas B. King, Kiekhaefer's new director of public relations, was prepared with the perfect inaugural use for the secret facility. King was considered by many to be a real "hot shot" promotions man who could pull off headline publicity programs with relative ease. He was an idea man, who complemented Kiekhaefer's dogged determination with inspiration and finesse.

King was aware of the reputation that Mercury products had unjustly received in the industry.

Kiekhaefer chose Lake X for its big water and total isolation. Always worried about "enemy spies," he often tested Mercury engines himself.

Mercury engines were beating everything in the water, but a whispering campaign had been started somewhere—Kiekhaefer blamed OMC—that Mercurys were "fast but won't last." The consumer who wanted a reliable, trouble-free engine to crank up on the occasional weekend to go fishing was hearing from his local Johnson, Evinrude, or Scott-Atwater dealer that he would be better off with a slower, more conservative, and dependable product rather than the fast but allegedly temperamental Mercury. It wasn't true, of course, for Mercury products were enjoying a most enviable service record throughout the industry, but it was one of those slanderous slogans that fell off the tongue so nicely that it sounded correct. After all, Mercurys were fast, and as a result, many people began to believe the rest of it. King's solution was to propose to Kiekhaefer that Mercury stage a 25,000-mile endurance run at Lake X, a distance equal to a complete circumnavigation of the world.

The resulting publicity would not only help to refute the "fast but won't last" rumor but could also showcase Mercury's latest and most powerful engine, the new 60-horsepower, six-cylinder Mark 75, at the same time. Thrilled with the idea, Kiek-

Kiekhaefer was ham-fisted at the controls of a boat, knowing only two speeds: off or full throttle. Here, Kiekhaefer delights some journalists on Lake X in 1957, propelled by a pair of his new six-cylinder, 60-horsepower Mark 75 engines.

haefer immediately assigned responsibility for the enormous undertaking, known as "Operation Atlas," to Strang and Wynne.

One of Strang's greatest strengths was his ability to analyze the most complex assignments from Kiekhaefer and issue a one- or two-page memo that could make the impossible look rather simple. Strang initially determined that the project would take about 40 days. In his memo to Kiekhaefer, he calculated that the circumference of the earth at the equator was 24,902 miles, and "it will thus be necessary to maintain a minimum speed of 25.939 miles per hour (let's call it 26 mph)." Strang understood, though, the unpredictability of weather and other contingencies, and so proposed that "it would be wise to shoot for a 30-mph average (34.6 days), so providing a time cushion." He suggested that the new Mark 75 engines be throttled back to a

Two later perspectives of Lake X, where *Operation Atlas* was launched. During *Operation Atlas*, there was nothing but a shack, several house trailers, and snakes.

somewhat effortless 4,500 rpm (compared to the top speed of 6,000 rpm) and turn a propeller of higher than normal pitch, sort of simulating an overdrive in a car, to "permit operation in the economy range with the possibility of good fuel consumption publicity."[4]

Strang also suggested that all major components of the engines selected for the endurance run be "Zygloed and Magnafluxed" before the run, referring to tests to reveal even the smallest cracks or manufacturing defects in crankshafts, pistons, rods, or castings. "A local surveyor," Strang suggested, "can measure and certify such course or courses as we may care to stake out." Twenty-five thousand miles is a brutal journey in a small outboard boat, and so Strang evaluated the endurance of the driving crews that would make the attempt, forecasting that it would be "difficult to get drivers to take shifts of more than four hours at a stretch. With each man taking two such shifts per day, it will require three drivers per boat on a seven-day basis."

Wynne contracted with the United States Auto Club (USAC), an organization with national stature and with a history of supervising record-breaking endurance and speed events in the automotive industry, to monitor the endurance run. USAC officials provided 24-hour supervision and lap counting, and made certain that the engines were not modified "except for routine maintenance" during the record-breaking attempt. Now, all that was left was to prepare Lake X for Operation Atlas.

Wynne established a base at the water's edge with a house trailer, an equipment trailer, and a mobile radiotelephone. When Kiekhaefer heard that it was illegal to have a mobile phone without having it installed in a car, he promptly secured a junk car with an active Florida registration, stripped it of tires and doors, and sank it up to the floor boards to make a sort of "telephone booth" that would satisfy the letter of the law. He had a giant antenna erected to improve reception, which was perfectly legal because the statutes "didn't say how high your antennae could be."

By September 10, 1957, Wynne had moved into the Lake Breeze Motel in nearby St. Cloud as preparations continued to commence Operation Atlas. In order to establish a clear course of at least five miles for the endurance run, 11 giant cypress trees needed to be removed from various locations around the lake.[5]

A Mercury employee named Wayne Meyer and a local scuba diver placed dynamite under the first tree out in the lake, lit the fuse, and moved a safe distance away. The huge explosion that followed lifted the tree nearly clear of the lake amid a tremendous shower of water. But the tree dropped right back into place as if nothing had happened. "So we went back and got a long rope and tied it to the tree and got on this big barge we had there, and while we blasted, we were pulling. Then we just dragged them to the side of the lake," Meyer said.[6] The

In 1971, not long after Carl Kiekhaefer left the company he founded, work began on what would become known as the MerCabo Test Center, near Placida, Florida, to replace the Kiekhaefer-owned saltwater test facility in Sarasota. Like its sister test facility at Lake X, MerCabo (which means "Cape Merc" in Spanish) became a grueling test ground for Mercury engines and products. Like Lake X, the original 35-acre site was eventually expanded to a 50-acre site, where engines, engine parts, and accessories, as well as boats, were run through a merciless, day-long cycle of abuse. Besides constant operation, engines and engine parts are left out in the sun to bake and sprayed periodically with saltwater.

course thus cleared was officially surveyed and measured, coming out to exactly 5.5366 miles for a complete circuit.

The endurance run was to be continuous, meaning that the exchange of drivers, the addition of fuel, and the accomplishment of minor repairs would all have to be made on the run, 24 hours a day, in daylight and dark, rain or shine, as the boats were flying around the course at more than 30 mph. Strang, Wynne, and a crew of drivers and mechanics developed a host of unique solutions to overcome every obstacle. Strang decided that two identical boats would be specially prepared to go the distance, with two additional boats standing by in case of hull failure or accident. Fifteen-foot Raveau family runabouts, designed by Marcel Raveau, were adapted for the unique assignment.

Windshields and windshield wipers were added, along with a 30-gallon fuel tank to reduce the frequency and danger of refueling operations. Automobile-style headlights were fitted to either side of the runabouts for nighttime operations, complementing lighted buoys that were placed throughout the course. Two special refueling and crew shuttle boats, featuring 50-gallon fuel drums elevated five feet above the deck on a cradle of angle iron, were built.

As proven in practice runs, the fuel boat could synchronize with the speed of the endurance boat to be serviced, and a three-inch flexible hose would be passed over to the driver, who would insert it into the fuel tank. Gravity pressure from the elevated supply tank would quickly fill the smaller tank, although the often-erratic motions of the boats on the water accounted for a certain amount of spillage. A fresh driver would then cross over into the endurance boat and grab the wheel while the previous driver crossed back into the supply boat. According to the endurance run logbooks kept by officials and Kiekhaefer employees, only once did a tired driver lose his footing and go overboard during the crew transfers.

A special observation stand was constructed for the USAC officials, led by Chief Steward Charles W. McDonald, under the direction of Duane Carter, director of competition for USAC. Carter had written to Wynne three weeks prior to the scheduled start of the run to lay down the conditions for authentication of the attempt. Among the requirements was that "all the component engine parts which may be required as replacements during the run must be carried in the boat during the run."

The most important condition of USAC certification, however, concerned inspection of the engines following the run. "After completion of the run, the engine will be disassembled and compared with another disassembled engine selected from stock. All the parts must pass and be certified by the USAC steward and his technical representatives to be stock as advertised and available to the general public."[7] This is the area where the ingenuity of

A helicopter trails an endurance driver at Lake X.

Endurance testing at Lake X meant not only long days but long nights. Most dangerous of all were the nighttime refuelings (right).

Kiekhaefer's crews and engineers was tested to the limit.

At 6:58 a.m. on September 11, 1957, USAC Steward McDonald punched his stop watch as the first of the two boats roared away from the starting dock, followed by the second boat within minutes. Thirty-four days, 11 hours, 47 minutes, and 5.4 seconds later, the lead boat crossed the finish line, having completed 4,516 laps of the Lake X course and 25,003.286 miles. The second boat finished only moments later. But what happened between the start and the finish was only partly observed by USAC officials.

By all accounts the engines performed amazingly well under the circumstances, but quite a number of unsupervised and wholesale replacements of parts became necessary as the laps added up. The first problem to surface was excessive

build-up of carbon deposits in the exhaust ports of the engines, even though "white" gasoline was being used to reduce lead deposits on spark plugs. The engines would slowly lose power, so that eventually the drivers were forced to use wide-open throttles just to maintain 4,500 rpm over the course.

Periodically, the heads were surreptitiously removed while the USAC officials were distracted and assumed that routine maintenance, like spark plug or distributor points replacement, was occurring. The heads would then be completely de-carboned. But while the heads were off, Kiekhaefer's mechanics also took the opportunity to replace complete distributors, complete sets of pistons, rod bearings, main bearings, crankshafts, carburetors, and gear case components, and at one point they even exchanged the entire power head. Kiekhaefer, unwittingly, would actively assist in the diversion,

for many of the clandestine replacements were done when Kiekhaefer would arrive and invite USAC inspectors for lunch in St. Cloud. Once, when Wynne reported to Kiekhaefer that he didn't think the engines would make it under the guidelines for the program, Kiekhaefer icily replied, "Yes they will, Jim. You just make damn sure that they do!"[8]

To prohibit overhauls, USAC had placed a crimped seal and wire around part of the engine, but mechanics quickly learned how to drill and saw around it when necessary or even move the seal from engine to engine. Naturally, when USAC tore down the engines at the finish and the parts were compared with a stock engine taken randomly from Kiekhaefer's line in Fond du Lac, the compo-

Endurance testing at Lake X (below left) had to be certified by the USAC (below) to become a world endurance record. But the USAC officials who inspected "unadulterated" engines (left) weren't infallible.

United States Auto Club

USAC

To Whom It May Concern:

OFFICIAL USAC RECORD

This is to certify that the 25,000-mile endurance run of the Mercury Mark 75E outboard engine, Serial No. 1098258, has been successfully completed. The run was continuous (with refueling while underway), except for pit stops designated in Official Records for normal servicing, with a stock six-cylinder 60 horsepower Mercury outboard chosen at random from production, powering a five-place 15-foot family runabout hull. At the completion of the run, the motor was immediately impounded and held in the custody of the duly accredited USAC officials for inspection. The motor was completely disassembled, thoroughly inspected, compared to another similar model chosen at random from production by USAC officials, and was found to be in stock production specifications.

STATISTICS:

Location of run:	Lake "X" in Florida	
Date:	Start —	Sept. 11, 1957 at 06:58:58.40
	Finish —	Oct. 15, 1957 at 18:46:03.80
Total elapsed time:	34 days, 11 hours, 47 min., 5.4 seconds	
Average speed:	30.205 miles per hour	
Average fuel consumption:	3.8 gallons per hour	
Average miles per gallon:	7.9 miles per gallon	
Total distance traveled:	25,003.286 miles	
Laps:	4516	

Dated: Thursday, October 24, 1957

Signed: *Duane Carter*
Duane Carter, Director of Competition, USAC

C.W. McDonald
Charles McDonald, Chief Steward, USAC

nents matched perfectly, because only stock parts were substituted during the run. Kiekhaefer was never fully aware of the lengths his loyal crews went to to guarantee his success in Operation Atlas.

Nighttime operations were the hardest on the crews and the equipment. The lights mounted on the bows of the boats were very unreliable, and the constant jarring would break either the filaments or the glass lenses. Quite often, a second driver or mechanic had to lie across the speeding deck in the middle of the night to replace lights as the boats sped around the course. Eerily, the pink eyes of Lake X's many alligators would reflect the lights as the boats made their laps, and drivers were able to estimate the size of the 'gators by the distance between the eyes. One night, one of the drivers inadvertently ran over a rather large alligator, kicking the engine up against the shock absorbers. The entry in Wynne's official log for the evening was, "Ran over alligator which surfaced just in front of boat! Engine kicked up. No damage to boat or engine. Damage to alligator unknown."[9]

Kiekhaefer reaped a public relations bonanza when the results of the endurance record were announced. Strang prepared some calculations for Kiekhaefer to throw around attesting to the brutal punishment endured by his engines. Each engine, Strang figured, had made 225 million revolutions, and the total number of sparks or explosions per engine was a staggering 1.35 billion. Kiekhaefer confirmed to the press that "there were no mechanical or electrical failures, and the batteries were still fully charged at the end of the run." Kiekhaefer and King, supported by savvy new public relations arrival Frank Scalpone, were quick to capitalize on this "evidence" that Mercury was both fast and would last. Kiekhaefer was so pleased by the success of his new Mark 75 engines that he instructed USAC to keep them in official quarantine because he wanted to run them another 25,000 miles to

shut down once and for all the vicious, allegedly OMC-inspired rumors that Mercury outboards were temperamental, delicate, and fickle.

Wynne, for one, had experienced enough of the mosquitoes, snakes, spiders, and sweltering environment of Lake X to last a lifetime and asked Strang to have someone else manage the second half of Kiekhaefer's proposed 50,000 mile, twice-around-the-world endurance run. He returned to overall supervision of Kiekhaefer's proving grounds at Siesta Key and Oshkosh and was delighted to encounter civilization once more.

The second 25,000 miles at Lake X was pretty much a repeat of the first effort, though 17-foot models of the same boat were used for more stability as a more windy and harsh season for boating was fast approaching. One night, one of the endurance drivers fell asleep at the wheel and before he could recover, crashed into the densely wooded shoreline and was killed. Though Kiekhaefer and the Lake X crews were deeply saddened by the event, the engine was put on a backup boat and completed the distance. This tragedy, along with the potential for future injuries in normal testing activity, was among the reasons that Kiekhaefer contributed heavily to the construction and renovation of the nearby St. Cloud Hospital. Altogether, Kiekhaefer would donate more than $300,000 in funds and services to the hospital to ensure that whenever Kiekhaefer Mercury test crews were injured, they would receive the very best emergency medical treatment.[10]

Kiekhaefer and his able group of engineers, drivers, mechanics, and public relations professionals had pulled off the largest, most organized, and exotic of all endurance feats in marine industry history. It was a truly remarkable undertaking, representing a record that is yet unbroken. And given the extreme difficulty in reproducing the feat today, the record may stand for all time.

The Pro Max series of racing engines, introduced in 1997, is considered to be among the best built high-performance engines in the world.

CHAPTER SIX

RACING THROUGH THE YEARS

No one more than I can attest to the wisdom of "walking alone" and "not running in packs."

—Carl Kiekhaefer, 1962[1]

MERCURY MARINE EMPLOY-ees have always had a special relationship with speed. And after Carl Kiekhaefer masterminded the record-breaking endurance run in 1957, the "fast but won't last" stigma diminished, leaving the company to concentrate more effort on racing. Much of the history of outboard motors has been tied to boaters' desire to skim over water like a skipping stone, with perhaps no one so obsessed with fast boats as Kiekhaefer himself. But Kiekhaefer wasn't simply obsessed with boats that went fast—he wanted boats that were faster than anybody else's. And these he made. Since the company's foray into racing in the late 1940s, Mercury has compiled a list of marine racing titles that is unparalleled in the industry. Kiekhaefer also saw the unwritten value of racing, something that could help the company even through hard times. As in auto racing, fast, sleek, and winning boats were a way to keep Mercury's name in front of the general public. It was an advertising bonanza.

"With other marine companies, racing is a lot of fun, something they enjoyed doing," said Fred Hauenstein, technical director for Mercury Marine's Hi-Performance Business Unit. "But they didn't take it as an absolute cultural thing that they had to win races. The Mercury people have always felt that racing is their life."[2]

"Our goal was to just wipe out everybody," recalled Larry Lohse, one of the few remaining Mercury employees who followed Kiekhaefer to Kiekhaefer Aeromarine Motors and then back to Mercury. On Mercury's 60th anniversary, Lohse was still with Mercury as director of engineering in the company's Hi-Performance Business Unit. He said:

There were times we raced with such passion that we took the first 10 places in a race, either with our own boat or people using our equipment. One time, Carl was on the phone to someone at our racing center, and he was really chewing him out. Afterward, I asked, "What was that all about? I thought we did quite well." Unfortunately, out of 10 places, we didn't take seventh, and Carl just didn't like that.[3]

1940s: The Beginning of the Racing Bug

Mercury's penchant for racing began in 1947, when an ambitious new Mercury owner prepared to enter the Albany-to-New York race with a 10-horsepower Mercury Lightning. The owner and engine won their division handily, putting the outboard industry on notice that Mercury was off to

---

The Mercury Racing logo. Historically, fast engines and the Mercury name have been synonymous.

the races. Within a year, Kiekhaefer Mercury engines had won a handful of distinguished racing events, and Kiekhaefer began to see that a new and enormous opportunity was blossoming to publicize engineering achievement.

By the following year, Kiekhaefer had successfully lobbied the American Power Boat Association (APBA) to officially recognize stock outboard racing, and he was pleased to see these new events attracting large crowds and expanded media exposure.

Stock outboard racing steadily rose in popularity, but it quickly became clear that the stakes weren't the honor or ability of the drivers or even the reputation of the boats. The races were between outboard brands, and with few exceptions, the real battle was between Kiekhaefer Mercury and OMC products.

The 1948 Albany-to-New York Outboard Marathon was the first opportunity for the two competitors to go head to head. On the morning of June 13, the 16th running of the race began in a miserable, raw, and soaking downpour. The rain and fog were so dreadful that the record number of 180 drivers could scarcely see the 300 feet across the Hudson River at the Albany Yacht Club, where the race began. The finish line was a long 134

miles downriver at the US Navy float at 72nd Street in New York City.

At the 9 a.m. gun, six different classes were off and running. Class I was limited to motors of no more than 12.5 cubic inches, which included an even dozen of the Mercury 7.5-horsepower, 11-cubic-inch Rocket outboards; three 7.9-horsepower, 12.41-cubic-inch Champion Lite Twin outboards; four 7.5-horsepower, 11-cubic-inch Martin "60" engines; and a lonely 7.9-horsepower, 11-cubic-inch Firestone. The Mercury engines, in line with Kiekhaefer's strategy of underrating his engines, pulled somewhere around 14 horsepower, while the other engines actually ran close to their advertised power. The Mercury entries, led by a 16-year-old Indiana schoolboy named Leon Wilton, took the first five places in the class, followed by Champion, Martin, and Firestone.

But because Mercury and OMC raced mostly in different classes, both would claim victories in the same races for many years, though they would seldom race against each other. The real winners of these grueling contests were consumers. The reliability of outboard motors was being proven, event after event, and both OMC and Mercury were designing products that could endure the punish-

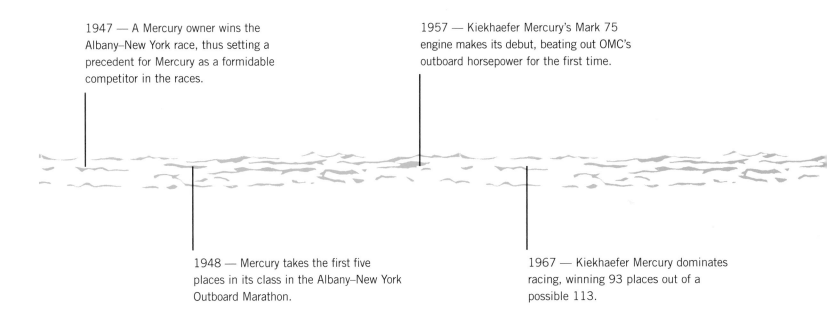

1947 — A Mercury owner wins the Albany–New York race, thus setting a precedent for Mercury as a formidable competitor in the races.

1957 — Kiekhaefer Mercury's Mark 75 engine makes its debut, beating out OMC's outboard horsepower for the first time.

1948 — Mercury takes the first five places in its class in the Albany–New York Outboard Marathon.

1967 — Kiekhaefer Mercury dominates racing, winning 93 places out of a possible 113.

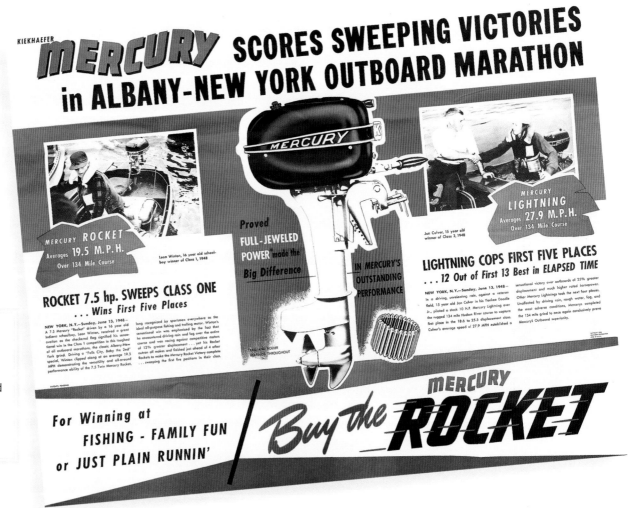

Carl Kiekhaefer broke with marine industry practice of overrating engines; he underrated the horsepower of his engines to give them an edge in racing.

1971 — Dr. Robert Magoon wins six first-place finishes driving Kiekhaefer's *Aeromarine I.* Kiekhaefer and Magoon are declared APBA US national offshore racing champions.

1985 — Driving a MerCruiser, George Morales breaks the record-finishing time in the Miami–New York Chapman Offshore Challenge.

1973 — Mercury officially forms its Hi-Performance Division to promote the company's presence in racing.

1996 — Mercury shuts out OMC by setting six APBA outboard bass boat speed records.

ment of long-distance racing, largely at the hands of amateur drivers.

The field of nearly 200 entrants in the 1948 Albany–New York race was, by a wide margin, the largest in the history of outboard racing. Even in the pouring rain and blinding fog that hampered both men and machine, an amazing 141 competitors completed the 134-mile race. Only a few years before World War II, that number would have been unimaginable.

1950s: Need for Speed

When Kiekhaefer sanctioned Strang's design for a six-cylinder, in-line, 60-horsepower engine, he signaled the start of a race for speed and outboard horsepower that would endure for decades to follow. When the first Mark 75 engine rolled off the assembly lines in Fond du Lac in 1957, Kiekhaefer had, for the first time, taken the lead in outboard horsepower over rival OMC and its 50-horsepower, V4 "Fat Fifty." After that, Mercury seldom fell behind the enemy in the race for outboard horsepower.

When government contracts for production of target drone aircraft engines were canceled following the Korean War, Ted Jones left the Kiekhaefer organization and returned to work building the fastest boats in the world. His three-point hydroplane designs would capture world record after world record, powered by the most powerful inboard engines in existence. In the nine years between 1950 and 1958, Jones' designs captured an incredible eight APBA Gold Cups, the most coveted prize in boat racing history. His *Slo-Mo-Shun IV* and *V* unlimited hydroplanes monopolized

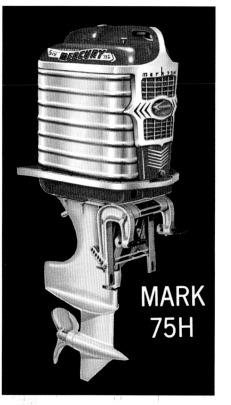

MARK 75H

The Mark 75 engine was adapted with special carburetors to allow the engine to run on pure alcohol in an attempt to break the world speed record on water.

the coveted trophy from 1950 to 1954. His *Miss Thriftway* design won it again in 1956 and 1957, followed by his codesign of *Hawaii Kai III*, which captured the cup in 1958. Kiekhaefer was eager to use a smaller version of this basic Jones configuration to establish a new world speed record for outboards. The world record hadn't been held by an American since 1937.

The 100-mph barrier, in fact, had just been broken by Italian Massimo Di Priolo near Milan in 1956. His boat was propelled by a specially designed, one-of-a-kind, supercharged 160-horsepower outboard engine. Even with this enormous engine, the Italian barely passed the mark at 100.3 mph, and the record was not universally trusted.

In an attempt to break the record and move the title for speed into an American's hands, Kiekhaefer contracted with Hubert Entrop and Jack Leek of Washington state on March 14, 1958. Entrop, a model builder for Boeing Aircraft wind tunnel tests in Seattle, would build the boat based on a Jones design, while Leek would serve as engine mechanic to specially prepare a 60-horsepower Mercury Mark 75 for the record-setting effort. In his agreement with the men, Kiekhaefer insisted that "every precaution shall be taken to maintain secrecy during boat construction and tests preliminary to the official run in order that information shall not leak out to the press in advance of the successful conclusion of the project."

Kiekhaefer insisted that the record attempts be made on Lake X so that he could control not only security but publicity. A stock engine was modified with special carburetors built by Strang to allow the engine to burn pure alcohol, and a special racing lower unit was used with a very thin, high-speed propeller. Normally, the engine would develop 60 horsepower at 5,500 rpm, but with this arrangement, the engine developed 83 horsepower at 7,500 rpm. Entrop's first trials on Lake X fell short of expectations and the record, reaching only 96.134 mph.[4] Kiekhaefer, with his usual bulldog diplomacy, let Entrop and Leek understand in no uncertain terms that they had failed and that they had better figure out a solution. Entrop felt insulted by Kiekhaefer and, according to Strang, "finally just pulled up stakes and left." Strang would later calm Entrop down and persuade him to continue the attempt for the record back in Entrop's home state of Washington.

On the morning of June 7, 1958, with Kiekhaefer personally directing each step, Entrop made two runs in opposite directions across Lake Washington to challenge the record. His first run was timed by official observers of the APBA at slightly over 109 mph while the second was clocked at just over 106 mph, producing an average run of 107.821 mph to establish the new world record.

Kiekhaefer was very excited about having established the new record. Not only had Entrop brought the record back to the United States after a lapse of 21 years, but he had smashed the standing US record by almost exactly 30 mph. Most new records beat existing speeds by a few tenths of a mile per hour or by a few miles per hour. Not only was this the first time that a production outboard had exceeded 100 mph, but the new Kiekhaefer Mercury record also annihilated the old records by the widest margin in history.

Kiekhaefer's acquisition of the new world speed record for Mercury in 1958 signaled the start of a never-ending race for higher and higher speeds between Mercury and OMC.

In March 1960, a new 14-foot hydroplane, *Starflite Too* (named after the new 75-horsepower, V4 Evinrude *Starflite II*) dashed through the timing traps across the still waters at Lake Havasu, Arizona, at a sizzling 114.65 mph, smashing the Kiekhaefer record by over 7 mph. Kiekhaefer responded at Lake Washington two months later, on May 5, 1960, with a new world record of 115.547 mph. Again, Kiekhaefer and Strang used a modified 60-cubic-inch Mercury Mark 75H, beating the one-third larger Evinrude engine by less than one mile per hour. Kiekhaefer was careful to point out that he used this "smallest of the Merc six-cylinder engines because the Union of International Motorboating (the world sanctioning organization for speed records) does not recognize records set with engines over 1000 cc (61 cubic inches)." This meant that the OMC record "wasn't recognized" and that his was.

Eventually, Kiekhaefer grew weary of this see-saw battle between OMC and Mercury and decided to increase the odds in his favor. Kiekhaefer learned OMC was preparing a response to the recent Kiekhaefer record. On September 17, 1960, a new boat christened *Starflite III* boosted the stakes in the outboard record race to a blazing 122.979 mph, topping the Kiekhaefer mark by more than 7 mph. More important to Kiekhaefer was formal powerboat racing, and that became his obsession of the 1960s.

At Lake Washington, the proven Mark 75 again broke the world speed record, taking the record away from OMC.

1960s: Powerboat Racing

Offshore powerboat racing, or ocean racing, became more of a political item on Kiekhaefer's marketing agenda than a sporting one during most of the 1960s. Kiekhaefer was almost constantly embroiled in heated arguments with race promoters, APBA committee chairmen, and, occasionally, competitors. In 1962, Johnny Bakos drove his boat to victory in the Miami-Nassau race at a record average of 48.6 mph, propelled by a pair of 327-cubic-inch MerCruiser sterndrive packages. In this, one of the toughest and most demanding of all open-passage ocean races, six of the first 10 finishers were powered by Kiekhaefer's engines. The following year, *Mona Lou*, driven by Odell Lewis, set a new speed record for the same race at 55.4 mph. That time, seven of the first 10 finishers were powered by Mer-Cruiser sterndrives. Then, for a period of several years, Kiekhaefer, disgruntled over racing venues, rule changes, and official personalities, withdrew most of his factory participation in racing.

Wynne, campaigning a wide variety of boats, engines, and races, became one of the most consistent winners in the sport. He built up an unbeatable lead in driver points in 1965, and when the season was over was declared the World Champion offshore driver. Near the end of the 1966 season, Wynne created a furor by winning the celebrated Miami-Nassau race with a turbine-powered, 32-foot aluminum boat, the *Thunderbird*. Wynne's unique boat, powered by a pair of 450-horsepower Pratt & Whitney jet aircraft engines driving twin propeller shafts, won the race in wild seas rather handily but was ruled illegal following the victory. Wynne, though, was awarded the driver's points for the race nonetheless, which helped the Kiekhaefer alumnus to become World Champion for a second year in a row. Kiekhaefer had long been enamored with the potential for turbine power in the marine industry, and he purchased the *Thunderbird* turbine boat.

Renaming it the *Mona Lou II*, he unsuccessfully lobbied the APBA and race promoters to allow the new technology to compete with traditional piston-powered engines. Arguments for and against the turbines were loud and many, and confusion

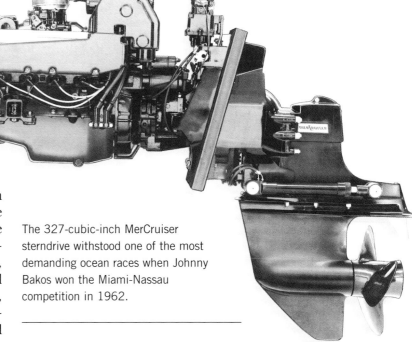

The 327-cubic-inch MerCruiser sterndrive withstood one of the most demanding ocean races when Johnny Bakos won the Miami-Nassau competition in 1962.

over the unfamiliar powerplants left the fate of the boat unresolved.

Kiekhaefer faced obstacles entering *Mona Lou II* in the 1967 Sam Griffith Memorial Race from Miami to Bimini and back. He grew furious when his turbine-powered boat—the same boat Wynne had been allowed to enter a year earlier in the same event—was ruled ineligible. "For a period of three weeks before the race, turbine power was publicly declared legal," Kiekhaefer angrily wrote in a letter, "declared illegal two weeks before the race, [and] declared legal again one week before the race...."[5] For a while, Kiekhaefer seriously considered pulling out of racing altogether, feeling that maybe Mercury needed to "change our image." He said:

In the minds of our dealers, we are a dynamic, progressive, fast-acting, and hard-hitting company. ... With "esprit de corps" like this, can you imagine how their enthusiasm would waver if we tried to change our image into that of a stodgy old manufacturer who built products ideal for school teachers and little old ladies?[6]

Bluster as he might, Kiekhaefer was privately determined to get back into racing with a flourish. In 1967, the year of Mercury's return to racing,

Kiekhaefer entered his products and teams in a total of 27 races. Considering the various divisions within the races, his remarkable record showed the level of his determination and the durability of his products. He won 43 first places out of a possible 50, and 93 places (first, second, or third) out of a possible 113. Kiekhaefer Mercury dominated the race courses throughout the year, with Mercury outboards and MerCruiser sterndrives collecting more prize money and trophies than all other competitors combined.

It was during the 1960s that Mercury's Hi-Performance Department had its informal beginning in the trunk of Dick Snyder's car. At the time, Snyder was in charge of the Hydrodynamics Department, and he attended a number of races in the Midwest over weekends to see how well the latest Mercury engines stood up. When he saw an engine fail, Snyder asked the driver to take the broken part back to Oshkosh to determine the problem and sent a replacement part to the racer. "After a while, it got to where a lot of the guys had the broken parts ready for me when I showed up," Snyder recalled. So he brought replacement parts with him. "I became like a little bitty store with a half-dozen of these and a half-dozen of those, and filled my trunk up with broken parts."

Snyder quickly realized he needed a mechanic to help him find out if certain parts of an engine were breaking from faulty design or from operator error. He enlisted the help of a young mechanic named Gary Garbrecht, who (with much prodding on Snyder's part) agreed to come with him on the long drives to races, sometimes as far away as West Virginia. Garbrecht's enthusiasm grew with each visit, as he determined the problem with a Mercury engine and then fixed it with the parts the men brought with them in Snyder's trunk. Snyder said:

It got to be that between his time and my time and the size of my trunk, something had to be done. In conversations with Kiekhaefer, we determined

that Gary would leave my department, and we would set up the first true high-performance department, with him heading it up. Some years later, in 1984, I was asked to take charge of the department, which then had more than 120 people in it, selling more than $12 million a year in product.[7]

Property was purchased near the Mercury facility in Oshkosh, and Garbrecht brought several more mechanics in, beginning Mercury's first department dedicated to high performance.

1970s and 1980s

Throughout the 1970s and early 1980s, offshore racing began to resemble the early days of stock car racing, a time when moonshine runners outran the law at night and competed with each other during the day—except that many offshore racers ran drugs from cargo ships outbound from Colombia. According to estimates, more than a third of South Florida-based offshore racers were in some way involved with drug-running and its companion crimes, money-laundering and income tax evasion.[8]

John Crouse, who wrote the authoritative *A History of Offshore Powerboat Racing*, noted that the sport had become "thoroughly tainted," prompting major backers such as Bacardi Rum, Benihana Japanese Steakhouses, and Anheuser-Busch to cease team sponsorships.[9] Mercury Marine would move away from factory-sponsored teams in 1980, but its engines dominated the sport. The closest competitor to Mercury, as it happened, was Kiekhaefer, who had begun a new business

The *Mona Lou II*, purchased by Carl Kiekhaefer, was powered by a controversial turbine engine, which was subsequently declared illegal for use in racing.

in 1970 called Kiekhaefer Aeromarine Motors (KAM) after selling the Kiekhaefer Corporation to Brunswick in 1961.

Kiekhaefer had purchased one of the first 36-foot Cigarette hulls from Don Aronow in North Miami, Florida, and installed a pair of 496-cubic-inch MerCruiser sterndrives, carefully reinforced and meticulously modified by himself and the KAM engineering staff. Mercury had dominated offshore racing almost from the moment that Kiekhaefer had introduced the MerCruiser sterndrive in 1961 while he was still with Brunswick. But Kiekhaefer was certain that much more could be done with the same basic equipment if preparation, accessories, fine-tuning, and absolute attention to detail were combined with the right driver. These were the same basic tenets that had won Kiekhaefer three national stock car championships and a greater percentage of victories in APBA competition than all other marine manufacturers combined. "Consistency," Kiekhaefer was fond of saying, "thou art a jewel."

Selected to pilot the *Aeromarine I* was two-time APBA offshore outboard racing champion Dr. Robert Magoon of Miami Beach, Florida. Though Magoon had never competed in an inboard boat, Kiekhaefer recruited him for his superb driving and navigating skills and knew he would be up to the rigorous challenge of a sustained year-long campaign.

Magoon pushed the MerCruiser engines and drives to six first-place finishes out of nine, along with a second and third, during the 1971 racing season. Kiekhaefer's *Aeromarine I* was the first boat in APBA racing annals to win six national championship races in a single season, and Magoon became the first driver in history to win the Hennessy "Triple Crown," with victories at all three of the races (held in New York; Long Beach, California; and Key West, Florida) sponsored by the famous cognac distiller, Jas. Hennessy & Company of France. KAM and Magoon were declared the 1971 APBA US national offshore racing champions.

Mercury Marine's Hi-Performance Division was formally established as a business in 1973. For the next two decades, its sole mission was limited to product development and the promotion of Mercury Marine's image through racing. Of all the factors that contribute to winning races, preparation is one of the most important, noted racing pro Earl Bentz. Bentz raced for Mercury between 1973 and 1981 and was a member of the famous "Black Angel" team, along with Bill Seebold and Reggie Fountain.

Bentz began racing for Mercury shortly after breaking his back. Traveling well in excess of 100 mph, his boat had gone airborne and flipped over. Mercury called him while he was recovering in the hospital, and upon his release he began racing for Mercury, even while wearing a back brace.

Opposite page: *Aeromarine I* and driver Dr. Robert Magoon took the 1971 APBA national offshore racing championship using MerCruiser sterndrives modified by Kiekhaefer.

Above: *Aeromarine III*, also operated by Magoon (inset), was a sister boat to *Aeromarine I*.

The Black Angels took victory after victory, and Bentz himself won five national championships. He said friends who raced for OMC envied the amount of time he and his teammates spent testing their boats and engines. "The OMC guys would be on the race course trying to test their equipment that day for the race, while we'd be ready because we had gotten it done the day before. Gary Garbrecht would have us out on the water while it was still dark."[10]

Horsepower naturally played a huge part, and Mercury's commitment to winning gave it the advantage in power. With the craft built by Bill Seebold, it wasn't surprising that Mercury teams dominated tunnel boat racing. Bentz said drivers worked with Seebold to develop the boats and spent many hours behind the wheel at Lake X or Lake Havasu testing under all kinds of weather conditions.[11]

Hi-Performance began production of the consumer Big Block 454-cid V8 MerCruiser 370 Typhoon engine with TRS drive. The naturally aspi-

rated carbureted engine would become the building block for the multimillion-dollar boating market (along with the 1990 acquisition of KAM's highly touted Sport Boat Accessories line).

When Charlie Alexander decided to end Mercury's factory-sponsored teams, racing took on a whole new look. Now Mercury sold race packages to anyone who wanted them. And the technological innovations were no longer just in outboards but also in the MerCruiser line. Powerboat champion George Morales of Fort Lauderdale became a poster boy for MerCruiser in the mid-1980s when he won three straight Superboat titles in his *Maggie's MerCruiser Special*. In 1985, he broke an 11-year-old record in the Miami–New York Chapman Offshore Challenge, completing the grueling trip in 19 hours.[12] (Morales' streak ended in 1987, following his conviction for drug-smuggling. He was sentenced to 16 years in prison).[13]

Such endurance races appealed to Mercury's "Hi-Perf" workers since Mercury's competitors were still trying to tag it with the "fast but won't last" label. Hi-Performance technician Gerry Celichowski recalled one memorable race that proved Mercury's durability with both a winning effort and a little sex appeal:

Above: Carl Kiekhaefer and Dr. Magoon.

Right: In 1987, *Miami Vice* actor Don Johnson (left) won the Mississippi River Run, which ran from Louisiana to St. Louis, for Mercury Marine.

One race that I'll always remember is the Mississippi River Run—from Louisiana all the way up to St. Louis. In 1987, we were working with Wellcraft boats, and actor Don Johnson was the driver. It was his first race, so we followed him in a sea plane and made all the fuel stops and checked for breakage. It was a long, grueling race—one full day and the next day till around 2 p.m. Overnight, we worked on the boat almost till dawn. And he won the race.[14]

The emphasis on endurance was a "cultural shift," said Dennis Banks, senior vice president for engineering and technology in 1998. "The culture at Mercury has always been one gigantic speed shop— very creative, very instinctual." But that changed as technology improved. Banks continued:

When people were stuck going 20 mph, here came Carl Kiekhaefer and Mercury in the 1950s to show you how to go 40 mph. That was of high value back then. But the challenges we're facing

now are different. People are saturated on speed. Once you have a bass boat that will run 70 or 80 mph, is it really a powerful incentive to go 100 mph? How many average people have the courage to go 80 mph?[15]

One purpose of racing was to transfer the new technologies into innovations for the average customer. One such innovation from Mercury included the MerCruiser 320 port fuel-injected engine, the first fuel-injected consumer sterndrive package offered by Mercury Performance Products in the mid-1980s.

Meanwhile, KAM introduced a revolutionary throttle and shift control for sport boats in 1984. The Zero Effort Controls featured a canted handle with throttle and shift controls designed to fit comfortably in the hand. The throttle used ball and spring detents (catches that lock the movement of one part of the mechanism, much like a ratchet) to provide tactile feel and resist "creep."[16]

In 1988, KAM debuted its new sterndrive, which brought victory to racers during the 1988 APBA Offshore World Championship in Key West,

AWARD FROM "THE ENEMY"

IT CAME AS A SHOCK TO CARL KIEKHAEFER WHEN he learned in early 1976 that he was to be awarded the prestigious Ole Evinrude Award for "immeasurable contributions to the sport of boating." Kiekhaefer was absolutely thrilled, and perhaps more than any other honor he would receive in his lifetime, the Ole Evinrude Award represented for him the pinnacle of marine industry achievement.

In the six years since Kiekhaefer had left Mercury, he had completely discarded the competitive passion that he had demonstrated toward Evinrude in three decades of engineering and marketplace warfare. Not surprisingly, Charlie Strang was selected by OMC Chairman Ralph Evinrude to deliver the speech on the occasion of Kiekhaefer's receipt of the Ole Evinrude Award on February 22, 1976.

At the Key Biscayne luncheon, held during the Miami International Boat Show, Strang and Evinrude showered praise on Kiekhaefer's career and enormous contributions to the industry and to the pleasure of boating enthusiasts around the world. Kiekhaefer listened, dabbing his wet eyes with a handkerchief, as "a distinguished crowd of boat manufacturers, corporate and company personnel, and awed media members watched the history-making event of one marine giant honoring another."[1]

Ralph Evinrude said, "Carl Kiekhaefer galvanized the marine business into action. His gift for 'making things go' will long remain memorable in the marine field," adding, "I can't think of a finer man to represent the marine industry than that great catalyst for the trade...." Strang spoke at length of his friend and mentor's accomplishments and attempted in conclusion to circumvent Kiekhaefer's professed modesty. "If I know him, in accepting this award, he will probably ascribe most of this success to a 'team.' True, any achievement as great as Carl's calls for the help of others. ... But I was there ... saw the team change through the years ... saw the team members come and go ... with the one solid, stable factor always Carl himself. He did it his way, and he can't take that away from his legend, his innate modesty notwithstanding!"[2]

The unique circumstance of Kiekhaefer receiving this honor from the Evinrude Foundation was covered by hundreds of newspapers and magazines throughout the country—especially since Kiekhaefer gushed with sincere appreciation to Ralph Evinrude:

I am sorry only that we didn't get to know each other better during the heat of the marketplace over the past three decades.... [The press and my friends] feel, as I do, that it must have taken considerable courage to select a former competitor, but usually with the final thought that some high principles remain in the minds of our industry leaders such as yourself.[3]

A year later, when Ralph Evinrude was being honored for his 50th year of service to the marine industry, Carl and Fred Kiekhaefer were invited to Evinrude's table of honor during the gala banquet in Milwaukee. For all of Kiekhaefer's contributions and success in the industry, he still felt out of place seated next to Evinrude and confessed as much to Jim Jost. "I could well believe that there were others who deserved a spot at Ralph's table in view of the tremendous history of [Evinrude Motors] and I felt a little out of place in all this distinguished company," Kiekhaefer said. "I am just wondering if Ralph Evinrude himself didn't think I was somewhat of an impostor."[4]

Florida. Once again, Don Johnson won, racing in the Superboat class with Bill Sirois at the throttle. The drive racked up four consecutive US-1 offshore championships.

The KAM drive began to eat into Mercury's share of the consumer sterndrive market, spurring the industry rivals towards greater cooperation. Following Mercury's acquisition of Kiekhaefer Aeromarine Motors in 1990, the sterndrive was renamed the MerCruiser Six Drive and continued to win more offshore races than any other propulsion unit. That year, which saw the return of the Kiekhaefer legacy to Mercury Marine, the Hi-Performance Division introduced the first mass-produced, warrantied, supercharged marine engine, the MerCruiser 525SC. Engineers in the division had recognized that consumers had been installing after-market blower kits on engines not designed to handle the increased power.

The over-stressed engines would fail, and customers would put in a warranty claim. Based on the 454 block, the 525SC proved so reliable that the initial warranty period of 90 days was extended to a full year.

In 1996, Mercury reclaimed its crown lost to OMC by setting six APBA outboard bass boat speed records. The records included the Bass 150-horsepower class (88.952 mph), the 175-horsepower class (89.734 mph) with Mariner

Above: Innovations for racing boats often filtered down to the level of the average customer.

Below: Kiekhaefer Aeromarine's Zero Effort Controls offered drivers the convenience and safety of operating shifting, throttle, trimming, and K planes with one hand.

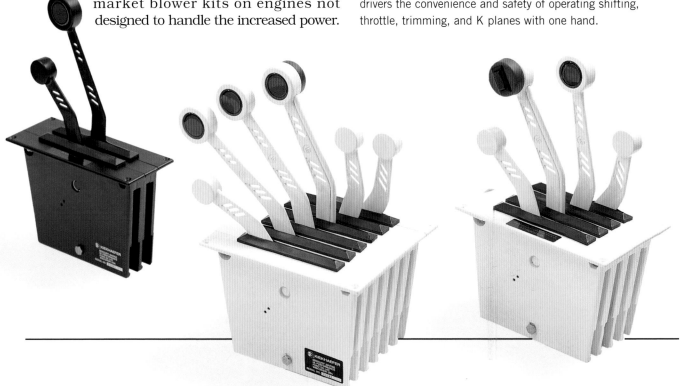

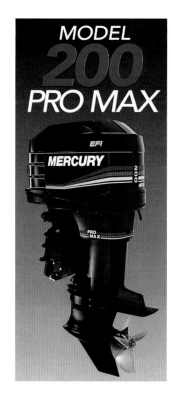

outboards, and the 200-horsepower class (94.112 mph) with a Mariner Super Magnum 200. The Pro Bass 200 Unlimited class was won with a Mercury Pro Max 200 (100.956 mph), and the record in the newly established Pro Bass Unlimited class fell to a Mercury 2.4 Litre EFI (102.568 mph), while the Mercury 200 DFI set a new world record in the Pro-Stock Bass Low Emission class (100.136 mph).

A year later, defending Rouen outboard champions Andre Larue and John Castelli, wtih Formula 1 veteran Kay Marshall, made history with their fourth-place finish in *Popeye*, powered by a Mercury 200-horsepower OptiMax low-emissions outboard. The trio completed 605 laps, just 149 laps behind the third-place boat, which was powered by a Mercury 300-plus-horsepower S3000.

Mercury has maintained its racing heritage through the most difficult of times, whether through factory-sponsored teams, as in the past, or by maintaining the most complete business line of the highest-quality products. "We may not have factory-sponsored teams anymore, but we are very intent on supporting all the independent racers," noted Senior Vice President Jim Hubbard. "It is helping to maintain our image as the best and the fastest."

That image runs like blood through drivers and the Hi-Performance clan alike. "You never get it out of your blood," said Bentz, who today is president of Triton Boats. "It's either in your blood to be competitive or it's not."[17]

Left: The Pro Bass 200 Unlimited Class was won with a Mercury Pro Max 200.

Below: Andre Larue, John Castelli, and Kay Marshall, powered by a 200-horsepower OptiMax, finished fourth at the 1997 24 Hours of Rouen. The engine was the only low-emission unit that accepted the challenge, and it competed against engines rated at more than 300 horsepower.

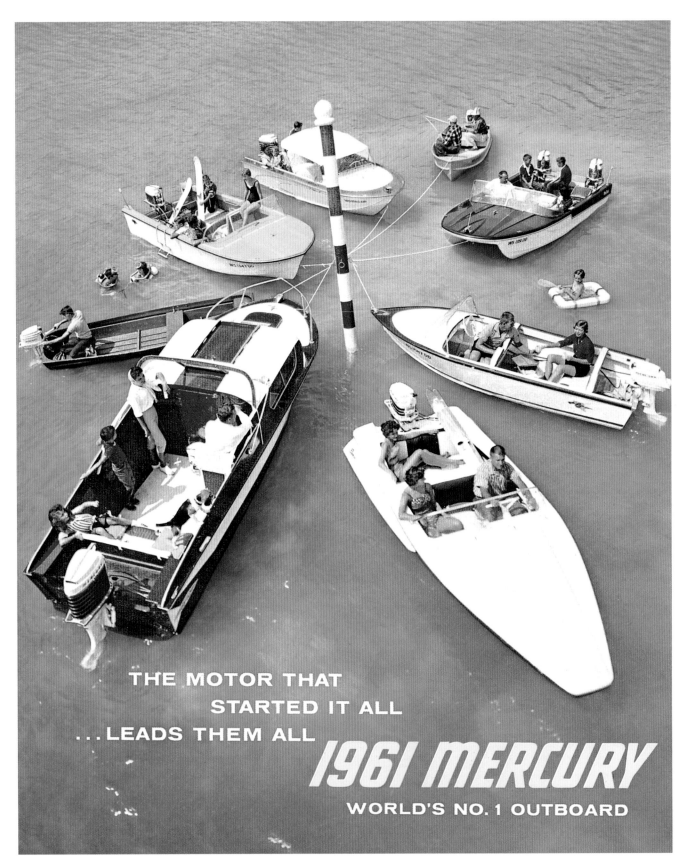

This 1961 promotional piece stressed the family benefits of Mercury outboards, not just their speed.

CHAPTER SEVEN

MERGING INTO THE SIXTIES

Despite persistent rumors, the Kiekhaefer Corporation is not for sale, nor are there any negotiations under way for sale or merger. ... We repeat, we have no interest other than staying strictly on course in our own field, which has been the design and production of better outboard motors. ...

—Carl Kiekhaefer, February 1961[1]

THOUGH CARL KIEKHAEFER AND MERCURY Marine would one day compete to produce the fastest engines, Kiekhaefer's split from the company was still several years away. But the separation really began on the morning of September 30, 1961. Kiekhaefer was crying in his bedroom with his long-time secretary Rose Smiljanic comforting him. "I won't sign," he wept, "I'm not going to go through with it." His close friend Al Puelicher, president of the Marshal & Ilsley Bank, told him firmly, "You've got to go through with it."[2]

Kiekhaefer had worked his way through crisis after crisis without shedding a tear—building innovative outboard motors in a converted barn, winning auto racing titles with no previous experience, repelling two stockholder rebellions, and surviving wartime restrictions by reinventing the chainsaw.

What reduced him to tears in September 1961 was an impending deal to sell the company to a larger corporation. Although he first considered a merger in 1947, now that it was here he was having trouble accepting it—even though he had spent the waning years of the 1950s actively pursuing one.

Merger Mania

In a letter he never mailed, Kiekhaefer wrote to US Senator Alexander Wiley in 1957, "The combined tax loads of the State of Wisconsin and the federal government make it impossible for us to carry on the necessary research and expansion to continue long in business. It is one thing to meet normal competition, but it is quite another to be taxed to death."[3]

At the time, Kiekhaefer estimated he had "created his own industry of 2,500 employees and had created some $75 million in tax money to say nothing of payrolls."[4] But it wasn't just taxes that had done him in. The racing bug helped.

"You just couldn't seem to get it across to him. He had this real penchant for [auto] racing, and he'd spend the money right and left, and we didn't have the money to spend," said Donald E. Castle, the controller from 1952 to 1957. "I couldn't meet payrolls, and you know, he was spending a million dollars for racing—Christ, for automobiles! So, it wasn't all the most enjoyable period of my working life."[5]

Fortunately, Kiekhaefer had a wonderful relationship with Puelicher. "If it hadn't been for Al Puelicher and the Marshal & Ilsley Bank, there would be no Mercury company today," Castle maintained. "I'd call Puelicher many times and say, 'Al, I've got a payroll of 50-some thousand dollars coming up Friday, and I don't have any money as you

In the 1960s, Mercury began manufacturing more parts and accessories for its engines, such as this Quicksilver propeller.

well know.' Because they had our bank account. He'd say, 'Well, I'll put some money in for you.'"[6] Slowly, Mercury and the Kiekhaefer empire had begun to unravel.

During those years, Kiekhaefer fielded dozens of casual inquiries from larger organizations that were searching for solid companies to acquire in order to diversify. As a matter of course, Kiekhaefer politely declined the offers. But as severe cash shortages began to disable his operations in the mid-1950s, he began to accept the idea of merging Mercury with a larger, financially stronger partner.

Besides the obvious increased opportunities that a sizable investment in manufacturing facilities and product development would bring to Mercury, Kiekhaefer had other reasons to consider a merger. He had fashioned Mercury into the second-largest outboard manufacturer in the world. Like an industrial czar, Kiekhaefer had neglected to develop an organization that could survive without him. He had acquired a cadre of bright and talented engineers and manufacturing management, especially Charlie Strang, but Kiekhaefer was still the absolute nucleus around which all activity at Mercury revolved. Kiekhaefer began to fear that if something were to happen to him, Mercury might not survive.

His anxiety over the succession of leadership at Mercury was magnified extensively one afternoon in the fall of 1956 when he became convinced that he was going to die. Mercury was introducing the newly announced six-cylinder, 60-horsepower Mark 75 outboard motor for the 1957 model year at the annual Mercury dealers and distributors meeting. The announcement banquet was being held at a large restaurant between Fond du Lac and Oshkosh, and Kiekhaefer was to be the featured speaker during the evening ceremonies. Kiekhaefer and Strang were together in the engineering department following the meal when Kiekhaefer came to Strang and said, "Oh my God! I think I'm having a coronary!" Pete Humleker, Kiekhaefer's executive in charge of industrial and personnel relations, was in the lab at the time, and Strang told him, "Get Carl in the car. Get him to his house, and I'll have a doctor waiting with everything he needs by the time you get to Fond du Lac."[7] Kiekhaefer's "coronary" was a false alarm, but it triggered a sense of mortality.

Another equally strong inducement to considering a Mercury merger was the exposure of Kiekhaefer's personal estate to federal and state taxes because he owned 90 percent of the stock of both

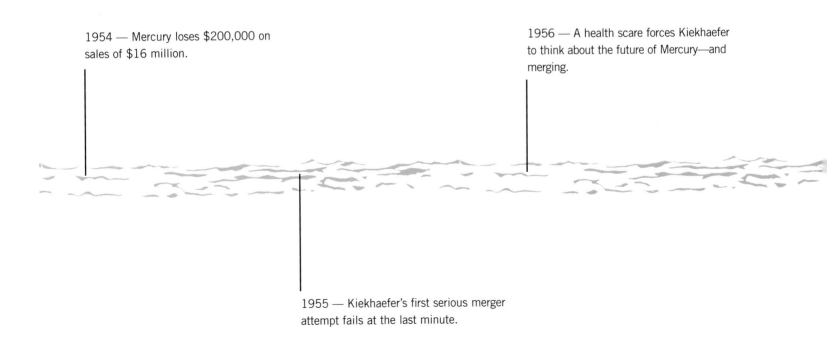

1954 — Mercury loses $200,000 on sales of $16 million.

1956 — A health scare forces Kiekhaefer to think about the future of Mercury—and merging.

1955 — Kiekhaefer's first serious merger attempt fails at the last minute.

the Kiekhaefer Corporation and Kiekhaefer Aero-marine Motors. Any outright sale of his holdings would subject the estate to severe tax liabilities. Tax laws have since changed, but the penalties in the mid-1950s for owning such a large percentage of a growing business could be devastating, not only in an outright sale but also in case of death. The surviving family estate would also be taxed heavily.

Kiekhaefer was against taking Mercury public because of the constant agitation he had experienced with stockholders, initial investors, and family alike. He began to seriously consider a merger that would allow him to align his companies with a much larger and more powerful organization and reduce his tax exposure by taking a combination of cash and stock from his merger partner. If a smaller portion of a transaction involved cash, his tax liability would be appreciably smaller, while taxes on stock received would be deferred until sold. Lastly, he knew that for Mercury to grow fast enough to compete equally with OMC, he needed to invest significantly in new plant facilities and new die-casting equipment and undertake greater research into new technologies and product development.

By 1954, Kiekhaefer's empire was beginning to lose money. When the contract with Disston for production of chainsaw engines was terminated in early 1953, more than $460,000 in annual profits disappeared overnight. Even though sales of Wizard motors to Western Auto Supply increased by nearly $1 million between 1953 and 1954, only a nominal profit was realized because of production problems encountered in converting Mercury models to Wizard models. On top of these losses, sales of Mercury outboards fell by more than 11,000 units in 1954 alone, and when calculations were completed for the bottom line, Kiekhaefer had lost nearly $200,000 on sales of almost $16 million for the year.

For a second time, Kiekhaefer considered a merger with Food Machinery and Chemical Corporation (FMC). Years earlier, as Mercury was still growing by leaps and bounds, Kiekhaefer had entertained the possibility of an alliance with the giant industrial firm. But in May 1957, Benjamin Carter, the executive vice president of the machinery divisions, wrote Willis Blank to tell him that Mercury had grown too big to be of interest to FMC any more.

During the years 1957 through 1961, Kiekhaefer and his chief executives were almost perpetually distracted by wave after wave of prospective

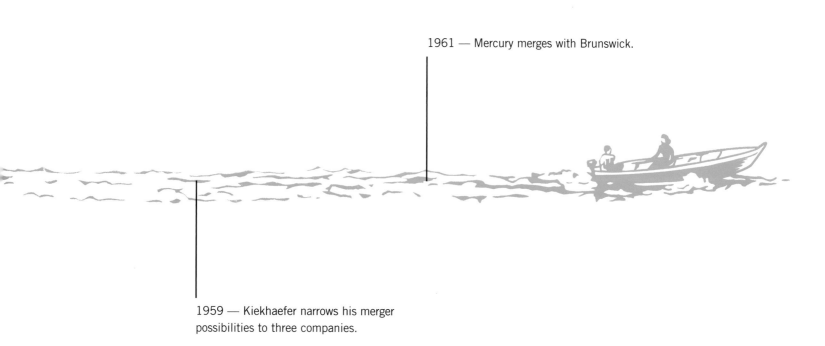

1961 — Mercury merges with Brunswick.

1959 — Kiekhaefer narrows his merger possibilities to three companies.

merger partners, from National Automotive Fibres of Detroit (NAFI), to the giant Borg-Warner Corporation of Chicago, to Motorola. There were also intermittently serious discussions with Chrysler.[8]

The Bowling Bride

In the closing years of the decade, a three-way race for making a deal with Carl Kiekhaefer began to shape up among Chrysler, American Machine and Foundry Company (AMF), and Brunswick Corporation. Of the competition, most interesting was the quiet battle for control of Kiekhaefer Mercury that ensued between bowling industry rivals AMF and Brunswick.

AMF had become one of the most popular stocks on Wall Street due to a combination of engineering ingenuity and executive talent. In 1943, Morehead Patterson took over control of AMF from his father, Rufus Lenoir Patterson, who had founded the company in 1900 and invented the first automated tobacco handling machine. These complex machines could weigh and bag tobacco, as well as roll cigarettes and cigars. By 1940, AMF machines were rolling over a million cigars a year. The company also developed baking and stitching machines but was in danger of stagnation by the time the younger Patterson stepped in. Following World War II, Morehead Patterson "decided that the company had to grow or die."[9] In his search for new products, he came upon a crudely built prototype of an automatic pinsetter for 10-pin bowling.

An automatic pinsetter is a remarkably complex device, and many inventors had failed to conquer the combination of accuracy, speed, safe pin handling, and ball return. An inventor named Fred Schmidt, working in a henhouse in Pearl River, New York, had patented a device using strong vacuum gripping of pins. Robert E. Kennedy, a salesman for Brunswick, learned of the new device and formed a partnership with the inventor. Brunswick was already heavily involved in the manufacture and sales of pins and balls for the sport and should have recognized the potential of the new machine. But when Kennedy approached Bob Bensinger, who was Brunswick's president at the time, he was surprised to be turned down flat. Bensinger, who became chairman, later recalled his justification in a book on Brunswick history prepared by Chicago journalist Rick Kogan. "Who needed an automatic pinsetter? Not the bowling proprietors—they didn't have the money. Even if they did, why should they buy? There were plenty of pin boys around."[10] Kennedy promptly took his remarkable device to rival AMF, where Morehead Patterson quickly made a deal.

It would take AMF six years to make the cantankerous contraption work reliably, but when the company introduced a version in 1952, the AMF Pinspotter, Brunswick was stunned. "When we heard that, it was like a death pall hit the company," a Brunswick executive remembered. "What the hell

The New York branch of Mercury.

St. Cloud, Florida, is home to the Special Products Division of the Kiekhaefer Corporation, where plastic and aluminum marine parts and accessories are produced.

are we going to do? Fold up our tents and walk away?"[11] Brunswick developed its own device but fell nearly four critical years behind in getting a competitive machine to market. By 1961, AMF would install 68,000 Pinspotters under lease for an average annual gross of $68 million. The international potential for the new machine was also realized, and AMF leased an additional 3,000 machines in 17 foreign countries.

Since 1957, various brokers and agents had attempted to get Kiekhaefer and AMF in the same room to explore a merger, but serious discussions didn't begin until 1960. As it turned out, AMF had been carefully watching Kiekhaefer's progress for years, waiting for the right moment to make an offer.

In May 1961, AMF presented Kiekhaefer with a most tempting offer, which would amount to more than $30 million in cash and stock over a four-year period, and leave Kiekhaefer in place as president of Mercury. Meanwhile, Brunswick Corporation had for several years been struggling for Kiekhaefer's attention. In 1958, Kiekhaefer had arranged to entertain Brunswick-Balke-Collender Company President Benjamin Edward "Ted" Bensinger at Tommy Bartlett's spectacular water ski show at the Wisconsin Dells. Bensinger was impressed by the power and beauty of the Mercury outboards used exclu-

sively in Bartlett's highly regarded shows and commented, "The water ballet and show were terrific."[12] He also spoke with Blank about the potential for getting their two companies together, and both agreed that "it might not be amiss for us to 'touch base from time to time.' "[13]

Brunswick's Story: "Gambling Furniture"

John Moses Brunswick, a 26-year-old Swiss immigrant, began building carriages and fine furniture in Cincinnati, Ohio, in 1845. In this same year, young Brunswick saw his first billiard table, an elegantly crafted example imported from England. Though billiard tables had arrived in the United States before the American Revolution, they were mostly considered instruments of bawdy establishments and quickly gained a reputation for attracting drunkenness and gambling. When US President John Quincy Adams had a table installed in the White House, he was soundly criticized for having "gambling furniture."[14] Like bowling, the early history of billiards was replete with many variations in both rules and equipment, but before Brunswick built his first table in 1845, slate beds and rubber cushions had become the norm. In the early part of the 19th century, a French infantry captain named Minguad "whiled away his sentence playing billiards in prison."[15] He discovered that by gluing a patch of leather to the end of his tapered cue stick, he was able to manipulate the path of the ball by hitting it somewhat off-center. He became so enamored with perfecting what would eventually be referred to as applying "English" to the cue ball that he asked to be kept in jail a month longer than his sentence required.[16]

When news spread of the high-quality billiard tables built by Brunswick, his business mushroomed. By 1858, Brunswick had expanded to 75 employees, including his two half-brothers, and was building $200,000 worth of tables a year. By 1873, Brunswick merged with Julius Balke's Great Western Billiard Manufactory of Cincinnati and by 1879 with Phelan & Collender of New York, his two largest billiard table competitors. The company, which moved to Chicago after the great fire, would be known as the Brunswick-Balke-Collender Company until the name was shortened in 1960 to Brunswick Corporation.

In 1912, Brunswick anticipated the onset of Prohibition sentiment and discontinued a $4 million sideline manufacturing elegant bar and tavern fixtures. In the 1920s, Brunswick diversified into automobile tires, phonograph cabinets, phonograph machines, and eventually phonograph records featuring the voices of such musical idols as Al Jolson, Duke Ellington, and Cab Calloway. By the eve of the Great Depression, Brunswick sales were nearly $30 million. Well-timed divestitures of music division assets helped to nurse Brunswick through the worst years to follow. Following World War II, the great bowling pinsetter war with rival AMF would dominate Brunswick thinking for decades to follow.

When AMF unveiled its latest and most reliable Pinspotter in 1952, a flurry of pinsetter development began at Brunswick. Benjamin E. "Ted" Bensinger, the third Bensinger president of Brunswick since his grandfather became president in 1890, borrowed $16 million from a private investor to fund a massive race to develop a competitive device, and in 1956, the first Brunswick pinsetter was installed. Unfortunately, AMF had already installed more than

9,000 rival Pinspotters throughout the country. But Brunswick's new machine proved so popular that $30 million in orders flooded the Chicago headquarters. By the end of 1956, Brunswick had installed 2,000 machines, 7,000 by 1957, and when Bensinger began feeling out the Kiekhaefer Corporation in 1958, more than 11,000 Brunswick devices were in use. The company's growth was nothing short of spectacular. Sales of $33 million and profits of $700,000 in 1954 swelled to sales of $422 million and earnings of $45 million by 1961.

Near the end of 1960, rumors spread that Brunswick was also considering a merger with Kiekhaefer's perpetual rival, Bob McCulloch and his Scott-Atwater company. When Kiekhaefer heard that Bensinger was holding talks with McCulloch, he refused further discussions. Brunswick, though, was on a shopping spree, and between 1958 and 1961 purchased 18 companies, ranging from MacGregor Sports Products to Owens Yachts and Larson Boats. Bensinger, avoiding confrontation with the unpredictable Kiekhaefer, would phone Blank in Fond du Lac when he was certain Kiekhaefer was out of town. Blank would record his conversations with Bensinger and play them for Kiekhaefer when he returned. Bensinger attempted to convince Blank that Brunswick was to be a force in the boating industry and that he was determined to acquire an outboard manufacturer. Bensinger said:

One way or another, we have come to a corporate decision, and that is that we're going to have to be in that business. ... We're going to be a dominant factor, or try to be, in that marine operation. ... This is going to be, as you can imagine, over the next few years, a battle of survival. You folks are one of the two or three well-established companies in the field on the outboard end.

[W]e haven't had any serious negotiations with anybody, including yourselves. But that doesn't mean we aren't going to be having plenty of discussions with others, and I hope, as well as yourselves. ... What's best for Brunswick? Should we try and merge with Kiekhaefer or Outboard Marine or West Bend or McCulloch? Should we import

Founded in 1900 as a manufacturer of tobacco-handling machines, AMF was the first to build a reliable pinsetting machine.

some motors? Should we do some things on our own? We don't know. I'm candid to admit it. ... The only thing we have a firm conviction on is one way or another we're going to be in the game.[17]

Proposals and counter-proposals began to flow from all three suitors in the spring of 1961. AMF, Chrysler, and Brunswick jockeyed for emotional position with the volatile founder of Mercury, and a considerable portion of Kiekhaefer's time was spent evaluating and ultimately rejecting various offers and suggestions. Early in the year, Kiekhaefer removed Chrysler from consideration, believing that he would be swallowed by the giant automaker and become an insignificant and powerless division. More to the point, Chrysler had strategically blundered by stipulating that Kiekhaefer would have to step down as president of the company and take orders from a Chrysler-appointed executive. The battle for ownership of Mercury narrowed to AMF and Brunswick.

In November 1960, Bensinger offered Kiekhaefer $25 million for Mercury, $18.75 million in cash and $6.25 million in Brunswick stock over a six-year period. By January 1961, Bensinger changed the offer to $25 million in immediate cash. The following month, Bensinger raised the offer to $30 million, $25 million in cash and $5 million in stock. But on March 7, 1961, Brunswick financial analysts discovered that Mercury's entire net worth was only $15 million and that 1960 profits after taxes were a paltry $42,000. The offer dropped $5 million overnight to $25 million. Kiekhaefer angrily broke off negotiations and began to look toward AMF. Robert C. Anderegg, Kiekhaefer's new controller, remembered the differences in approach between AMF and Brunswick. "Brunswick didn't go near into the analysis that AMF did. I think Ted Bensinger was just determined he was going to get Mercury one way or another and paid a lot less attention to the details. He just plain wanted to buy the company."[18]

Kiekhaefer had become alarmed by the swirl of rumors circulating the country that he was planning to merge. It seemed that every time he spoke to the press, all it wanted to know was who he was negotiating with and when a deal would become final. Kiekhaefer correctly assumed that Mercury sales would suffer as a result of this widespread speculation and issued a terse press release attempting to convince the public that his company was not for sale, even as he was in the midst of almost daily negotiation. It read:

Despite persistent rumors, the Kiekhaefer Corporation is not for sale, nor are there any negotiations under way for sale or merger. ... We feel we can serve the industry best by continuing in our present form and concentrating on our own field of endeavor.

It is true that in recent years we have been approached by a number of reputable firms who have suggested merger or sale; however, we repeat, we have no interest other than staying strictly on

Brunswick's pinsetting machine revolutionized not only bowling but the company itself.

LINING UP TO GET FIRED

CARL KIEKHAEFER NEVER OWNED UP TO THIS wild but true story because he felt it made him sound like "an oddball." The most popular version is still being repeated today and has appeared in both *Boy's Life* and *Reader's Digest*. Adding a few minor changes, it becomes the Kiekhaefer "Coca-Cola driver" story.

> *Carl Kiekhaefer had decided to make a surprise tour of one of his factories one day. Walking through the plant, he noticed a young man lazily sitting on a crate of soft drinks. "Just how much are you being paid a week?" the boss angrily asked him. "A hundred bucks," answered the lounging guy.*
>
> *The boss pulled out his wallet and peeled off five $20 bills. "Here's a week's pay," he shouted. "Now get out and don't come back!"*
>
> *Wordlessly, the young man stuffed the money into his pocket and took off. The plant manager, standing nearby, stared in amazement. "Tell me," Kiekhaefer barked, "how long has that guy worked for us?" "He didn't work here," replied the manager. "He was just delivering Coca-Cola for the soft-drink machines."*[1]

Actually, Kiekhaefer fired more than one person who didn't work for him. Ted Karls was driving a truck for Anchorage Transfer and Storage in the early 1950s and made a scheduled delivery of packing cardboard to the Kiekhaefer Mercury facility in Fond du Lac. After he had backed his tractor-trailer rig to the loading dock, Mercury personnel told him they would unload the shipment, and he was to wait for his signed delivery receipt. "Because I didn't have to do nothing, I was just standing there by the rail, with my foot up there, smoking a cigarette," Karls said. He had been waiting about half an hour when Kiekhaefer came through the loading dock, moving like a freight train. Even though Karls didn't know the busy industrialist personally, he recognized him from his periodic deliveries and said, "Good morning, Carl. How are you?"

Carl snorted, "Good—What are you doing?" "Nothing," Karls responded. "When are you going to do something?" Carl demanded. "When that trailer's empty," Karls said, motioning to the truck. "You ain't gonna stand here that long. You follow me," Kiekhaefer said brusquely. Karls followed Kiekhaefer through the plant to an office, where a young lady was seated behind a desk.

"How much do you make a week," Kiekhaefer demanded. "I make $140 a week," Karls said. "OK, write him a check," Kiekhaefer told the girl. "You're fired!" he told Karls, and continued on his journey through the plant.

Karls took the check from Kiekhaefer's obedient employee and returned to his truck, which had been unloaded in his absence. He told the shipping dock workers that Kiekhaefer had fired him and had given him a check, and they told Karls, "You're the second one." Karls left the plant and stopped at a nearby grocery store to cash the check. The cashier, who knew that Karls drove for Anchorage Transfer, asked, "When did you start working for Mercury?" Karls explained that he had just been fired by Kiekhaefer himself, and the cashier responded that he had cashed another check only two weeks before for a driver with Railroad Express trucking in Oshkosh as Kiekhaefer had "fired" him also. The cashier ribbed Karls a little because the other driver had received $160, $20 more than Karls. Word spread amongst drivers at both Anchorage Transfer and Railroad Express about Kiekhaefer's hair trigger and no-questions-asked dismissals with pay. "The guys all laughed," Karls remembered, "and every time somebody would go out there, they'd just stand around and wait for Kiekhaefer to come and fire them. But nobody else ever got fired."[2]

course in our own field, which has been the design and production of better outboard motors.[19]

Brunswick attempted to soothe Kiekhaefer's frayed nerves. Brunswick Vice President F. E. "Gene" Troy wrote Kiekhaefer a note of apology, trying to explain why Brunswick could often seem cold-blooded in its approach to making a deal. "I feel that through our wide experience in the field of mergers and acquisitions we have become somewhat callous to the personal feelings of others, and while this is not intentional, the impression sometimes created has worked to our disadvantage. If we seemed over-enthusiastic in our negotiations with you, it was an honest enthusiasm for a great product and greater opportunities."[20] Kiekhaefer ignored the overture and continued discussions with AMF.

AMF offered Kiekhaefer approximately $30 million in cash and stock with a payment schedule that stretched over nearly four years. Disturbing to Kiekhaefer was the lack of flexibility he perceived in an AMF merger. The language of the proposals and the inferences AMF would make in negotiations led Kiekhaefer to believe that they were insincere in promising him the freedom to run the company in his own fashion following a merger. He considered the benefits of establishing a separate engineering consulting company to raise capital rather than accept a Mercury-Brunswick merger. Finally, exhausting all the feasible alternatives available to him, he grudgingly admitted that his best opportunity was with Brunswick.

By June 1961, Kiekhaefer had received four different proposals from Brunswick headquarters in Chicago. Among the various plans was one that would provide Kiekhaefer and Blank with $34 million in Brunswick stock, based on the average price of the stock 10 days before and 10 days after a formal closing. Among the various terms defined in the prospective agreement was Kiekhaefer's ability to personally purchase the Siesta Key saltwater proving grounds property at Midnight Pass near Sarasota, the house at Winter Haven, a house in Fond du Lac, and, most remarkably, the enormous properties of Lake X. In the case of Siesta Key and Lake X, he would be able to lease these facilities back to Brunswick on favorable terms while maintaining a most lucrative investment opportunity.

Kiekhaefer agonized over every detail of the proposed agreement and almost daily vacillated between acceptance and rejection. His moods would swing widely, one moment beaming with pride over a condition of sale that favored him, the next moment scowling and agitated over a paragraph that limited his freedom. Even when the hundreds of nuances involved in the transaction were ironed out, Kiekhaefer was still unsettled about giving up control of the empire he had carefully built for more than 22 years. He demanded of Bensinger—and received—a separate and confidential letter to guarantee his autonomy as president of Mercury and the job security of his top executives following the closing. "It is contemplated," Bensinger wrote, "that the present Kiekhaefer operation will be continued as a separate subsidiary of Brunswick, and, without commitment as to term by either party, you will be made its president and act as its chief executive." Kiekhaefer would also be elected a vice president of Brunswick Corporation and be given two seats on the board of directors. It would be up to Kiekhaefer to fill the second seat on the board with an individual of his choosing.

The preliminary "Agreement and Plan of Reorganization" between Brunswick Corporation and the Kiekhaefer Corporation was typeset and delivered to Kiekhaefer near the end of July 1961. Closing of the merger was actually a two-step process. His signature on the agreement would authorize both corporations to prepare all of the necessary closing documents and Kiekhaefer to prepare deeds of title to Kiekhaefer properties and facilities for delivery at the closing. Strang remembered when the moment of truth arrived for signing the preliminary agreement. Strang was sitting with Kiekhaefer in his office on July 29, 1961, when he was preparing to sign the papers. "I said, 'Carl, it takes you 10 minutes to get rid of what took you 22 years to build.' He looked at me a minute and says, 'Yeah,' and went ahead and signed it."[21]

Within 24 hours of signing the preliminary agreements, Kiekhaefer received a warning from Arthur A. Burck, a prominent Wall Street consultant who had tried in vain to get Kiekhaefer to consider a merger with Studebaker-Packard earlier in the year. The letter cautioned against a merger with Brunswick, suggesting that the price of the stock was artificially high. Burck wrote:

R. F. Bensinger (left) was chairman and B. E. "Ted" Bensinger was president of Brunswick when Kiekhaefer Corporation was acquired.

Was lunching today with a group of invest-ment bankers and was jolted by a rumor that you were selling for $33 million in Brunswick shares. This jolted me because in the opinion of those pre-sent—as well as my opinion—Brunswick stock is way overpriced. In other words, the important thing is not the immediate market value you get, but where the stock will be a year from now—this is what counts."[22]

It was the only formal warning that Kiekhaefer received against a merger with Brunswick, and so he discounted it, assuming that the consultant was simply sore that his proposed merger with Studebaker-Packard hadn't materialized. After all, Brunswick was experiencing record sales, and the tremendous popularity of bowling seemed to ensure high profits for many years to come. Another more subtle warning came from his longtime advisor and attorney Alan Edgarton in Fond du Lac, who said, "Carl, if I know you at all, I don't see how you'd ever work with somebody unless you were the boss. I'm not trying to hurt your feelings, but you're that kind of fellow."[23]

There were 60 days between the signing of the initial agreement and the scheduled closing meet-ing at Brunswick's Chicago headquarters. "I'm sure from the first of August on, Carl had begun already to have second thoughts," Mercury Controller Bob Anderegg remembered. "He talked to his attorneys and actually tried to find ways that he could wiggle out of the deal. Between the first of August and the end of September, he tried every which way to wiggle out of it." According to Anderegg, Kiekhaefer at one point told his attorneys, "The hell with it! Breach the contract!" But cooler heads prevailed, and he calmed down.[24] As the closing day approached, Kiekhaefer became more anxious and unsettled, and he was nearly impossible to be around.

Signing It Over

On that morning in September 1961, after Kiekhaefer cried in his bedroom, he washed his face and prepared to leave. Two cars left Fond du Lac for the long drive to Chicago. Kiekhaefer and Smiljanic drove one car, while Anderegg and Edgarton followed in another. Assembled in the Brunswick boardroom were Bensinger, a phalanx of Brunswick attorneys, and rows of neat stacks of papers to be signed by both parties. Following a few nervous minutes of greeting, Brunswick handed Kiekhaefer the first set of papers to sign. Nobody really knew what Kiekhaefer was going to do, and the tension was nearly suffocating to everyone in the room. "It was a question of 'go' or 'no go,'" Edgarton remembered. "If you knew Mr. Kiekhaefer, you'd know it was a possibility [that he could walk out]. I knew it because I'd been into some situations … where he just had enough and walked out. But I think that in back of it all was the [question], 'What will I do? Where will I get the funds to keep this whole organization going and do what I want to do worldwide?' " Kiekhaefer was unhappy, Edgarton remem-bered, but it was too late. "Well, if you knew him … you could read it as well as you could a news-paper. Because he was one person when he was happy and normal, and he was an entirely dif-ferent person when he was in a mood of that kind. He was just mad, and he wanted to put it off, but they weren't going to put it off."[25]

Kiekhaefer slowly began to sign. Anderegg and Edgarton sat on either side of Kiekhaefer, and as each document was handed to him, they would briefly explain what it was for and where he had to sign. "But after a while," Anderegg recalled, "there were just so many of them he just finally got to signing the papers and throwing them on the floor. He was just exasperated with the whole procedure."[26] And suddenly, it was over. "Then, the truth really hit him," Anderegg observed. "He had sold his company. I'm sure he had tears in his eyes. I never saw a man so dejected as he was on the way home from that meeting."[27] Anderegg and Edgarton again shared a car for the return trip to Fond du Lac, and both remembered being affected by Kiekhaefer's obvious agony. "We both thought the same

thing," Anderegg explained. "It was kind of a torture to see what Carl was going through and what he must be thinking. It was a quiet ride back for everybody, I'm sure."[28]

Kiekhaefer was in shock. The company didn't belong to him anymore. On the way home, he cried again.

Within days of signing the documents that gave Brunswick control of his empire, he received a memo from his new "boss," Bensinger. It was a boilerplate announcement to all Brunswick divisional presidents concerning an upcoming Brunswick board of directors meeting. Kiekhaefer then realized where he stood in the scheme of things. The terse memo gave Kiekhaefer only 15 minutes to explain to the board a lengthy list of subjects, including his original and revised budgets for 1961. The memo read:

By 1961, Mercury could advertise that it was number one in the world in outboards.

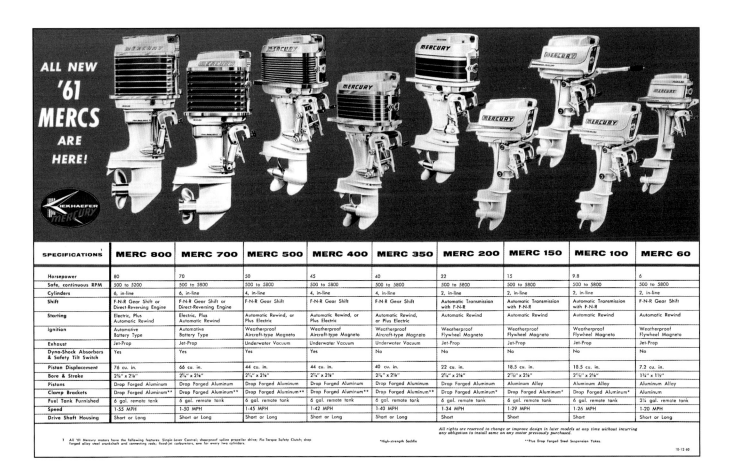

SPECIFICATIONS[1]	MERC 800	MERC 700	MERC 500	MERC 400	MERC 350	MERC 200	MERC 150	MERC 100	MERC 60
Horsepower	80	70	50	45	40	22	15	9.8	6
Safe, continuous RPM	500 to 5200	500 to 5800	500 to 5800	500 to 5800	500 to 5800	500 to 5800	500 to 5800	500 to 5800	500 to 5800
Cylinders	6, in-line	6, in-line	4, in-line	4, in-line	4, in-line	2, in-line	2, in-line	2, in-line	2, in-line
Shift	F-N-R Gear Shift or Direct-Reversing Engine	F-N-R Gear Shift or Direct-Reversing Engine	F-N-R Gear Shift	F-N-R Gear Shift	F-N-R Gear Shift	Automatic Transmission with F-N-R	Automatic Transmission with F-N-R	Automatic Transmission with F-N-R	F-N-R Gear Shift
Starting	Electric, Plus Automatic Rewind	Electric, Plus Automatic Rewind	Automatic Rewind, or Plus Electric	Automatic Rewind, or Plus Electric	Automatic Rewind, or Plus Electric	Automatic Rewind	Automatic Rewind	Automatic Rewind	Automatic Rewind
Ignition	Automotive Battery Type	Automotive Battery Type	Weatherproof Aircraft-type Magneto	Weatherproof Aircraft-type Magneto	Weatherproof Aircraft-type Magneto	Weatherproof Flywheel Magneto	Weatherproof Flywheel Magneto	Weatherproof Flywheel Magneto	Weatherproof Flywheel Magneto
Exhaust	Jet-Prop	Jet-Prop	Underwater Vacuum	Underwater Vacuum	Underwater Vacuum	Jet-Prop	Jet-Prop	Jet-Prop	Jet-Prop
Dyna-Shock Absorbers & Safety Tilt Switch	Yes	Yes	Yes	Yes	No	No	No	No	No
Piston Displacement	76 cu. in.	66 cu. in.	44 cu. in.	44 cu. in.	40 cu. in.	22 cu. in.	18.5 cu. in.	18.5 cu. in.	7.2 cu. in.
Bore & Stroke	2 3/4" x 2 1/8"	2 9/16" x 2 1/8"	2 9/16" x 2 1/8"	2 9/16" x 2 1/8"	2 7/16" x 2 1/8"	2 9/16" x 2 1/8"	2 11/32" x 2 1/8"	2 11/32" x 2 1/8"	1 3/4" x 1 1/2"
Pistons	Drop Forged Aluminum	Drop Forged Aluminum	Drop Forged Aluminum	Drop Forged Aluminum	Drop Forged Aluminum	Drop Forged Aluminum	Aluminum Alloy	Aluminum Alloy	Aluminum Alloy
Clamp Brackets	Drop Forged Aluminum**	Drop Forged Aluminum**	Drop Forged Aluminum**	Drop Forged Aluminum**	Drop Forged Aluminum**	Drop Forged Aluminum*	Drop Forged Aluminum*	Drop Forged Aluminum*	Aluminum
Fuel Tank Furnished	6 gal. remote tank	6 gal. remote tank	6 gal. remote tank	6 gal. remote tank	6 gal. remote tank	6 gal. remote tank	6 gal. remote tank	6 gal. remote tank	3 1/4 gal. remote tank
Speed	1-55 MPH	1-50 MPH	1-45 MPH	1-42 MPH	1-40 MPH	1-34 MPH	1-29 MPH	1-26 MPH	1-20 MPH
Drive Shaft Housing	Short or Long	Short or Long	Short or Long	Short or Long	Short or Long	Short	Short	Short	Short or Long

All rights are reserved to change or improve design in later models at any time without incurring any obligation to install same on any motor previously purchased.

1 All '61 Mercury motors have the following features: Single-Lever Control; shearproof spline propeller drive; Flo-Torque Safety Clutch; drop forged alloy steel crankshaft and connecting rods; fixed-jet carburetors, one for every two cylinders.

*High-strength Saddle

**Plus Drop Forged Steel Suspension Yokes.

10-12-60

The formidable 1961 Mercury lineup.

What you actually expected to have your subsidiary attain for 1961; the reasons—economic, personnel, or otherwise—that were responsible for your attaining the final objectives set; or the reason why the objectives were not attained. And, most important, what remedial steps you have taken during 1961 to get your house in order to assure a 1962 satisfactory result.... Be prepared to discuss your Management Team or organization (a) as it was; (b) as it now is; (c) as you plan it to be for 1962."[29]

Kiekhaefer would soon experience an emotional and even life-threatening trauma as he realized the true consequences of his merger with Brunswick. Not since he left the family homestead more than 40 years ago had Kiekhaefer suffered such a crisis of identity and self-worth. Though he proudly displayed the stock certificate for 600,000 shares he had received from Brunswick, he had difficulty savoring his good fortune. Among the terms of the agreement signed on July 31 was that Brunswick would pay 600,000 shares to Kiekhaefer for 100 percent of the Kiekhaefer Corporation, after which Kiekhaefer would distribute 10 percent of the shares to Blank. The agreement also stated that if the price of the shares amounted to less than $34 million when the closing took place in Chicago, Brunswick would give Kiekhaefer additional shares to make up the difference. But, the agreement went on to specify, if the price of Brunswick stock were to rise during the interim period, Kiekhaefer would still receive the whole 600,000 shares. In fact, on the day of closing, Brunswick stock had risen to nearly $63, a gain of $6 from the signing of the preliminary agreements. That day, Kiekhaefer was handed Brunswick stock certificates worth $37.725 million. He and his family would keep $34.357 million while Blank would receive around $3.3 million. The recent rise in stock value was an extra personal bonus of more than $3.5 million for Kiekhaefer alone.[37] Unfortunately, the disagreeable task of informing the world of his decision destroyed any sense of financial victory he may have felt.

He directed Tom King, who had become Mercury vice president of marketing, to immediately wire all distributors of the merger before word leaked to the press. Of greatest concern to Kiekhaefer was that distributors might feel they would be forced to represent Brunswick's boatbuilding interests, or that Brunswick outlets would become Mercury dealerships. Kiekhaefer outlined his "official" reasons for merging, including:

1. You automatically become a partner in a well-diversified, 116-year-old corporation internationally known for its products for the leisure-time market and with gross sales which will, with the addition of Mercury, be approximately $450 million in 1961.
2. The addition of 90,000 Brunswick stockholders and employees as Mercury boosters.
3. The opportunity for a combined Brunswick-Kiekhaefer program of engineering research.”[30]

If Kiekhaefer's reasoning seemed unconvincing, it is because Kiekhaefer himself wasn't sure about the future with Brunswick. Within days of the merger, a picture of Bensinger standing with Kiekhaefer next to a Mercury outboard was printed in hundreds of newspapers across the country. Kiekhaefer is glowering at Bensinger, who displays a decidedly nervous smile as he tentatively rests his

Following the sale of the Kiekhaefer Corporation to Brunswick on September 30, 1961, Brunswick President Ted Bensinger nervously leans on one of Carl's engines for a publicity photograph.

Brunswick's 1961 annual report
introduced its new subsidiary, the Kiekhaefer Corporation.

arm across Kiekhaefer's engine. The picture captured the essence of the newly emerging and uncertain relationship between the two men.

Worst of all, almost immediately following the merger, Brunswick stock began to fall. After Kiekhaefer had received a handsome dividend check in the months following the merger, the dividends abruptly stopped. Kiekhaefer was prohibited by Securities and Exchange Commission regulations from selling more than 1 percent of his holdings each six months because he was now technically an employee of Brunswick Corporation and subject to insider trading rules. Bensinger offered to assist Kiekhaefer in selling additional shares, if he wished,

through a secondary offering, which Bensinger could legally arrange. But Kiekhaefer was suspicious of Bensinger's motives and assumed that Brunswick wanted him to reduce his holdings to reduce his potential influence as a large stockholder and as a Brunswick director.

In fact, Kiekhaefer held the single largest block of Brunswick stock, a position of strength that he felt was more important than selling off shares in a declining market. What Kiekhaefer didn't realize was that Brunswick shares would plummet from $63 on the closing day of the merger to only $6 in less than a year. The bowling boom that had catapulted Brunswick stock ever skyward had busted, and pinsetter customers stopped making payments. Relative to his holdings on the day of closing, Kiekhaefer had been wiped out. Blank, Kiekhaefer's loyal counselor who eagerly pushed for the sale, quietly sold his stock without even informing Kiekhaefer, and managed to liquidate his shares before the stock's dramatic decline.

Even though Brunswick was in the throes of a precipitous avalanche of debt and despair, the Kiekhaefer Corporation was having a banner year, spurred on by the quick acceptance of important new products and by increased sales of standard lines. Within a few months of the merger, Kiekhaefer was ready to face the world again and was preparing to take on OMC for dominance in the marine industry.

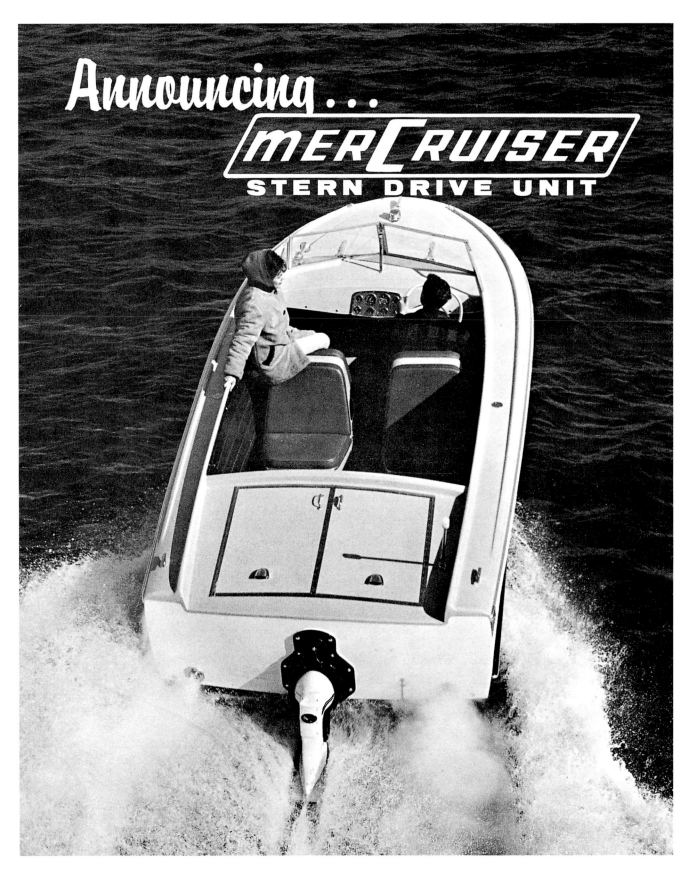

The cover of this brochure touted the MerCruiser sterndrive but not the intrigue that led to its invention.

CHAPTER EIGHT

THE STERNDRIVE CONSPIRACY

That is a horse s—t idea. Now, if you took the engine and you stood it on end, and put it on top of the gear box, you'd have an outboard motor. Then you got the right touch!

—Carl Kiekhaefer on the sterndrive, 1951[1]

UNTIL THE LATE 1920s, THERE WERE REALLY only two ways, excluding wind and oars, to propel a boat through the water: inboard or outboard engines. Both had drawbacks. The four-cycle inboard engine, usually converted from an automobile, was big and heavy and had to be mounted at an angle so that the propeller shaft would place the propeller far enough into the water to do some good. This meant that the propeller was usually pushing away at an angle between 10 and 15 degrees down in the water rather than pushing directly in line with the direction of the boat. This imperfect angle of attack reduced the efficiency of the propeller considerably. V-drive transmissions helped inboard installations to move the bulk of the engine back toward the transom, but the angle of the propeller in the water remained about the same.

The biggest advantage that inboard engines had over outboard engines was horsepower. In 1957, Carl Kiekhaefer made the most powerful outboard engines in the world at 60 horsepower. Inboard engines, available from about 65 horsepower to many thousands of horsepower, could be installed in boats ranging anywhere from 14-foot runabouts to ocean-going freighters, all relying on the same basic installation. Inboard engines, though, also needed a rudder to steer and a strut to hold the propeller shaft in place under the water. Most also needed a "skeg," or narrow plate of steel that would

strike the bottom before the propeller would be damaged. Each of these steering, strength, and protection elements represented a performance penalty in the form of parasitic drag under water. For large, slow boats, the effect of this penalty was negligible, but for small boats, all the iron and steel dragging through the water slowed them down no matter how large the engine or how efficient the propeller. Lastly, the propeller shaft of an inboard engine had to protrude through the bottom of the boat through a big hole, which required vigilance to keep it secure and not allow leakage into the boat.

The outboard motor, lacking only large horsepower, did away with many of the troublesome features of the inboard engine. The underwater components were all streamlined, the bulk of the engine was far aft, out of the way, and steering the outboard-equipped boat was accomplished by turning the propeller itself rather than dragging a big rudder through the water, so the boat didn't slow down in a turn. A skeg to protect the propeller was already built into the outboard, and if it hit the bottom or an object in the water, the whole works tilted up to protect the propeller

---

The MerCruiser was the first sterndrive for marine inboard engines of 125 to 200 horsepower.

and shaft. The only drawback with outboards was the limitation of power.

In 1930, Johnson Motor Company unveiled a very practical solution called the Johnson Tilting Stern Drive. A four-cycle gasoline engine was mounted nearly up against the inside of the transom, connected through a shaft to what was essentially a lower unit of an outboard motor protruding from the back of the boat. The four-cycle automobile or marine engine could be up to 60 horsepower, whereas the most powerful outboard motor available then was the Johnson 34-horsepower Sea Horse. The new sterndrive seemed to do everything an outboard could do and more. Warren Ripple, president of Johnson Motor Company, concluded that the new device would revolutionize marine transportation, and the reason for its acceptance would be the ability for the propeller to tilt up like an outboard when an obstruction was encountered.

Johnson literature waxed poetic about the "revolutionary," "amazing," and "epochal" new sterndrive that would "obsolete the past."[2] The public, however, remained skeptical, and sales were almost nonexistent.

By 1931, another sterndrive unit was marketed by the Morse Chain Company, the Marine

The 1930 Johnson Tilting Stern Drive (shown here on a Ludington runabout) was expected to "obsolete the past." Though this effort solved some of the problems associated with inboards, it created others.

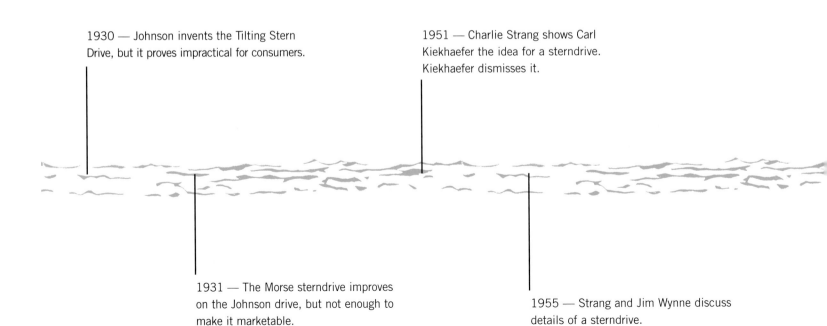

1930 — Johnson invents the Tilting Stern Drive, but it proves impractical for consumers.

1951 — Charlie Strang shows Carl Kiekhaefer the idea for a sterndrive. Kiekhaefer dismisses it.

1931 — The Morse sterndrive improves on the Johnson drive, but not enough to make it marketable.

1955 — Strang and Jim Wynne discuss details of a sterndrive.

Division of Borg-Warner Corporation, under the name Silent Chain Drive. The Columbian Bronze Corporation, a leading supplier of propellers to boat and engine builders, also produced a version of the device, as did the American Outboard Drive Corporation, with a new design by Joseph Van Blerck. The K. E. Ahlberg Company of Culver City, California, introduced a new inboard-outboard motor that used a tractor, or pulling propeller, rather than a traditional pushing propeller. A similar, though larger and slower, version of this tractor drive was also built and marketed by Gifford-Wood Company of Hudson, New York. The engineers and corporate executives of these various sterndrive producers seemed ecstatic about the obvious benefits of these new propulsion systems, but again, the public wasn't interested.

For one thing, almost nothing was easy about getting one. The interested buyer had to supervise the marriage of a boat, an engine, and a drive system—all supplied by different people, each of whom adamantly refused to take responsibility for the outcome of the combination. Boats weren't built with sterndrive units in mind, so owners had to modify their interiors to accommodate the new devices. Interior seating configurations had to be

moved, engine beds and hatches had to be modified and relocated, transoms had to be strengthened, the old inboard propeller shaft holes had to be plugged and sealed, and tricky alignment holes had to be drilled through the transom—usually right through the name on the stern of the boat—and the sterndrive had to be mounted. None of these steps were easy, and all of them had to be figured into the cost of the new drive.

But even once each of these time-consuming and costly installation steps was completed, the owner ended up with less speed than the original inboard installation and less flexibility than an outboard boat, at an ultimate cost approaching twice either one. When engine problems developed, the engine builder blamed the sterndrive. When sterndrive installation problems were encountered, the engine builder was blamed. When boat performance was questioned, the boatbuilder blamed the engine and the sterndrive. The public quickly caught on to this closed circle of design and performance finger-pointing and kept away from the new product.

When the Great Depression stalled all manner of boat and engine sales in the early 1930s, the sterndrive products offered by Johnson and the

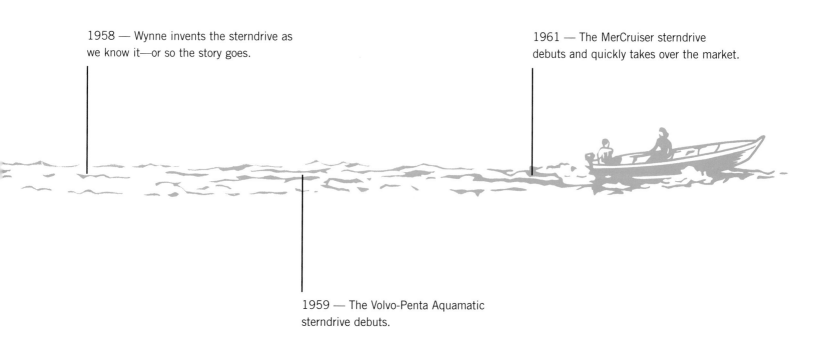

1958 — Wynne invents the sterndrive as we know it—or so the story goes.

1961 — The MerCruiser sterndrive debuts and quickly takes over the market.

1959 — The Volvo-Penta Aquamatic sterndrive debuts.

others were among the very first casualties. Johnson's miraculous new device "that obsoletes the past and opens a vista of tomorrows extending as far as human conception can visualize,"[3] was out of production in only two years. By the time the United States entered World War II, the concept had been abandoned by all manufacturers. The brilliant new idea was a complete failure.

Reviving the Sterndrive

In 1958, so the story goes, a former Kiekhaefer employee named Jim Wynne invented the first true sterndrive.

Wynne, then 28, had quit working for Kiekhaefer in December 1957. He enjoyed his job as head of Kiekhaefer's various proving grounds, but he was increasingly upset with what he considered to be Kiekhaefer's juvenile emotional antics. At the time, Wynne had been placed in charge of the Siesta Key, Florida, saltwater proving grounds. After his stint at Lake X supervising the first 25,000 miles of the 50,000-mile endurance runs, it seemed like paradise to Wynne. A small fleet of yellow test boats would run most of the day, building time on engines in the warm waters of the Gulf of Mexico just south of Sarasota. Other operations included static testing of components hung by strings into the tidal saltwater to observe the effects of exposure to both sea and sun. Mercury learned much from these operations—from protective paint finishes and the proper balance of sacrificial zinc anodes to component metallurgy to slow the advance of electrolysis from contact with the sea.

Although Kiekhaefer tried to lure Wynne back (even offering Wynne, a car buff, a 1952 Jaguar XK120), he wasn't interested.[4]

It was during this independence from Kiekhaefer and the Kiekhaefer Corporation, as the story would be told and retold, that Wynne invented the sterndrive. Between 1958 and 1991, an estimated $20 billion would be spent on sterndrives and parts in the worldwide marine industry. If one takes into consideration the value of the boats that have been designed for the sterndrive market, the figure is considerably higher. If the value of trailers, accessories, fuel, and other expenses that naturally accompany ownership of this type of boat are figured in, the impact on the world economy of the introduction of the modern sterndrive conceivably approaches $75 billion. It is the most financially significant product introduced in the marine industry since the internal combustion engine.

The popular public story, and the carefully guarded secret story concerning the development of the modern sterndrive, are altogether different.

The Fiction of the Sterndrive

"In trying to build a sterndrive, I first looked at all the inboard-outboards that had been built since way back in the 1920s," Wynne repeated in public many times. He continued:

They all had something that didn't work. For example, some would steer the boat like an outboard motor, but they didn't tilt. Some tilted but didn't steer properly. It seemed to me that if a sterndrive was going to be successful, it had to do everything that an outboard motor did because that was the competition.

The idea was to get something that steered and tilted just like an outboard motor but with the engine inside the boat covered up like an inboard with a full transom. Use of a four-cycle automobile engine was also more efficient at that time. Essentially what I wanted was the bottom half of an outboard motor mounted outside the boat so that it would swing back and forth for steering and also tilt up and down. The drive shaft had to go through the transom of the boat, which meant that it had to bend.

I had seen the front-wheel-drive mechanism of a car, which does the same job, and this was the tipoff that a certain type of universal joint that I used originally—a constant velocity joint—was the answer.

The steering and tilting axes ran through the center of the universal joint, and this allowed it to move in two directions at the same time.[5]

In another interview, Wynne explained just what, in 1958, the breakthrough concept was that would make the modern sterndrive more successful than the Johnson drive of 1930:

The basis of the patent was the use of a double universal joint in the horizontal shaft behind the

Jim Wynne with the first prototype of the Volvo-Penta Aquamatic sterndrive at the New York Motor Boat Show in 1959.

transom, so that the drive could both swing back and forth for steering and also tilt up about the center of the universal joint. This allowed all the torque being transmitted by the shafts and the gears to be completely encased inside the housings. It was a practical way of making an outdrive.

Other outdrive units had attempted to steer the lower end while holding the upper portion stationary. This required the steering mechanism to restrain all the torque that was in the vertical shaft going down to the underwater unit. There were a lot of units around [back in the 1930s] that had that problem.[6]

In simple terms, what Wynne revealed was that the difference between the modern and the old sterndrive was a pair of universal joints, similar to the hand's "OK" sign joined by the ring with another OK sign from the other hand, or to links connected in a chain. When one turns, so does the other, even though the motion of one can be started from almost any angle to the other. Every car has one between the transmission and the drive shaft. In his interviews with virtually every boating publication in the world, Wynne was asked the question, "How did you come to build the first one?" He answered:

I left Mercury at the end of 1957. As we know, I had a little run-in with Carl at Christmas. I started working on this inboard-outboard idea in February or March of 1958.

I started developing a prototype, just a crude working model using old outboard parts (mostly Mercury), in my parents' garage in the spring of 1958 and applied for some patents.

I purchased an engine that I had seen at a Volvo car dealership and that Volvo-Penta was marinizing (modifying for use in boats)—a little 1.6-liter, 80-horsepower unit that seemed to me just the right size. I ordered it without the reverse gear because I wanted to bolt it directly onto the sterndrive.[7]

The public story continues that after Wynne ordered the Volvo engine without a reverse gear, the Volvo representative in the area became curious about the intended application. They met, and after Wynne disclosed information about his new prototype, the enthusiastic Volvo representative arranged a meeting with Volvo headquarters in Sweden, from which an exclusive deal was struck for use of the new drive. Volvo introduced the new sterndrive at the 1959 New York Motor Boat Show, and the course of marine industry history was forever changed. Wynne was hailed as one of the most significant inventors in the marine industry and was mentioned in the same breath as Ole Evinrude—and even Kiekhaefer. In 1989, Wynne was inducted into the National Marine Manufacturer's Association Hall of Fame, an honor that had been bestowed only on eight other individuals, including Evinrude, Kiekhaefer, Christopher Columbus Smith (Chris-Craft), and Gar Wood.

Wynne testing the Volvo-Penta–powered craft over a solid oyster bed.

For several decades, Wall Street and industry analysts attributed the invention of the sterndrive to Wynne, but in 1991, that all changed when the real story was first revealed.

What Really Happened

While Charlie Strang was working toward his master's degree in mechanical engineering at M.I.T., he remained an avid outboard racing enthusiast. He grew interested in mounting an assault on the US outboard speed record held by Clint Ferguson of Boston since a 1938 run of 78.121 mph. Strang knew that the only thing holding back another record was the current horsepower limitations of outboard engines. In 1948, as Strang began to address the problem, the largest American outboard engine was the 33.4-horsepower Evinrude Speedifour. It was impossible for Strang, as a student at M.I.T., to attempt an independent design and prototype of a larger power head, so he began to look at the more powerful engines used in auto racing. "There was an engine in England that was very popular," Strang said, "called the Coventry Climax. It was a fire pump engine during World War II, and after the war they converted it for racing. It was aluminum, very light, and it was only about a one-liter engine. They used it in a lot of race cars in Europe."

Strang's idea was to mate this light, horizontal engine to the lower end of an outboard and then mount the entire thing outside of the record-attempting boat, hoping that officials would still consider it an outboard. When he discovered that the setup wouldn't be legal from a competitive standpoint, he abandoned his goal of taking the

outboard record. He continued to refine his combination of an automobile engine with an outboard lower unit, this time with the engine inside the boat and the drive unit outside. In his engineering invention ledger, Strang drew different versions of his design and then dated and signed the pages, which was the suggested M.I.T. procedure. One of his entries during 1948 was for his final version of a modern sterndrive, complete with the universal joint linkage which would ultimately be patented, not by Strang, but by Wynne. In his explicit drawing, Strang even identified the universal torque transmitter by its scientific name of Hookes Coupling, and further labeled and identified the tilt and swivel pin features within the coupling. The drawing showed features exactly as they would appear later in the modern sterndrive and in the patent application submitted exactly 10 years later by Wynne.

When he had finished tinkering with his idea in the pages of the ledger, Strang didn't know what to call his new drive. He was a fan of comic books in his younger days and remembered a voluptuous siren named Appassionata Von Climax from one of his favorites. Since he had considered joining his new drive to the Coventry Climax engine, he named the new sterndrive after this imaginary seductress, and the AVC drive—the modern sterndrive—was born.

Strang was convinced that the new sterndrive had an enormous financial and practical potential in the marine industry. As an avid outboard racing enthusiast, an engineering scholar, and a highly regarded journalist within the marine industry, he was in exactly the correct position to analyze the possibilities for the new concept. From Strang's unique and well-rounded perspective, the AVC drive would fill a critical need in boating propulsion left wide open by the extreme difference in horsepower available between the largest outboard and the smallest typical inboard engine.

In the summer of 1951, after only two weeks in the Kiekhaefer Corporation's employ, Strang disclosed his idea to Kiekhaefer. These were the heady days in transition between Kiekhaefer's two-cylinder Lightning-style models and the beginnings of his new—and significantly more powerful—four-cylinder Thunderbolt. Kiekhaefer was flush with success over the introduction of his new 25-horse-power masterpiece and had his marketing gun sights firmly on OMC and its even larger outboard models. So, when Strang proudly explained the enormous potential he imagined for his new AVC drive, Kiekhaefer wasn't the least bit interested. "I was passionate about the idea," Strang remembered. "And the first thing I did was show Carl this concept, and that's when, you know, he said I was nuts. I showed the drawings and everything to Carl, and he said, 'Oh, that's ridiculous,' and he wanted no part of it."[8]

Strang was swept into the maelstrom of Kiekhaefer activity, which would soon include the Mexican Road Race and a blizzard of engineering challenges both on the track and on the water. He kept thinking about his AVC drive, though, and his first-hand experience with the powerful Chrysler, Ford, and Chevrolet automobile engines used in stock cars left a lasting impression on him.

One evening in 1955, aboard Kiekhaefer's slow and onerous Beech-18, Strang and Wynne were flying down to Texas to testify in a product liability case concerning a Mercury outboard motor. It was a long and boring flight in the drafty twin-engine aircraft, and they listened intently to the Sugar Ray Robinson vs. Carl "Bobo" Olson middleweight boxing fight on the radio. After Robinson recaptured the crown from Olson, the conversation drifted into engineering and the potential speed of outboard motors. It was aboard this flight that the greatest conspiracy in the history of the marine industry began.

"It was a long, slow flight down to Texas," Strang recalled, "and I started sketching this thing up to Jim and he got very excited about it, and he talked to Charlie Alexander about it." Charles "Alex" Alexander had been promoted to engineering vice president of Mercury, reporting directly to then-executive vice president Strang. Wynne also reported directly to Strang. A secret series of conversations ensued between Strang, Alexander, and Wynne about the possibilities for the AVC drive. Strang remembered when the decision was made to develop the new

---

Wynne inspects the outdrive following the rough ride, which failed to damage the unit.

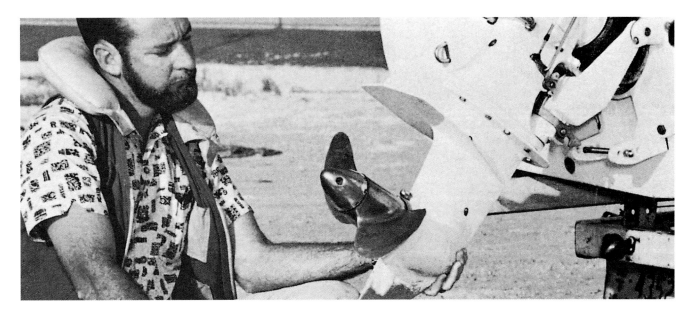

product themselves, secretly and without Kiekhaefer's knowledge. "Jim and Charlie and I said, 'What the hell.' Maybe we could start a company and make this thing since Carl didn't want it."

Wynne had been appointed chief engineer of Mercury proving grounds. Strang had become Kiekhaefer's closest friend and most trusted confidant and was second in command as executive vice president. Alexander occupied the most sensitive engineering position in the company, that of vice president of engineering. These three men, arguably Kiekhaefer's most crucial and most highly trusted executives, were actively conspiring to build what would become the most significant product in marine manufacturing behind Kiekhaefer's back.

In the spring of 1958, Wynne, who had been gone from Mercury for less than 90 days, "invented" the sterndrive. Strang and Alexander remained at Mercury and continued to support his development of a prototype AVC drive through surreptitious meetings and phone calls. A company had been formed, Hydro Mechanical Development, headed in principle by Wynne—the only one of the three on the outside. Lacking sufficient funds to mount the expensive tooling and manufacturing of the drive, the men decided to seek outside assistance. In a brazen move, the three met in Indianapolis in early 1958 in the office of John Buehler, president of Indiana Gear Works, manufacturer of various types of bezel and other gears as well as the US licensee of the Hamilton Jet Drive of New Zealand. The three had settled on approaching Buehler because of his existing gear production abilities—a critical element in the manufacture of the sterndrive—as well as his well-known foray into boat jet propulsion, a possible indication of a willingness to invest in novel ideas.

Buehler was quite novel himself, as Strang remembered:

We walked in and this huge fat man wearing a Boy Scout uniform, shorts and all, says, "We're a Scouting family." He gave us the scout signal (salute) and everything else. Then he took us into his office, and I'll never forget his office because it was a gorgeous office, enormous, and he had mounted animals all around the walls—but it was the ass-end of the animal! And there were arrows sticking out of them. He was a real weirdo, funny as hell.[9]

Strang, Alexander, and Wynne tried their best to persuade Buehler, sitting in his Boy Scout shorts and hat under the rear end of a moose with arrows sticking out of it, that the new sterndrive would revolutionize the boating industry. But Buehler was stubbornly convinced that his Hamilton Jet Drives were going to take over the industry, so "why waste time on anything else?"

Back in Florida, Wynne completed the "cobbled-together" prototype of Strang's AVC drive in his parents' garage. One of the lessons Wynne had learned from Kiekhaefer was the value of secrecy. He covered the windows of the garage, speaking with no one about his project until the prototype was completed and tested. He borrowed a 20-foot fiberglass boat from Woody Woodson, the founder of Thunderbird Boat Company in Miami, and installed the new drive system. Wynne carefully covered up his new unit and towed it to Pelican Harbor on the Intracoastal Waterway in Miami before dawn. After a few trial runs and some adjustments, he was satisfied that the concept would work.

Shortly thereafter, John Jarnmark, the New Jersey-based general sales manager for Volvo-Penta, made a routine sales call to Wynne as a follow-up to the sale of an 80-horsepower engine delivered without the reverse gear. Wynne told Jarnmark that he was working on a special marine application of the engine that could conceivably produce many more orders for Volvo. Jarnmark was interested in finding out more, but Wynne was at first reluctant to fully disclose the idea. Once Wynne had filed the patent applications based on Strang's drawings and universal joint concept, he invited Jarnmark to Miami to see for himself. Jarnmark was most impressed with the concept and installation of the Volvo-Penta engine, and sent photos, diagrams, and descriptions of the device to the home office in Sweden.

In the meantime, a friend of Wynne, Ole Botved, the manufacturer of Botved-Coronet outboard boats and cruisers in Copenhagen, Denmark, invited Wynne to join him as one of three copilots in an attempt to cross the Atlantic Ocean in an outboard boat. Wynne, always ready to tackle an unusual challenge, agreed. The voyage, from Copenhagen to New York, was designed as a publicity venture to generate business for Botved's boat line and to establish a new world record for outboard-powered boats. Since Wynne had already helped to establish Kiekhaefer's first 25,000-mile endurance run at Lake X, Botved wanted Wynne's expertise as an outboard mechanic and driver. A small freighter would steam alongside the trio, providing fuel for the crossing and standing by to pull them aboard during severe storms or in case of mechanical failure.

Wynne flew to Copenhagen, and during the period devoted to preparations for the transatlantic attempt, he traveled to Sweden and met with Harald Wiklund, the president of Volvo-Penta. Wiklund, a remarkable individual, was president of Volvo-Penta for 28 years, from 1949 until 1977. When he took on the job of president in 1949, the company was generating sales of a few million Swedish kronor a year, and when he left, Volvo-Penta, except for outboard motors, was the world's largest supplier of marine engines, with sales of more than a billion kronor annually. When Wynne walked into his office in 1958, Wiklund had been president for nine years and had already put Volvo-Penta on a course of growth that was making the Swedish marine engine the envy of the world. Wiklund was quite impressed with the idea brought to him by Wynne, and it looked as if a deal

might be struck. Wynne was still operating under the assumption that Strang would leave Mercury—perhaps any day—and join him in the sterndrive venture. But Strang was leaving all of his options open and kept delaying his decision, which was making Wynne nervous. Wynne knew that Strang's direct involvement would be critical to the success of any manufacturing venture, and he was concerned that he alone didn't have the expertise to create a company to build the drives without Strang. But now that Volvo was showing a sincere interest, he phoned Strang to find out his intentions once and for all. Would Strang really leave Kiekhaefer? If not, what was he supposed to tell Volvo-Penta?

Strang was in Fond du Lac when the call came from Sweden. "I remember I was eating dinner at home one night," Strang recalled, "and Jim called. He said, 'There are some people over here called Volvo. I was out with them last night, and I told them about the AVC, and they're real excited about it. ... They want to do something about it.'"

Dimension drawing for the Aquamatic 100.

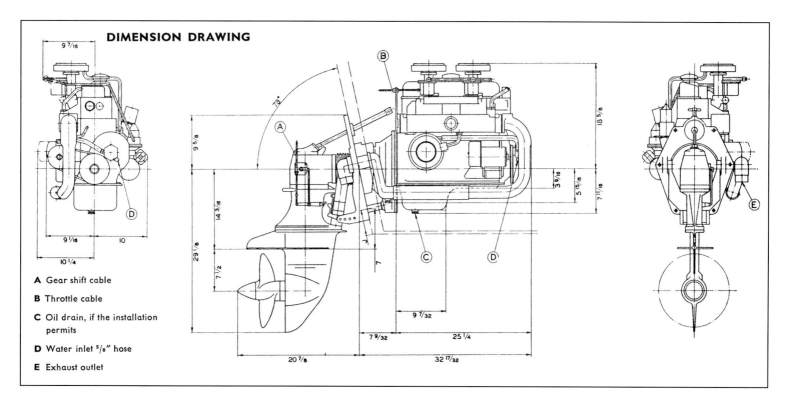

DIMENSION DRAWING

A Gear shift cable

B Throttle cable

C Oil drain, if the installation permits

D Water inlet ⁵⁄₈" hose

E Exhaust outlet

Strang's mind was spinning. Kiekhaefer had recently proposed that Strang head up a public Kiekhaefer Corporation as president. The war with OMC was entering perhaps the most crucial phase in Mercury history, as Kiekhaefer declared, "The Mercury organization, this year, is like a boxer in a ring who has just scored and is moving in for the knockout. There is no stopping our organization at this time. Never before have we seen dealer morale and plant morale so high, but we must move with aggressiveness and intelligence even though our competition may appear to be groggy at the moment. We want to be on the lookout for sleepers. It may be a lot tougher in the next round."[10]

Strang was busier than he had ever been, and his prospects for advancing into the presidency of Mercury were tantalizingly close. On the other hand, he knew the enormous potential for his new sterndrive. Wynne was waiting on the other end of the line. If Strang said he would leave Kiekhaefer, Wynne would merely negotiate to buy Volvo-Penta engines at a volume discount. If he told Wynne to go ahead alone, he would negotiate a license agreement with Volvo-Penta under the pending patent, and Volvo-Penta would manufacture the drive and combine it with their engines as a package. Strang took a deep breath and told Wynne, "Jim, do what you want with it."[11]

Wynne met again with Wiklund and proceeded to negotiate the license agreement. "We spent two days together, and I guess I sold him on the idea," Wynne said. "He was very astute, very receptive, and we signed a letter of intent for them to build this thing under the ideas of the patent that I had filed for."[12] Wiklund remembered that Wynne was actually not very well prepared. "You know, the only thing that Jim had to give me was an idea. He had no drawings or nothing. We had to make all the drawings. I bought the idea and the patent rights from him, but he had no idea about the construction of the whole thing."[13]

Wiklund guaranteed Wynne $7 (US) for every unit that Volvo-Penta produced over the lifetime of the patent. After sales initially faltered, Wiklund renegotiated with Wynne, and a figure of $3.50 per unit was agreed upon; plus Wynne received a generous 12.5 percent of all future license income Volvo-Penta might receive from other builders, which would eventually include Mercury. "In the beginning," Wiklund said, "he got too much money for it, you see, because the only thing he had was the idea, and we had to do the whole job. ... We sent him many millions from Sweden."

A tacit and somber understanding was reached between Strang and Wynne, that Wynne would claim credit for the invention of the drive to protect Strang's position with Kiekhaefer. If Kiekhaefer were ever to find out that his most trusted friend had secretly given perhaps the most significant invention in the marine industry to a competitor, their relationship would, of course, be shattered. More than this, however, as Volvo-Penta quickly began to make plans to manufacture and promote the new sterndrive, Strang and Wynne both understood that Strang could very well be held liable for the disclosure, as he had continued to develop the idea while on the Kiekhaefer payroll, even involving Wynne and Kiekhaefer head of engineering Alexander. It would bring about a scandal of enormous proportions. So the bond of secrecy was made, and a conspiracy begun that would endure for more than 30 years.

The Conspiracy Continues

Volvo-Penta began a crash program to complete engineering drawings and prepare production tooling for the AVC drive, which the company called the Aquamatic. Though a capable engineer himself, Wynne was unable to answer the many technical questions that Wiklund and his chief marine engineer, Neil Hanson, were asking. As a result, Wynne had to disclose the true origin of the invention to Wiklund and the engineer and swear them to secrecy. A series of clandestine meetings took place during the late summer of 1958 between Wynne, Wiklund, Strang, and Hanson. Strang would correct errors in the engineering specifications and make direct changes to the drawings spread out on motel beds. Strang remembered the secret encounters:

I had a half-dozen surreptitious meetings with the chief engineer of Volvo, who'd come over with the drawings, and we'd go over the layouts together. [For example,] I was at the boat races in Lakeland, Florida, and Jim and the chief engineer of Volvo tracked me down, and we were sitting on the floor of the motel room going over the drawings and so on.[14]

It was a most dangerous business for Strang, who was risking his entire career by conducting these secret engineering briefings with Volvo-Penta and Wynne. Strang knew well that Kiekhaefer had spies within the company. One report back to Kiekhaefer, and the game would be up. Wiklund felt he spent more time in aircraft that summer than behind his desk in Gothenburg, Sweden. "I was Scandinavian Airlines' biggest customer. They say Columbus discovered the United States. I discovered it, too, in my own way," he said.[15] With Strang's brilliant guidance, the Volvo-Penta Aquamatic drawings were finalized, and Swedish engineers rushed

to complete tooling for the new sterndrive in the fall and early winter of 1958.

The Aquamatic was unveiled with great fanfare at the 1959 New York Motor Boat Show in early January. It had taken Volvo-Penta engineers less than six months to produce the tooling for the prototype unit, and it drew some of the largest crowds of the show. Wynne answered questions about "his new invention," and hundreds of photos were taken with Wynne, looking most distinguished in his carefully trimmed beard, leaning on the Aquamatic. Ingemar Johansson, the Swedish heavyweight boxing champion of the world, also made an appearance to pose with Wynne and the new drive. Kiekhaefer was stunned to see the crowds formed around Wynne and the new sterndrive at the Volvo booth and was miffed that he was continually fielding questions from his own dealers and distributors about the merits of the new drive. It took him almost a year, but Kiekhaefer finally got his hands on an Aquamatic, had it installed on an 18-foot Dunphy boat, and tested it himself at Lake X.

Kiekhaefer hated the Volvo-Penta drive before he even got in the boat. He never once recalled talking to Strang about the AVC drive years earlier, and he never would.

Kiekhaefer, who was known among the test crews as perhaps the most ham-fisted, indelicate, and clumsy of boat drivers, got the boat going around the Lake X test course at a little over 31 mph. His comments, all contrary to just about everyone else's concerning the new unit, would come back to haunt him. Kiekhaefer's test report on the new sterndrive is a classic example of a biased evaluation:

> *Volvo engine: Extremely noisy, even though compartmented with sound-absorbing material as liner. Noise is combination of intake and mechanical. Gear whine noticeable at part throttle although not at high speed.*
>
> *Steering extremely dangerous. Spun out boat at first hard left turn. Except for center position,*

REF. 5320

AQUAMATIC 100

DATA

Max. output	100 h. p.
Type of operation	four-cycle
Valves	overhead
Number of cylinders	4
Capacity, total	108.6 cu. in.
Bore	3.313"
Stroke	3.15"
Compression ratio	9.5:1
Total weight	465 lbs

● Cuts fuel cost over 50 %
● More speed — more power for your money
● Easy trailing and beaching
● Rugged 100 h. p., 4 cycle engine
● Needs no expensive oil mixture
● Inboard prestige and style — outboard mobility
● More cockpit room in the boat
● Easy to install.

The Aquamatic 100 opens new and greater frontiers to inboard-outboard propulsion since it is capable of powering boats up to 24 feet in single installations and up to 30 or more feet in duals.

The Aquamatic 100 has two major components—engine and drive. The 4 cylinder, inboard engine develops 100 horsepower. The economy of operation will amaze you as the average fuel cost is less than one half that of outboard engines of comparable power.

The outboard drive of the Volvo Penta Aquamatic steers and overcomes underwater hazards in the same way as conventional outboards. The entire unit tilts up easily and locks in place for convenient trailing and launching. And the quick handling response of propeller steering and single lever control is yours with the Aquamatic.

Promotional piece for the Aquamatic 100, designed in secret by Charlie Strang at Mercury.

steering force so violent as to twist wheel out of hand.…

Installation costs must run considerably higher than an outboard since one large hole must be cut into the transom to take the engine mount. … A water pick-up, in addition, must be installed on the underside of the boat.…

The Volvo outboard-inboard drive, aside from its cost and weight disadvantages, has all the other disadvantages of an inboard installation, and while a certain segment of the public might go for it, I do not believe it is a threat to outboard motors at this time. … Gone too is the stimulant of annual model changes. Styling plays no part. The product does not advertise itself, being hidden, and has all the romance of a 371 diesel power plant![16]

For Kiekhaefer, it was only part of a nearly two-year-long tirade against the new sterndrive. Wynne was helping Volvo-Penta write and produce its Aquamatic advertising campaign and brochures, and the strategy was extremely upsetting to Kiekhaefer. "Don't buy an outboard," Volvo's exhibit signs shouted, "before you have seen and tested the revolutionary Volvo-Penta from Sweden … that combines inboard efficiency and safety with outboard flexibility and speed."[17] This approach was irritating enough to Kiekhaefer, but then Wynne invaded two of the territories long claimed by Kiekhaefer: speed and endurance.

Wynne had learned very well from Kiekhaefer the promotional advantages of racing and endurance. He urged Volvo-Penta to ship him one of the few hand-built and precious prototypes following the introduction at the 1959 boat show. Guessing correctly that the very conservative Volvo organization might forbid him from entering the new unit in a race, Wynne secretly prepared another of Woody Woodson's 18-foot Thunderbird boats to accommodate the new Aquamatic. In April, Wynne entered the boat in the Miami-Nassau race and took aboard as his copilot the editor of *Popular Boating*, Bill McKeown.

The magazine, which today is called *Boating*, was and is the most widely read journal of the sport, and McKeown's presence aboard was a stroke of promotional fortune for Wynne. Wiklund later told Wynne, "Jim, you're stupid," and "If I had any idea that you were going to put that thing in a race, I would have personally come over there and taken it away from you."[18] Wynne had installed the sterndrive in a little 16-foot deep-V fiberglass hull designed by Ray Hunt and built in Massachusetts by Marscot Plastics. Wynne and McKeown won their class in the race and came in fourth overall, a remarkable accomplishment for the unknown drive system.[19] In the process, Wynne garnered a landslide of positive publicity for the Aquamatic and set his sights on future races.

In June, Wynne established four new world records in the nine-hour Orange Bowl Regatta marathon in Miami, handily beating Mercury entries from Kiekhaefer, along with the most powerful engines available from Evinrude, Johnson, and Scott-Atwater. As if Wynne were not satisfied with setting four new world speed records, averaging better than 31 mph for the whole nine hours of the race, he also upset nearly every other contestant in the marathon by making only a single pit stop for fuel, an Orange Bowl Regatta first. The combination of Strang's design and Wynne's promotional abilities had united to thrust Volvo into the headlines of the marine industry press. Sales of the Volvo-Penta Aquamatic, sluggish at first, began to rise, and Kiekhaefer began to realize that some Volvo-Penta sterndrive sales were made at the expense of his new 70-horsepower Mark 78A motor, the world's most powerful outboard. Both Wynne and Volvo-Penta were becoming well-known from these adventures, and Wiklund believed that Volvo-Penta had made Wynne a star. "You see, Jim Wynne was nothing before we started with the whole idea of the Aquamatic," Wiklund said. "Then, we built him up. We paid him a lot, of course, because he gave us the idea, but also, we built up his name. The Aquamatic has meant a lot for Jim Wynne."[20]

Many of Kiekhaefer's dealers and distributors began asking when Mercury would come out with a sterndrive, and Strang felt obligated to approach Kiekhaefer on the concept once more. Strang, as the actual inventor and principle engineer of the Volvo sterndrive, was intimately familiar with the potential for the device, but now he had to be most careful when discussing the idea with Kiekhaefer.

Finally, in early 1960, more than a year after the Aquamatic had been introduced, Kiekhaefer authorized Strang to at least begin thinking about the possibility of a Mercury sterndrive. He was, however, absolutely convinced that the idea would still fail in the marketplace. In a strange sort of reverse psychology, Kiekhaefer was allowing Strang to begin his own design work while looking forward to telling him later, "I told you so."

As late as June 1960, Kiekhaefer tried to negotiate an agreement with Wiklund for Mercury to be the exclusive sales agent for the Aquamatic in the United States, selling the Swedish drive at Mercury dealerships. Not even Volvo-Penta itself would be able to make a single sale in the United States under Kiekhaefer's proposal. Kiekhaefer also wanted Volvo to actively enforce any infringements on the basic patent to prevent OMC and others from building a sterndrive. The deal began to unravel when Kiekhaefer balked at the guarantee of purchasing a minimum of 10,000 units a year for three years.[21] He was sure that the marketplace wouldn't absorb this many of the new drives, especially because at that time Volvo-Penta was considering attaching no engine larger than 100 horsepower to the Aquamatic package. Kiekhaefer reasoned that if the Volvo agreement was successful he could avoid the major design and tooling costs of a competitive drive, while at the same time preventing the entry of other sterndrives into the market and protecting his own large-horsepower outboard sales.

But sales of the Aquamatic were in trouble. Wiklund had tooled Volvo-Penta up for an initial run of 10,000 units. At the end of 1959, he had sold less than 3,000 and was embarrassed to be sitting on an enormous inventory of 7,000 sterndrives. Though boatbuilders were candidly enthusiastic about the promise of the sterndrive, they were reluctant to buy. "All of the boatbuilders said, 'This is something we need,'" Wiklund remembered. "It was easy for them to sell a boat without any engine, and the consumer could buy an outboard engine. So I had a big problem in the beginning."[22] Wiklund turned to his old friend Captain Botved, the father of Ole Botved, who had crossed the Atlantic with Wynne in the *Coronet Explorer*. He made a deal with Botved to make Aquamatics available, interest-free, for a full year if he would install them in his line of Coronet boats. "They started installing the Aquamatic in their boats, and stopped selling the boats without engines," said Wiklund. "It was a success, and after two years, we began to have a very good success with

Jim Wynne aboard a 16-foot Ray Hunt-designed deep-V in June 1959.

Inset: Strang (left) was the real inventor of the sterndrive. Wynne took credit as part of a conspiracy of silence that lasted many years.

the inboard-outboard. It seemed like the Americans were afraid to go with it at first."[23]

At the Mercury sales meeting in the fall of 1960, Kiekhaefer admitted the possibility of a future Mercury sterndrive, but again, he characterized the sterndrive concept as an almost sure loser. "The outboard-inboard may well come into the picture next year, though the Volvo-Penta undoubtedly will not be a factor. Our plan will be to let someone else go first, someone else try the rotten stairway, someone else walk into the haunted house, someone else walk first out on the thin ice."[24] But when he spoke to his distributors a few months later on January 13, 1961, he threw down the gauntlet to consumers. If they wanted it, he would build it. He said:

When the customer really starts wanting and ordering these things, that's the time to look into it. But up to now it seems to me that most of the interest has been generated by just someone else (Volvo) who wanted to get into this over-advertised, over-promoted marine industry. In view of

Above: The new 140-horsepower MerCruiser I.

Right: On the sterndrive, a crank was used to rotate the prop.

that, do you still want an outboard-inboard drive? If you folks tell me that you want one, we're ready to build one.

[I]f the public wants to buy it without any engineering reasons like they buy golf bags and like women buy hats, perhaps we shouldn't knock the idea. If the public wants to buy it, we should build it. If this is the age where people do such things, perhaps we're wrong in condemning them. We've debated it many times. Should we blast this thing out into the open? With a few well-placed ads I'm sure we could cure the whole idea of the outboard-inboard drive. But is that a good way to do business? Is the public tired of outboard motors?[25]

Strang continued development of a Mercury sterndrive. Fortunately, Kiekhaefer did not think it was unusual that Strang could move so quickly with the drawings. Strang wasn't concerned about infringing on the Wynne patent or on the Volvo-Penta license because Wynne and Volvo were aware that the drive was Strang's idea in the first place. "[Kiekhaefer] was concerned about patenting it," Strang recalled. "Well, I wasn't the least bit concerned about patenting it 'cause I knew damn well that Volvo would never open their trap if I was involved in this thing, because they knew where it came from."[26]

Kiekhaefer learned that OMC was working on its own version of a sterndrive. Though most details

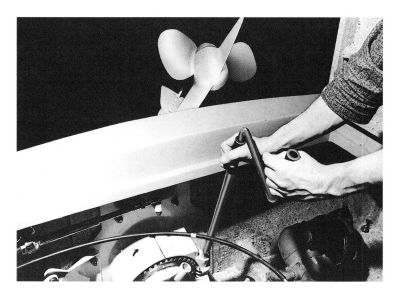

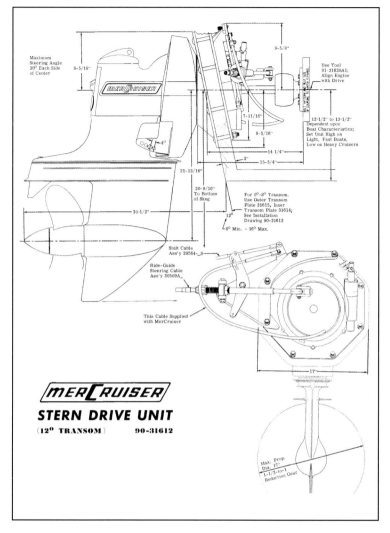

Above: MerCruiser sterndrive dimension schematics.

Right: The MerCruiser I sterndrive unit featured dual shock absorbers, exhaust through the propeller hub, a rubber-mounted engine, and a rubber-cushioned horizontal drive shaft.

When OMC announced its new V4, two-cycle, 80-horsepower sterndrive, dubbed the OMC-480, Kiekhaefer was jubilant. His MerCruiser was designed to attach to four-cycle, automobile-style engines ranging from 125 to 200 horsepower. Even his new 80-horsepower outboard could easily outperform the new OMC sterndrive. OMC added a number of deluxe features to its sterndrive, such as electric shifting and an automatic oil-mixing system, in order to make up for the small power. These features raised the price to $900, a price comparable to the 80-horsepower Mercury outboard.

Kiekhaefer initially offered the MerCruiser only to engine builders, who would package the engine and drive together for sale to boatbuilders. Mercury would then warrant the drive to the engine builder, who would then be responsible for

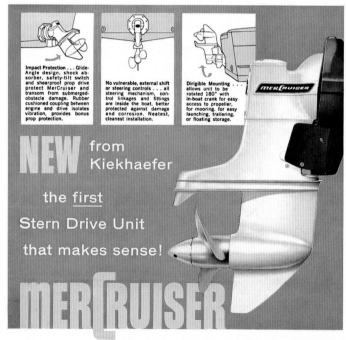

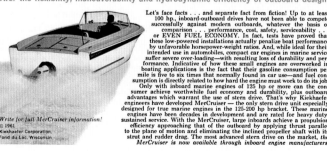

about the OMC drive were lacking, he discovered the company would announce it to its dealers at the Chicago Boat Show on March 25, 1961. Kiekhaefer then moved up the dates for the announcement of the Mercury sterndrive to a press luncheon March 23, followed by a large display in the Mercury booth on the opening day of the show, March 24, beating OMC to the punch. A week before the press announcement, the name MerCruiser was selected for the Mercury sterndrive.[27]

the consumer warranty. He took astute advantage of the strategic errors committed by both Volvo-Penta and OMC. Both had married their sterndrive device to low-horsepower engines, limiting their marketing appeal considerably. Once a deal was consummated with General Motors, Kiekhaefer was able to offer his MerCruiser sterndrive Power Package with dependable 110- and 140-horsepower marinized Chevrolet engines, designed and built by the best minds in Detroit.

To consolidate his hold on the high-power segment of the industry, Kiekhaefer had Strang design a second drive, somewhat stronger and with advanced features, to handle 225- and even 310-horsepower engines. The two drives became known as the MerCruiser I and the MerCruiser II. More than two-and-a-half years late in entering the market with a sterndrive, Mercury, by the end of 1961, had captured the bulk of the market by offering two models and a wide, powerful range of engines.

The MerCruiser sterndrive greatly improved upon the Volvo-Penta model, and Kiekhaefer Mercury didn't have to worry about patent infringement on the designs.

Orders from boatbuilders began to mushroom, and within the first year on the market, MerCruiser orders began to pour in from virtually every established boatbuilder in the country.

Kiekhaefer was now reeling in the glory of having the hottest new product in the industry. By 1962, as OMC would later document, only three years after Volvo-Penta's introduction of the Aquamatic, no less than "16 manufacturers were producing sterndrives."[28] Once Kiekhaefer opened up the sale of the new drive directly to the more than 2,500 boatbuilders in the United States, the MerCruiser would outsell all other sterndrives combined and eventually capture an incredible 80 percent of the worldwide market. For all of its work in the outboard motor trenches against the enemy, it would be the sterndrive that would eventually push Mercury ahead of OMC as the world's largest manufacturer of marine propulsion. OMC would maintain its lead in strictly outboard production, but because of the MerCruiser sterndrive, Mercury products would power more boats than any other brand in the world. Kiekhaefer's dream of overtaking OMC was finally coming true.

The conspiracy between Wynne and Strang had actually worked to Kiekhaefer's advantage. This secret relationship made possible Kiekhaefer's own entry into the sterndrive market after letting someone else go first.

Wynne's patents wouldn't actually issue for 10 long years because another individual, unknown to Strang, Wynne, or Alexander, had filed an application only two weeks after Wynne. More confusing to the patent office, the other inventor, C. E. MacDonald of Seattle, had actually constructed a similar prototype before Wynne had tested his in Miami. After 10 years of engineering and legal debate, the patents, based on Strang's universal coupling, were issued to Wynne on April 9, 1968.[29] Wynne would be rewarded handsomely by Volvo-Penta under terms of the licensing agreement reached in the summer of 1958. But, during the entire 17-year life of the patent, which didn't expire until 1985, Strang would never accept or receive a cent for his invention. "Charlie once said to me," Wiklund recalled, "'You gave Jim a lot of millions, but I didn't get anything.'"[30] Strang would eventually become chairman of the board and chief executive officer of OMC during Kiekhaefer's lifetime, and he swore an oath of silence to never disclose the incredible story behind the invention of the modern sterndrive while Kiekhaefer was still alive.

Outdoors magazine showed off the sleek new Merc 1000 in 1962.

CHAPTER NINE

CRISIS OF CONTROL

I cannot think of one single advantage which the Brunswick merger has produced.

—Carl Kiekhaefer, 1963[1]

FROM ALL APPEARANCES, THE BEGIN-ning of the new decade should have been known as the gold-en age of the Kiekhaefer Corpora-tion. In one glorious 12-month period, Carl Kiekhaefer introduced the Mer-Cruiser sterndrive, sold the company to Brunswick, and then capped it off by introducing the first 100-horsepower production outboard motor in the world. Everything seemed to be going Kiekhaefer's way. OMC would announce that it would discontinue the manufacture of pri-vate brand outboards, shutting down the produc-tion lines for Gale, Buccaneer, and Sea King for all time. Kiekhaefer had long predicted that OMC would abandon private label outboards, believing that Johnson and Evinrude dealers didn't appreciate competing against these virtually identical OMC products sold through catalogs and chain stores without regard to territory or price restrictions.

Yet within weeks after Kiekhaefer closed the sale of the Kiekhaefer Corporation to Brunswick, a crisis of control began that would fan Kiekhaefer's paranoia into a roaring emotional blaze. Brunswick Corporation was a large, diversified organization with a conservative bureaucracy managing such unrelated divisions as bowling, health and science, sporting goods, school equipment, and defense products. As a management principle, Brunswick subscribed to the conservative and methodological canons of the American Management Association.

In fact, Ted Bensinger was so enamored with AMA techniques that L. A. Appley, the president of the New York–based organization, was elected to Brunswick's board of directors. Kiekhaefer's organization, at the other extreme of management practice, moved lightning-fast with its lean organization, highly disciplined in the rigors and tactics of industrial and competitive guerrilla war-fare. Those skills had effectively broken a 30-year lead and virtual monopoly enjoyed by OMC in the marine industry.

For better or for worse, Kiekhaefer made intu-itive decisions based on decades of experience in the volatile marine marketplace. The decision-making process resembled a dictatorship—Kiekhaefer made the decisions and his subordinates were expected to move heaven and earth to carry them out.

By contrast, Brunswick's personnel submit-ted recommendations to committees for evaluation and analysis and engaged in long-term plan-ning and policy conferences. The potential for conflict between the organizations was immedi-ately obvious, and Kiekhaefer had extracted a letter

The 25th anniversary logo of Mercury Marine. Instead of celebrating, Carl Kiekhaefer was regretting his decision to sell the company.

from Bensinger that promised the Kiekhaefer Corporation autonomy as far as management was concerned. Kiekhaefer would soon stretch the meaning of autonomy far beyond the letter's intent.

Meanwhile, the introduction of the MerCruiser sterndrive and the 100-horsepower outboard had convinced Charlie Strang that Mercury was finally in a position to challenge OMC for supremacy in the industry. Only one week after Kiekhaefer had signed the Brunswick merger papers, Strang jubilantly described how OMC, displaying a growing engineering weakness, had copied many Mercury design features:

> We find that they are still trying to climb aboard the Mercury bandwagon without admitting it. Once again they have copied or imitated some of our older features in one form or another. Now ... they are claiming these features as "firsts" and are devoting most of their sales pitch to these so-called "firsts."
>
> If this report of new competitive outboard features seems brief, it is solely because the competitors don't really have much that's new to talk about. Contrast this with the Mercury line for '62. The whole line—not just one or two models— offers single-lever controls, fixed jet carburetion,

and the exclusive Jet Prop exhaust. New horsepower in four of the seven basic models. Major changes in the famous fours. A brand-new, ultra-compact 10 that will completely capture the 10-horse field. And, despite competitors' propaganda saying it is impossible to build outboards greater than 75 or 80 horsepower, we have broken the barrier with the Merc 1000—a 100-horsepower beauty that is lighter and more compact than their 75s!

> 1962 will be our year![2]

OMC's engineering hibernation coincided with Mercury's own remarkable string of successful advances, and Strang's own star continued to rise. In October 1961, he was elected president of the American Power Boat Association (APBA). Capping a 25-year association with the APBA, Strang had for years been the organization's chief measurer and inspector and had been chairman of the stock outboard technical committee and a member of the outboard racing commission. Jimmy Jost, Strang's close friend and fellow Mercury employee, was elected senior vice president of the organization. Again, Mercury had scored a decisive victory against OMC. The visible prestige that would

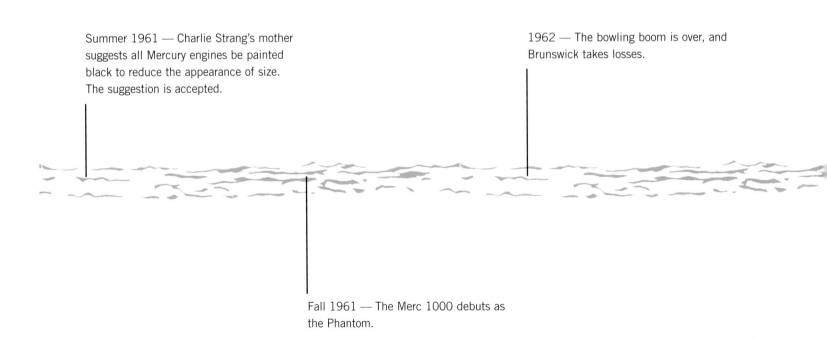

Summer 1961 — Charlie Strang's mother suggests all Mercury engines be painted black to reduce the appearance of size. The suggestion is accepted.

1962 — The bowling boom is over, and Brunswick takes losses.

Fall 1961 — The Merc 1000 debuts as the Phantom.

accompany the Strang and Jost elections was further proof of Mercury's continued dominance in racing.

Motherly Advice

In the basement of the engineering research building in Oshkosh, a tradition began in 1961 that would literally change the face of Mercury outboard motors for all time. The stark-white Mercury outboards had been the standard signature for Mercury products since Kiekhaefer had abandoned his program of offering a wide range of outboard colors to consumers during the mid- to late 1950s. This program reached its zenith in 1958 when Mercurys were offered in such exotic decorator colors as Marlin Blue, Gulf Blue, Sunset Orange, Tan, Sarasota Blue, Sand, Mercury Green, and Silver combinations. Kiekhaefer had advertised Mercury as "The most colorful name in outboards." Kiekhaefer also claimed that Mercury had "taken outboards out of the dark ages and put them into the bright, beautiful age of color—and you know color is here and will stay."[3] OMC had also gone through a similar, nearly psychedelic phase of colorful paint schemes for its products, but by the

early 1960s, the colors were standardized white for Johnson outboards and white and blue with red trim for the Evinrude line.

The introduction of the six-cylinder, in-line Mercury engine had spawned a number of industry jokes about its tall, nearly soaring appearance compared to the stodgy and rotund products of the competition. "Tower of Power" was the most complimentary of these characterizations, while the "UN building with a girdle" was the description of the new engine most favored by OMC. The competition delighted in scaring prospective six-cylinder Mercury buyers with the possibility that the new engine was too tall to tilt up properly on some models of boats and could even tip over if a driver tried to turn too sharply.

As the original 60-horsepower engine grew to 70, 80, and finally to 100 horsepower by the summer of 1961, the engine seemed to grow taller and taller until the new model began to look somewhat out of proportion even to Mercury designers. Strang and a small crew of engineers and stylists tried desperately to figure out a way to make the new 100-horsepower outboard prototype appear smaller and more compact. Their meeting lasted well into the night, and as the midnight hour approached, Ann

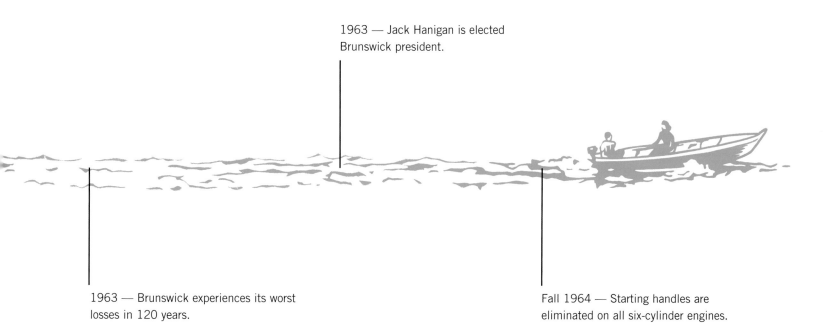

1963 — Jack Hanigan is elected Brunswick president.

1963 — Brunswick experiences its worst losses in 120 years.

Fall 1964 — Starting handles are eliminated on all six-cylinder engines.

Strang, Charlie's mother, "wandered into the building to find where her long lost son" had gone. Strang was explaining to her what they were trying to accomplish with various cowling configurations when Ann galvanized the group with a simple observation. "Well, a large woman always wears a black dress. Why don't you paint it black?" "Just for the heck of it," Strang said, "we painted one black, and the engine looked like it shrunk about 20 percent!"[4]

Introduced in the fall of 1961 as a 1962 model, the world's first 100-horsepower production engine was originally named the Phantom, owing to its mysterious and somewhat sinister appearance and power. But when double-page ads were placed in the nation's leading magazines announcing the great leap forward in the race for outboard horsepower, an insurmountable legal conflict over the name ensued. Thereafter, the trailblazing engine was simply known as the Merc 1000. It was Mercury's first black engine; it would be the

last engine Kiekhaefer would build before he sold his company to Brunswick Corporation and, conversely, the first engine built under Brunswick ownership. As the first 100-horsepower engine available to the public, it was also a significant milestone in the evolution of the outboard motor.

Two years prior to the introduction of the Phantom, when the Merc 800, 80-horsepower engine had become the world's most powerful, Kiekhaefer confidently announced that the sheer size of the motor would make a manual starting rope obsolete. He said:

I'm sure you will agree with us that there must come a time when the engine size is such that not even a strong man can crank it over, much less a woman or youngster. It is many years since automo-

Above: The new Merc 1000, the first 100-horsepower outboard.

Below: The Mercury lineup—all in black for the first time.

biles, trucks, and tractors were cranked, and you realize, of course, that inboards have never had cranking means.

If an engine won't start with a good battery, certainly it won't start with hand cranking.... Let's remember this. The manual starter and the auxiliary sheave for a starter rope are as ridiculous on a high-powered outboard motor as a hand crank on a high powered inboard.... Throw away the crank![5]

As logical as his arguments against hand cranking large engines were, Kiekhaefer's distributors and dealers were equally adamant that consumers wanted the back-up plan of manual starting in case of dead batteries. So, when the Phantom was rolled out in the fall of 1961, poking out of the top of the massive black cowling was a diminutive pull handle, a temptation probably avoided by all but the strongest professional wrestlers and football linebackers. Not until the fall of 1964 was the decision finally made to eliminate the starting handle on all six-cylinder engines, starting with the 1965 line.

Clash of Titans

The first outward signs of the coming clash of management styles between Kiekhaefer and Brunswick's management surfaced less than two months following the merger. On January 5, 1962, Kiekhaefer sent a memo to all department heads, mail clerks, and switchboard operators at all plants. It read:

This memo is being issued as a reminder that all phone calls and correspondence from the Brunswick Corporation must be cleared through the Office of the President. This means incoming and outgoing calls and mail. After calls and correspondence have been screened, they will be referred to the proper parties for handling. This policy must be adhered to without exception.[6]

Kiekhaefer effectively shut Brunswick out of Mercury. No communication with the parent organization was allowed except through Kiekhaefer's office. After paying more than $34 million for Mercury, Brunswick wasn't even allowed to speak to any of the subsidiary's 4,500-plus employees except for Kiekhaefer. Brunswick executives care-

fully acquiesced to his unusual request. A few weeks later, Bensinger informed his own administrative staff in a cautiously worded memo to "advise Kiekhaefer who your deputies are and give him a brief description of their functions. This will help to expedite and improve communications between our two groups."[7] Kiekhaefer even forbade access to all plants by any Brunswick personnel unless first cleared by him personally.

The organizations clashed in style, temperament, and priorities. For his part, Kiekhaefer struggled to understand the need for a never-ending stream of status reports and updates. He resented the intrusion of new ideas (that were not his own) on ways to improve manufacturing facilities and processes and resisted suggestions on ways to cut costs and take advantage of Brunswick's buying power.[8]

Kiekhaefer had saddled Tom King with coordinating research for many of the Brunswick inquiries. King finally threw up his arms in disgust, telling Kiekhaefer, "The question must certainly be raised as to how Brunswick wishes our key executives to use their time. It can be devoted to such areas as selling effort, market research, modernizing facilities, research, and development, or it can be devoted to defending our policies, steel strapping studies, paper box studies, freight bill reviews, studies on inbound and outbound freight costs, etc."[9] Kiekhaefer summed up his feelings by writing, "If any studies are to be made, the entire Brunswick organization should be analyzed, laundered, and ironed. Unless this is accomplished in the reasonably near future, the prospects with Brunswick look dim. While Brunswick may not fail, it will have a long, hard climb back."

Brunswick was indeed in serious trouble. In the 24 months following the merger, Brunswick's overall sales plummeted from $426 million and profits of more than $44 million to $315 million and a net loss of more than $10 million. The value of its stock, the only compensation received by Kiekhaefer for the sale of his company, was falling at a steady and nauseating rate.

Brunswick, in a headlong dash for pinsetter sales against rival AMF, had eagerly helped finance bowling centers across the United States. For six years, Brunswick amassed a mountain of debt, asking as little as 10 percent down from chain after

Brunswick tried to "help" Kiekhaefer save money with his corrugated box purchases.

chain of bowling establishments and giving them eight years to pay. In 1962, the bowling boom finally ended, pinsetter sales fell dramatically, and hundreds of bowling centers informed Brunswick that they could not meet their payments. Brunswick had borrowed against the expected payments by bowling establishments and, by the end of 1962, was overwhelmed by nearly $360 million in debt. At the time, taking on debt seemed like a good way to take advantage of an industry that showed no sign of slowing. A Brunswick-financed survey, conducted in 1961, had optimistically and incorrectly concluded that the market could absorb 300,000 lanes at a time when just 125,00 lanes were in operation.

The value of Brunswick stock fell from a high of $75 in 1961 until it reached a low of $6. Kiekhaefer's dreams of uniting with a strong, rich partner to build the manufacturing facilities he needed to overtake OMC appeared shattered. He began to look for ways to reverse or somehow nullify the

sale of the Kiekhaefer Corporation to Brunswick, alleging that Bensinger was aware of the coming financial crisis and that Brunswick would be unable to live up to its promises. Kiekhaefer's attorneys had begun to work furiously on this strategy by the beginning of 1963, attempting to prove that Brunswick had artificially maintained the price of its stock until the merger was complete and then allowed it to plummet. Following a thorough investigation, however, they concluded that "it could be argued that during negotiations with Brunswick, Mr. Kiekhaefer could have apprised himself [of the declining fortunes of Brunswick] by investigation of these records," really placing the blame on Kiekhaefer's own lack of homework before the sale.[10]

Before long, Kiekhaefer began to hint at total rebellion against Brunswick, or failing that, resignation. He drafted a scathing letter to Bensinger in early 1963 that argued over old sores and opened new ones:

> In my judgment, I do not need to be crammed with a lot of management ideas and theories to make this division perform better. I do not agree entirely with your theory on "cross-fertilization" between divisional managers where the divisions are completely different types of businesses with no common grounds of product, marketing, manufacturing, engineering, or research and development....
>
> I am sure that this will not be your opinion, but in my opinion, I feel there has been a breach of good faith.... I am convinced that the future of Brunswick looks pretty glum for some time.... I feel that a thorough and complete discussion must take place between yourself and the writer in the very near future if there is anything to be salvaged of our relationship.[11]

The following day, Kiekhaefer further revealed his agony in a letter never mailed to Howard F. Baer, chairman of the Brunswick Aloe Division and fellow director. He wrote, "I also realize the tremendous ground one treads on when one doesn't agree with 'Nero.' I am of a disposition that if I cannot be proud, I cannot work at all. I am taking the only way out open to me, so I may again work with dignity, pride, and the joy of accomplishments."[12]

By the summer of 1963, as Brunswick continued a dramatic slide to its worst loss in 120 years of business, bankers, associates, and family members inundated Bensinger with hints that he needed outside help to get through the deepening crisis. One of the names that kept cropping up was that of Jack L. Hanigan, the executive vice president and general

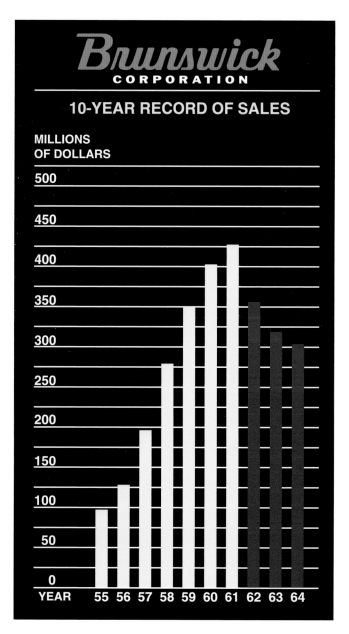

manager of Dow Corning Corporation. Hanigan, the short, husky, and tough 52-year-old administrator, had spent the last 26 years at Corning Glass Works and Dow Corning, working his way up through the organization in various assignments, including one as general manager of its Electrical Products Division. "My initial reaction was not to join Brunswick," Hanigan admitted. "A mutual friend set up the meeting between myself and Ted. I liked him a lot, and his company's problems presented some interesting challenges."[13]

Just as Bensinger had worked his persuasive magic on Kiekhaefer, so too was Hanigan soon won over to the Brunswick cause. On November 5, 1963, Hanigan was elected president of Brunswick while Bensinger moved up to chairman and CEO following the retirement of his brother and Chairman R. F. "Bob" Bensinger. It was a traumatic event for the Bensingers. Except for a short time before the turn of the century, Brunswick had been guided exclusively by the Bensinger family for 120 years.

Unfortunately, the tone of the relationship between Hanigan and Kiekhaefer was set in concrete within moments of their first meeting near the end of 1963. "So," Hanigan said brusquely as he shoved his hand in Kiekhaefer's direction, "you're the son of a bitch that's been making all the trouble here." Kiekhaefer was stunned. The Mercury division was setting meteoric sales records and breaking all profitability predictions while the rest of Brunswick was mired in a downturn.

It was the first of many clashes between the two, whose similar personalities provided a constant shower of fireworks between the two organizations. Hanigan was just as stubborn as Kiekhaefer, and the rivalry between the two powerful executives became so intense that staffers in both organizations would run down the hall scrambling to get out of the line of fire whenever the two men approached one another.

Kiekhaefer pressed Hanigan for money to modernize Mercury's manufacturing facilities and continually lobbied him for the expansion capital that he was originally promised by Bensinger.

The 1964 annual report showed Brunswick's discouraging drop in sales.

After becoming Brunswick president in 1963, Jack Hanigan (front) and Carl Kiekhaefer (rear) experienced an often-tumultous relationship.

Kiekhaefer assembled long, powerfully substantiated letters to Hanigan, pleading with him to release funds for new die-casting facilities, more room for manufacturing and inventory, and a host of essential machines crucial to new production techniques and model changes. To Kiekhaefer, it seemed as if Hanigan delighted in delaying every conceivable request or, worse, endlessly vacillating between approval and rejection.

The two waged their battles in tersely worded letters, exchanging literary blows for real and imagined slights. Hanigan would occasionally receive a letter with some minor complaint from an owner

of a Mercury outboard and would send it along to Kiekhaefer with a note scrawled across the bottom along the lines of: "Better look into these problems, Carl." Kiekhaefer would then reply by lashing out at Hanigan, sending bitter and flame-fanning letters in return that would, naturally, make matters even worse. He said:

> We would appreciate and would probably react accordingly if a pat on the back would come this way occasionally rather than the well-aimed kick in the pants that makes us feel as though we have been guilty of great oversight and that we have been lax and careless in inspection and manufacture and utterly stupid in engineering.[14]

Racked with despair, Kiekhaefer scribbled a long handwritten note to himself, summing up his deep feelings of resentment and remorse:

> We were promised complete autonomy of operation—which we had before the merger. In fact, to sum it all up, we are doing nothing more now than we could have done alone, without Brunswick. We would have had no difficulty borrowing short-term money as we always had from our own banks; we could have gone through with our preliminary discussions for long-term financing for any major capital expenditures and we still would have owned the company.
>
> I cannot think of one single advantage which the Brunswick merger has produced.[15]

The acrid relationship between Kiekhaefer and Hanigan came to a boil in May 1964 during a telephone conversation. Kiekhaefer told Hanigan that Strang and King, two of the top men at Mercury, were planning to resign because of him.[16]

In fact, weeks earlier, Strang, King, and Kiekhaefer had sat down at a typewriter and pecked out their resignations. They planned to launch a new venture and discussed various plans. It was Kiekhaefer, according to Strang, who decided against leaving Brunswick because of his sizable stock. The men agreed to drop the matter—that is, until Kiekhaefer blurted it out in a fit of pique, knowing that Hanigan would have been embarrassed by the loss of Strang's technical expertise and King's marketing ability. "He calls me in the morning," Strang recalled. "He said, 'I had a fight with Hanigan on the phone this morning, and I told him you and King were leaving because you couldn't stand his policies.' I said, 'Oh my God!' "[17]

Trapped, Strang and King had but one option: damage control. They decided to meet with Hanigan, acknowledge they did want to leave (to take advantage of the capital gains tax and start their own business) and try to negotiate a consulting contract to give them a head start on the outside. Strang and King met with Hanigan on May 24, 1964, in his office, where they explained their reasons. Hanigan's response took them by surprise: "You're leaving because you can't stand Carl!" Hanigan then disclosed his plan to fire Kiekhaefer. Hanigan spoke with members of Brunswick's board and believed he had the support to follow through on the threat. While Kiekhaefer was getting booted out, Hanigan planned to have the locks and guards changed at the plants. Kiekhaefer's belongings would be moved from his office to the parking lot.[18]

Strang and King were concerned that their resignations sparked the decision to get rid of Kiekhaefer, but Hanigan outlined his reasons, assuring the men that "this has been in the works for a long time." He continued:

Carl can't work for anybody! I don't see how anybody could work for Carl. Carl doesn't understand that he's sold the business. It isn't his to do with as he pleases. He's not a team man. I can't get the facts from him. I can't believe what he tells me because I've caught him in too many lies where I've had the facts from other sources. I don't get any cooperation on speeches or other corporate programs. All I get is excuses, phony excuses, and lies. The other division managers see this, and then they question my authority.[19]

Hanigan urged Strang to accept the position of president of the Kiekhaefer Corporation following Kiekhaefer's dismissal. He said someone was going to replace Kiekhaefer no matter what; it was just a question of who. The discussion between Strang and Hanigan seesawed over the next several days, with Strang resisting the thought of betraying his friend and Hanigan's insisting that it was in both Kiekhaefer and the subsidiary's best interests. In a phone call between Strang and Hanigan, re-

corded by Strang, the engineer revealed the depth of what troubled him:

I'm really honored that you offered me the opportunity … to be president of Kiekhaefer. The thing that's bothering me, though, is that even though you told me your decision to get rid of Carl was made before he brought you my resignation, I can't escape the feeling that my acceptance can only expedite his departure. And as much as I long wanted this thing for 13 years, I don't think I can accept it under these very unfortunate circumstances…. I really like Carl. I can't help it. And I don't want to have any part in hurting him.[20]

Hanigan tried to persuade Strang and King, who was also still planning to leave, to remain. He dropped (for a time) the plan to fire Kiekhaefer, who heard rumors of a scheme to unseat him and had lined up support on Brunswick's board. Kiekhaefer also heard rumors that it was Strang who originally tried to engineer his removal. Although Strang provided evidence to the contrary, the episode strained their friendship.

Strang and King left by the end of the summer of 1964. Their plan was to work together as a high-caliber marine industry engineering and marketing consulting firm, available to anyone who might need such a specialized service. They formed United States Executives, Inc., and one of their first clients was Rover, the small turbine engine manufacturer in England with whom Kiekhaefer had unsuccessfully negotiated for a manufacturing license. Strang and King drifted apart, though, and King began a search for a suitable corporate position for his talents.

Near the end of 1965, Strang was contacted by C. W. "Doc" Jones, a onetime Mercury dealer who had become an aggressive and dedicated OMC distributor and who maintained a high-performance machine shop in Phoenix, Arizona. Would Strang join him in an attempt to establish a new world outboard record? Strang knew that if he accepted Jones' challenge and helped OMC to beat the best that Kiekhaefer could build, there would be no turning back. Jones, intimately familiar with the products of both the Kiekhaefer Corporation and OMC, "knew that OMC had to have Charlie."

"We (OMC) were in all kinds of trouble with our outboard engines," Jones admitted. "I got Charlie to

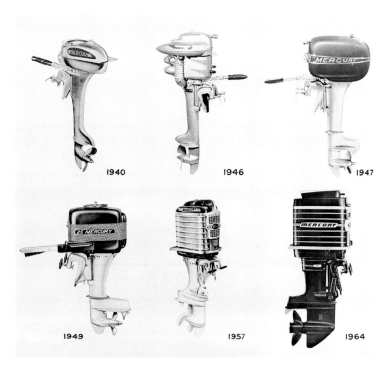

1940   1946   1947

1949   1957   1964

"Let's be realistic and recognize that these are wonderful years for Mercury," Kiekhaefer announced to dealers on the 25th anniversary of Mercury in 1964. "We are associated with a product that is enjoying a degree of popularity and public acceptance that is almost unmatched in history and certainly is without parallel in the industry."[23] Things were going Kiekhaefer's way in the marketplace, and he was rapidly closing the gap with his competitors. He said:

"While [OMC] has made its mistakes and has lost some of its dominance and stature in the marine industry, they will be like a wounded bear, ready to fight back with new weapons.... The boys that built our competitor's business, the old heads, have already retired and have left in their place a lot of youngsters who are fumbling around at the moment...."[24]

Whether due to Kiekhaefer's constant pressure or to Hanigan's skillful handling of resources, money became available for critical expansion at Mercury in 1964. For the three years following the merger, Kiekhaefer made relatively minor additions to facilities and argued vociferously that the golden opportunity to overtake OMC and become the world's leader in marine propulsion was slipping through their collective fingers. In 1964, Hanigan authorized a major expansion, and the Kiekhaefer Corporation embarked on the most ambitious building program in its history. But as Kiekhaefer prepared for construction of a mammoth, 180,000-square-foot distribution building in Fond du Lac and finalized plans for an even larger, 372,000-square-foot assembly building, a political blunder by Fond du Lac's city commission threatened the future of the company in Wisconsin.

The proposed $4.5 million investment, part of a forecasted $10 million expansion program, screeched to a halt in late February 1964. The city commission voted to annex the properties and buildings of the Kiekhaefer Corporation, which would add a substantial amount of taxable indus-

come out there and stay with me for six months. I personally talked to Ralph Evinrude ... and asked him to come out to Phoenix. The three of us went to dinner. And then they stayed up all night and talked. And Charlie saw me the next morning and said, 'They've offered me a job, but they won't tell me what it is.' "[21]

Strang was provided with a significant retainer of $50,000 to remain with Jones for the few months required to prepare for his arrival at OMC.[22] Clay Conover, OMC's celebrated chief engineer for the previous 16 years, was elected a vice president of OMC and general manager of Johnson Motors. On June 1, 1966, Strang joined OMC as director of marine engineering. From the exalted position of being Kiekhaefer's closest friend and most trusted confidant, Strang was about to become the enemy.

Meanwhile, Kiekhaefer promoted Charles Alexander to vice president of engineering and Armand Hauser to vice president of marketing. Though the Kiekhaefer Corporation felt the loss of Strang and King, the organization had confidence in Hauser, a 20-year veteran, and Alexander, who had been the chief engineer for the MerCruiser sterndrives. The loss of Strang and King had no effect on sales; in 1965, nearly 43,000 engines rolled down the production lines in Wisconsin.

try to fill city coffers. Kiekhaefer was furious. He told the city that he would not only halt his proposed expansion in the community but actually pull up stakes and move away, perhaps even to another state. Kiekhaefer published a terse statement of his convictions in the Fond du Lac *Commonwealth Reporter*:

The representatives of Fond du Lac made us a promise when we came to build plants and create a local industry, and that promise to a struggling small company was that the city would never annex the property upon which we built. That promise was broken ... when your city government did in fact annex our property. We consider that a breach of faith. ...

Because your city government and ours (for we live here also) broke the promise made to us many years ago, we are not willing to begin on this project in the Fond du Lac area until we receive from the city a simple statement that the city will never again annex our plants and lands unless we ask them to.[25]

The people of Fond du Lac erupted in a shower of support to keep the Kiekhaefer Corporation and its internationally recognized product line in the community. Dozens of prominent businesses and individuals lent their names and lobbying efforts to the cause. Kiekhaefer and project coordinator Hauser sat stoically with their arms crossed at public hearings that drew the largest crowds in local governmental history. In the face of nearly universal community support and Kiekhaefer's poker-faced bluff of moving the Kiekhaefer Corporation, the city commission relented and rescinded its plan of annexation. On April 26, 1964, residents were relieved to see the eight-column banner headline in the morning paper, which read, "Kiekhaefer Will Build Plant."[26]

Kiekhaefer gambled because Brunswick Corporation, not Kiekhaefer, had the final word on any decision to move all nine Kiekhaefer Corporation

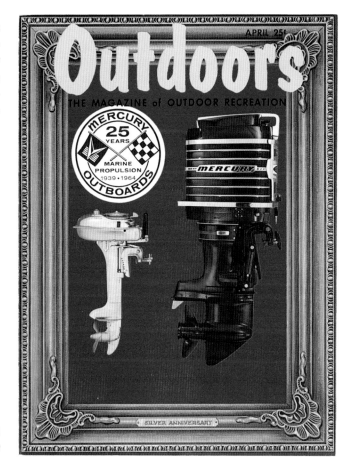

Above: *Outdoors* magazine celebrated Mercury's 25th anniversary.

Left: Kiekhaefer established a Mercury tradition of taking care of its dealers. Brunswick continues the tradition.

plants out of the city or, even more unlikely, out of the state. Fortunately for Kiekhaefer, the city decided to reverse the order of annexation, as very likely Brunswick Corporation, in the absence of Kiekhaefer, would have allowed the annexation to proceed unimpeded. Kiekhaefer, too, never wanted to leave, admitting that he felt a bond with the dedicated workforce he had carefully trained for more than a quarter-century.

Kiekhaefer stunned guests at the groundbreaking ceremony for his distribution center by driving an Euclid earthmover himself. He had bought two of the $65,000 twin-diesel machines a month earlier just for this occasion.

Construction of the new distribution building in Fond du Lac began on a July morning in 1964 as giant earthmoving machines, one driven by Kiekhaefer himself, lumbered down the service road to the groundbreaking site. Festivities had been coordinated for the occasion, including a long string of trailer-borne boats with MerCruiser sterndrive engines and Mercury outboards. The audience, including Brunswick Chairman Bensinger and President Hanigan, was indeed impressed.[27]

Over the next four years, Kiekhaefer supervised the construction of more than 1.5 million square feet of space for Mercury production, engineering, sales, and storage capacity. Most of the facilities were built in Fond du Lac, with major new facilities also built in Cedarburg and Oshkosh. Though Brunswick Corporation was still struggling to regain profitability following the collapse of bowling markets, sales and profits of Mercury products continued to soar. *FORTUNE*® magazine put it bluntly: "The leading money loser among the 500 largest industrials in 1965 was Chicago's Brunswick Corp., which racked up a deficit of $76,932,000."[28] *Forbes* was just as harsh, reporting in 1965 that "nearly $400 million of the company's $650 million in assets consists of accounts receivable for bowling alleys sold long ago. Until this mountain of bowling paper is substantially reduced, it will be hard to tell whether Brunswick is simply on the downgrade of the roller coaster—or heading into a bottomless pit."[29]

It seemed that the harder Kiekhaefer worked, the farther behind Brunswick was getting. He was rapidly making up his mind that it was time to get out.

In 1965, Mercury matched its speed with strength, pulling an elephant on specially designed water skis with a single 90-horsepower outboard.

CHAPTER TEN

RIFT BEYOND REPAIR

After having built a company that has produced over $1.5 billion worth of product with my name on it, I don't know whether any man is capable of two ventures of this type in his lifetime.... It's always easier, I suppose, to liquidate and buy tax-exempt bonds, but I wouldn't know what to do with myself since I don't like fishing or traveling.

—Carl Kiekhaefer, 1972[1]

CARL KIEKHAEFER'S NARROW ESCAPE from being fired naturally remained embedded in his memory and served as an invisible rock; his mind kept tripping over the belief that perhaps he wasn't paranoid enough.

Kiekhaefer lashed out in a letter he never mailed to fellow Brunswick board member Walter M. Heymann:

I do appreciate all you and Al Puelicher have done for me by keeping me from being fired several years ago in favor of Charles Strang. By first building his hopes with our company and then suddenly dashing them, Strang has become our worst enemy and is being driven on with a zeal that the devil couldn't match to become Outboard Marine's next president.

This treacherous act, namely Brunswick's negotiating with this man for a year or more behind my back, was a burden difficult to carry after I became aware of it. It was a narrow scrape not only for me but for Brunswick....[2]

Kiekhaefer's anxiety over being separated from Mercury grew, and he began to take steps that might ensure a new start following any irreconcilable differences with Jack Hanigan. As early as 1966, he and Hanigan began discussing ways to guarantee Kiekhaefer's smooth transition out of the company. Hanigan offered Kiekhaefer the possibility of being a third partner in a proposed new company with Brunswick and the British Rover Company. Kiekhaefer, though, had hoped he would be able to stay as president of the division if the new company were formed. "Well, this wouldn't be too bad," Kiekhaefer told Hanigan in a telephone conversation recorded by Kiekhaefer, "this wouldn't be too bad. But this means that I sacrifice something else in the process. That puts a new dimension on the thing. ... This means sacrificing my presidency here."[3]

Hanigan began to take Kiekhaefer to task for his frequent comments about leaving the company and slowly curved conversations around to what Kiekhaefer would expect should they ever part ways.

When Kiekhaefer asked Hanigan if he could get a two-year contract, he was surprised when the Brunswick president offered more:

I'd like to make it five years instead of two, if that would make you feel any better.... I want to be very clear with you that as far as I am concerned, we can do this in any way that you physically

---

A new logo for an old company. Carl Kiekhaefer revived the name Kiekhaefer Aeromarine and updated more than just the logo.

can handle it, but you said to me the other day that you'd like to get out and have something that was your own, and take pride in, and so forth. And I said it was all right with me. And I was trying to suggest a way that you could continue to be at Mercury and still be free to spend as much time as you wanted on [something else]. ... I don't want you out of there.[4]

Mercury's growth and profitability were continuing sources of pride and financial comfort to Brunswick, but Kiekhaefer continued to make the parent company's leadership feel impotent, unwanted, and meddlesome. Kiekhaefer seldom shared the division's success with Brunswick. He was the first to point out blemishes in Brunswick's management and the last to seek ways to benefit from nearly 125 years of business experience.

He also never ceased encouraging the Kiekhaefer organization to resent Brunswick. Jim Schenk, for example, was an impressionable 23-year-old when he joined the Kiekhaefer Corporation as a financial trainee in 1965. "I spent my young career being taught how to hate Brunswick. You were trained there from the day you walked in the door to dislike the parent. It was part of their indoctrination."[5] (In 1972, Schenk became the first to move from Mercury Marine to Brunswick. He eventually became vice president in charge of business development.)

Hanigan finally reached the end of his patience with Kiekhaefer and decided to take action. In a letter to memorialize a meeting that took place between the two men on October 8, 1969, Hanigan held nothing back, putting his true feelings about Kiekhaefer out in the open:

I cannot wait until your retirement date to replace you in charge of the Kiekhaefer Mercury Division. It is my opinion that your personality is so strong that a man strong enough to run this large a division would find it impossible to work for you. It is my hope, however, that a way can be found to have him work with you, not only until your retirement date but for many years after.

In listening to your comments over the past few years, I have come to have what I think to be a pretty good idea of what you want to do when you do retire. I am suggesting that this program be started now instead of waiting until 1971.[6]

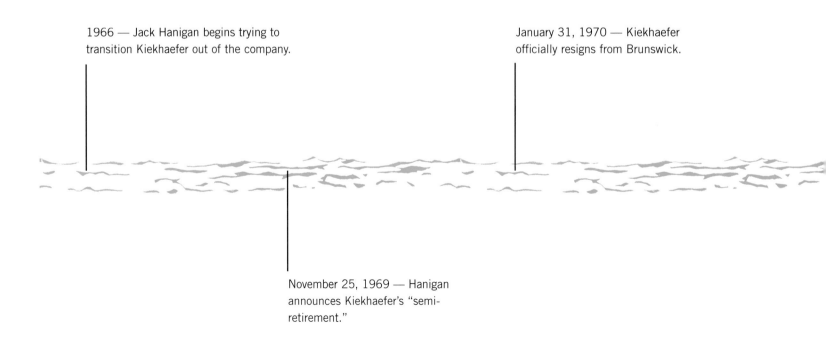

1966 — Jack Hanigan begins trying to transition Kiekhaefer out of the company.

January 31, 1970 — Kiekhaefer officially resigns from Brunswick.

November 25, 1969 — Hanigan announces Kiekhaefer's "semi-retirement."

October 13, 1969

Mr. E. C. Kiekhaefer
Kiekhaefer/Mercury
Fond du Lac, Wisconsin

Brunswick CORPORATION
OFFICE OF THE PRESIDENT

Dear Carl:

To recap our conversation of October 8, 1969:

I cannot wait until your retirement date to replace you in charge of the Kiekhaefer/Mercury Division. It is my opinion that your personality is so strong that a man strong enough to run this large a division would find it impossible to work for you. It is my hope, however, that a way can be found to have him work with you, not only until your retirement date but for many years after.

In listening to your comments over the past few years, I have come to have what I think to be a pretty good idea of what you want to do when you do retire. I am suggesting that this program be started now instead of waiting until 1971.

As I see it, what you would like is as follows:

To run your own show;

To continue to be associated with Kiekhaefer/Mercury;

To have your son associated with you;

To have a vehicle for possible capital gains in the future;

To be a part of whatever racing program Kiekhaefer/Mercury may have; and

To invent and develop devices in the marine field, as well as in other fields.

continued

69 WEST WASHINGTON STREET, CHICAGO, ILLINOIS 60602 U.S.A./TELEPHONE 312/441-7000

The letter from Jack Hanigan to Kiekhaefer mandating his early retirement.

Both men agreed to meet again in Chicago on November 6, 1969, to finalize plans for a smooth transition of control at Mercury. Following the meeting, Kiekhaefer began to draft the terms of separation from the company. Basically, the plan called for the establishment of a new division known as the Propulsion and Planning Division with Kiekhaefer as president at his existing annual salary of $100,000. Kiekhaefer would then be appointed "chairman founder" of the Kiekhaefer Corporation and basically step aside. His new division would have research and development authority in the fields of marine propulsion and snow vehicles along with responsibility for testing operations at Lake X and other sites. He would also be in charge of plant construction for Brunswick, air transport, and racing activities. This new division would lease space from Kiekhaefer at his modest facilities on "the ledge" (Kiekhaefer's home), at a generous price, and give him the option to buy out any equipment installed

September 1, 1971 — Kiekhaefer is allowed to begin directly competing with Brunswick.

1970 — Brooks Abernathy becomes president of Kiekhaefer Mercury.

November 23, 1971 — Abernathy changes the Mercury division's name from Kiekhaefer Mercury to Mercury Marine.

at the facility whenever the more or less open-ended agreement might lapse. Lastly, the agreement called for Kiekhaefer to "provide reasonable advice and assistance" to a new general manager of Mercury. Kiekhaefer would be given access to main plant facilities at all times and provide suitable office space at the main plant in addition to office space at the ledge.[7]

Brunswick's board of directors objected to the formation of this special division just to appease Kiekhaefer and decided instead to allow Kiekhaefer to build his own company, Kiekhaefer Aeromarine Motors, and appoint the new company as a consultant to Brunswick for research into marine propulsion and snow vehicles. This precarious relationship could be terminated with only 60 days' notice from either side. Under the new plan, Kiekhaefer Aeromarine Motors would be "free to develop its own interests outside of the marine propulsion field but will not compete with Brunswick in that field, at least prior to September 1, 1971."[8] Both Kiekhaefer

and Hanigan agreed to the loosely specified conditions on November 21, 1969, and joint announcements were prepared for release to the press, distributors, dealers, and employees.

To create an atmosphere of cooperation and a controlled transition, it was agreed that a meeting would be held in the Mercury auditorium four days later, on November 25, for Kiekhaefer to announce his "semi-retirement," and to introduce the new president of Mercury. Hanigan selected

Above: K. B. "Brooks" Abernathy was given the enviable title of president of Mercury, but at an unenviable time—at the announcement of Kiekhaefer's resignation.

Below: The ledge was the headquarters as well as the home of Kiekhaefer and his independent corporation. Inset shows the snowmobile test track where Kiekhaefer made many improvements to the snowmobile.

E. C. Kiekhaefer

K. B. Abernathy

K. B. Abernathy Succeeds Mercury's E. C. Kiekhaefer

On November 25 Brunswick Corporation announced changes in its corporate management.

Mr. K. B. Abernathy, formerly corporate treasurer and president of the International Division, was appointed president of the Kiekhaefer Mercury Division. He will report to Mr. J. L. Hanigan, president of Brunswick Corporation.

Mr. E. C. Kiekhaefer will continue as a corporate vice president and director of Brunswick Corporation, and was also appointed to the new post of chairman founder of Kiekhaefer Mercury. He will report to Mr. Hanigan on special engineering assignments.

Mr. C. E. Erb, in addition to his duties as vice president administration of Brunswick Corporation, was appointed president of Brunswick International Division.

In commenting on the changes in management in the Kiekhaefer Mercury Division, Mr. Hanigan stated: "This is a step to bring younger management into a position of top executive responsibility in this division. Mr. Kiekhaefer, who is one of the great pioneers in marine propulsion in this country, will be on hand to aid in this transition and simultaneously will be working on special projects where his considerable engineering talents will be available to the corporation."

Mr. Abernathy was born in Missoula, Montana on August 30, 1918, and raised in Evanston, Illinois. He is a graduate of Northwestern University and holds certificates from the Advanced Management Programs of both General Electric Company and the Harvard University School of Business.

From 1941 to 1945, he worked in accounting, marketing and manufacturing for General Electric. He moved to General Electric Credit Corporation in 1945 and was a regional manager in 1962 when he left to join Brunswick as assistant vice president and corporate credit manager.

He was elected treasurer of Brunswick in 1966, and in early 1968 was assigned the additional duties of general manager of the company's International Division. He has now been appointed president of the Kiekhaefer Mercury Division.

K. B. "Brooks" Abernathy, the bookish hero of Brunswick's campaign to collect massive delinquent receivables due from the bowling division disaster, as Kiekhaefer's successor. "We were owed $500 million at the time," Hanigan said, "which is quite a piece of change. He then took over as treasurer of the company and did a very good job of gathering all our money up, and sweeping it up from the nooks and crannies, and putting it where we could use it."[9] Hanigan had rewarded Abernathy by promoting him to head Brunswick's International Division, which also thrived as a result of his skills in money management.

One of Kiekhaefer's trademarks was being a little late to meetings. When he hadn't arrived at the auditorium within a few minutes past the 9:30 a.m. time for the dramatic announcement, Hanigan refused to wait and started the meeting without him. Assembled in the auditorium were about 100 Mercury executives and key employees. Hanigan strode up to the podium and read the press release that would be sent out following the meeting. As Hanigan announced the appointment of Abernathy as the new president, Kiekhaefer arrived at the level above the auditorium. The realization of what was happening just down the familiar flight of stairs seemed to shock him for a moment. Then, Rose Smiljanic, Kiekhaefer's secretary of more than 30 years, started to cry. He slowly turned around, his heart breaking that he wasn't permitted, after more than 30 years of leadership, to tell the assembled employees the news himself. He slowly walked to his car and drove away. As he drove through the gates for the last

Left: A story in the 1970 *Mercury Messenger* reported on the departure of E. Carl Kiekhaefer, founder of Mercury Marine.

Below: Kiekhaefer had difficulty adjusting to life as an entrepreneur instead of a lion of industry. "It is the team I shall miss the most," he said.

The 1965 Merc 500 with new silencing system bore little resemblance to the first Mercury engines 25 years earlier. But many of the earlier models' features were still standard 25 years later.

time, Hanigan explained to the astonished group that "this is a step to bring younger management into a position of top executive responsibility in this division. Mr. Kiekhaefer, who is one of the great pioneers in marine propulsion in this country, will be on hand to aid in this transition and simultaneously will be working on special projects where his considerable engineering talents will be available to the corporation."[10]

But following the official announcement, Hanigan made it very clear just who was in charge of the Kiekhaefer Corporation. He said:

I want to say to all of you ... that this is a very difficult thing for Carl to do. This place is his baby, and we want to make it as easy for him as possible by being just as polite and gentle as we possibly can be with him. However, there ought to be no question in anybody's mind that you are working for this man (Abernathy) now, not Carl. But don't make it too obvious if you can avoid it because he's contributed a hell of a lot to this business. The unfortunate part of Carl's style of management is that he, I think, would be here when he'd be 95 if left to his own devices. And you can't take that risk if you have stockholders to whom you're responsible. I've been worried for the last four or five years that a truck would hit him or something, and I wouldn't know what the hell was going on up here."[11]

Life without Kiekhaefer at Mercury was very frustrating for some who tried to orient themselves to the new regime, and several left the organization.[12] But Abernathy showed a remarkable amount of political acumen when he stepped into the oversized shoes so recently vacated by Kiekhaefer. One of his first moves was to eliminate Saturdays from the work schedule. Under Kiekhaefer, working Saturdays was virtually

mandatory. That went a long way to ease the transition. Abernathy also had the closed circuit cameras (used by Kiekhaefer to keep a watch on his people) taken out.

Relations between Abernathy and the Kiekhaefer organization were aloof because Abernathy knew he was replacing a phenomenon, reminisced Clem Koehler, a former Mercury employee: "Brooks didn't denigrate Kiekhaefer or his efforts, but you knew who was boss. Brooks kept a steady hand, and we made progress."[13]

After not receiving any instruction or communication from Hanigan, Abernathy, or anyone else from Brunswick for several weeks, Kiekhaefer decided to act. He felt betrayed by Hanigan and Brunswick and became convinced that the only way he could regain his pride was to renounce any agreements he had made with Hanigan and formally and completely resign. On December 30, 1969, he sent a short letter to Hanigan, Abernathy, and each member of Brunswick's board. It read:

The purpose of this letter is to inform you and the board of directors of Brunswick Corporation that effective on my 31st anniversary with Kiekhaefer Mercury, namely, on January 31, 1970, I am resigning as an officer and director of Brunswick Corporation, as a member of its executive committee, and also as Chairman Founder of the Kiekhaefer Mercury Division.[14]

From the ice-cold morning in the early weeks of 1939 to that ice-cold meeting in 1969, Kiekhaefer had worked an industrial miracle from the ruins and wreckage of an abandoned building in Cedarburg, Wisconsin. In the intervening 30 years, Kiekhaefer's vision and skills changed the face of the world's marine industry as well as the lives of countless men and women whom he nurtured in the process. His record is remarkable. The net worth of his company grew from $25,000 to more than $65 million. The floor space of his operations grew from 16,000 square feet to more than 2.5 million. His annual sales went from zero to more than $175 million, and the value of the products he sold would top $1.25 billion. He built more than 2 million engines of all varieties while his payroll exceeded $30 million a year. The good name of Mercury was distributed in 118 countries around the world by nearly 8,000 dealers and assembled and shipped by nearly 5,000 employees.

But Kiekhaefer soon felt discarded and abandoned by the company he had built. "Apparently they are attempting to erase all my contributions to the company I founded 30 years ago," Kiekhaefer admitted forlornly. "I guess this is my reward for hard work and sincere effort."[15] Of his decades of labor, Kiekhaefer was most concerned that somehow his remarkable contributions would be lost to the passage of time, the erosion of memory, and history itself. He said:

I just cannot understand what horrible crime I have committed to warrant a role like Nathan Hale's Man Without A Country. *I hate to see the time come when my only reminder of the past in the marine industry is by looking through the patent records.*[16]

As he approached his 64th birthday, the doors of the reborn Kiekhaefer Aeromarine Motors officially opened on February 1, 1970. Not since 1939

had Kiekhaefer been without the generous assistance of a large and well-developed organization. Now he was starting over with a skeleton crew of 13 wide-eyed and somewhat anxious individuals.

Kiekhaefer was most familiar with the marine industry and with the products he had invented, tooled, manufactured, and marketed for the previous 30 years. But a non-compete clause prohibited him from competing with Brunswick and Mercury products until September 1, 1971—a distant 20 months away.

His answer was to concentrate on the design of a small and versatile two-cycle engine, targeted to meet the special needs of the growing snowmobile market.

Kiekhaefer was no stranger to snowmobiles. Living in the heart of the American snowbelt, he had watched the introduction of snow vehicles and their growing popularity since the late 1950s. By the early 1960s, demand for snowmobiles began to rise steadily, and Kiekhaefer became enamored with the possibility of providing this unique product to Mercury dealers in the north to keep them active and profitable throughout the long winter season.

Kiekhaefer was convinced that Mercury expertise in two-cycle engine design and manufacture, in combination with engineering innovation in

The Mercury 150E snowmobile looked better than it ran. Mercury discontinued it when the product couldn't live up to the high standards Mercury set in the marine industry.

The 1973 product line brochure carried the new Mercury Marine name—without the Kiekhaefer name on top of it.

chassis and track design, would be sufficient to capture a large share of the burgeoning market. Spurring him on was the fact that in 1964, OMC had introduced Johnson Skee-horse and Evinrude Skeeter snowmobiles, powered by relatively under-powered 14-horsepower engines.

Longtime Mercury employee Billy Steele re-membered the Saturday morning meeting in Fond du Lac when Kiekhaefer, as president of Mercury, muscled his way into the snowmobile business. Kiekhaefer had recently visited a group of Canadian dealers and was impressed by their success in marketing snowmobiles in the winter months, "and all he would talk about was, 'We'll build snowmobiles.'"[17]

By June 1967, Mercury had finished its first prototype snowmobile and sent it to Aspen, Colorado. At Independence Pass, 13,000 feet high in the Rocky Mountains, test crews encountered difficult conditions of warm air and icy trails and began to uncover serious design deficiencies. The prototype was slow and heavy because of a 15-horsepower engine overwhelmed with Kiekhaefer's insistence on such standard features as electric starting, heavy-duty transmission, and nearly-bullet proof chassis and cowling.

The first snowmobile was so bad that one customer wrote to John C. Hull, who Kiekhaefer had tapped to develop the snowmobile marketing analysis, and said, "You know, this thing is so top-heavy and unstable that it fell over just sitting in my garage."[18] Dealers started getting snowmobiles back from unhappy customers. By the time engineers fixed the design, the market had peaked, ending Mercury's involvement in snowmobiles.

An Outboard by Any Other Name ...

On November 23, 1971, Abernathy announced a new name for the company, which remains today. "Effective immediately the name of this Division is changed to Mercury Marine Division of Brunswick Corporation. ... Out of respect for Mr. Kiekhaefer, there will be no company-initiated fanfare over this change."[19] Since the 1972 models of outboards, sterndrives, and inboards were already in production, "Mercury Marine" wouldn't appear until the 1973 model line, breaking a 33-year tradition of having the Kiekhaefer name appear on its products.

With his famous name reserved for his own company once again, Kiekhaefer continued to arouse angst in his erstwhile colleagues at Mercury Marine, who fretted over Kiekhaefer's expected introduction of a new sterndrive. His son, Fred Kiekhaefer, was convinced that the whole idea of the new sterndrive was developed only to worry and irritate Brunswick. "It was all smoke and hocus-pocus, and a strategy to keep Mercury Marine nervous about what he was doing. He liked his revenge from the way they treated him, and I think he deserved to get every ounce of it."[20]

MERCRUISER
RIGHT FROM THE START

The MerCruiser line grew not only more powerful in the 1970s but also quieter and more environmentally conscious.

CHAPTER ELEVEN

A New Decade, A New Era

I said, "Carl, there's nothing I can do about the past. Nothing. But I can do everything about the future."

—Jack F. Reichert, 1987[1]

I N THE EARLY 1970s, IT SEEMED MERcury Marine could do no wrong. From $150 million in 1970, sales almost doubled to $300 million in 1972. That year, Brooks Abernathy was promoted to president and chief operating officer of Brunswick, and the Mercury reins passed to another Brunswick-trained executive, Jack Reichert.

The announcement came as a shock to shareholders because Reichert had spent most of his career in the bowling division, where he started in 1957. Reichert helped develop Brunswick's retail bowling business and eventually was named vice president of marketing for bowling. In 1971, he transferred from bowling to Mercury and took over Armand Hauser's position as vice president of marketing. He was named president of the subsidiary the following year. Reichert's appointment underscored just how important Mercury Marine had grown in stature and sales within the Brunswick family because the position was considered the number two spot in the Brunswick Corporation.

Reichert had a different management approach than Abernathy, who had successfully concentrated on Mercury's financial side. Reichert believed the company needed to emphasize marketing to balance its engineering wonders. He understood the value of Mercury's high-performance image but knew

Mercury had to represent something more, explained Roger Patterson. Patterson was the first person under the rank of vice president to move from Brunswick to Mercury, preceding Reichert by three months. "I was looked upon as the corporate spy," he said. "But once you dig in to work, you really become part of the scenery, and they soon got to trust me."[2]

Patterson recalled Reichert's marketing directive:

I distinctly remember him saying, "We need to promote family boating. We don't want to lose the image of us winning races, but the market is bigger than that." So we promoted family boating to the point where the symbol virtually became a Sea Ray–style boat with outboards or sterndrives, with families enjoying what they were doing.[3]

It's a Small World After All

Reichert's vision and strategy coincided with the opening of what has become an international

---

A Quicksilver switch panel for boats powered by Mercury sterndrives, outboards, and inboards. The panel integrates instrumentation for easy identification.

symbol of family recreation: Walt Disney World in Orlando, Florida. The amusement park opened in 1972. With more than 30,000 acres of woodlands and waterways, Walt Disney World was a natural place for Brunswick Corporation to enter, and in fact Disney had approached Brunswick with the idea of establishing a Brunswick Marina, but the cost was prohibitive. Joe Swift, Mercury's genius publicist, instead offered to lend several engines to Disney for use on workboats and have Ed LeDuc, a crack service manager in the area, maintain the engines. "Ed LeDuc is one of the great, unsung heroes of Mercury," noted Clem Koehler. Koehler, who retired as director of public relations from Mercury in 1996, said LeDuc was responsible for making sure the engines remained in good—and safe—condition, day and night, in addition to his normal daytime duties.[4]

Disney's fleet of Mercury-powered boats grew to include both workboats and small rental boats,

From the time Walt Disney World opened in 1972, Mercury supplied engines, parts, and expertise. Pictured here are Water Sprites.

1972 — Jack Reichert is appointed president of Mercury after Brooks Abernathy becomes president and COO of Brunswick.

1974 — Under an agreement with a Yamaha subsidiary, Mercury introduces the Mariner.

1972 — Mercury Marine initiates new relationships with Walt Disney World and Yamaha; manufacturing plants are built overseas.

and LeDuc was soon joined by several more mechanics. The exposure Mercury received more than offset the cost, which was low to begin with because the well-maintained Mercury/Disney engines could be sold second-hand at a good price, and Disney purchased parts and oil from the company.[5] (This informal relationship continued to grow. In 1995, Mercury and Walt Disney World entered into a formal alliance.)

Production and sale of Mercury engines expanded overseas the same year that the seed to the Mercury/Disney relationship was planted. The first European plant was completed at Petit-Rechain, Belgium, which began producing outboards in 1972. Operating as Mercury Outboards Europe, SA, the plant initially housed 200,000 square feet of manufacturing and warehouse space along with 125 workers. Immediately following the completion of the Belgium plant, a facility was constructed near Petit-Rechain along the Meuse River. The new plant acted as a support facility, with a distribution, training, and service center, as well as a test base. To meet its growing demands worldwide, Mercury built additional assembly plants in Toronto, Canada, and Melbourne, Australia; distribution and service facilities later reached into such areas

1974 — The MerCruiser plant in Stillwater, Oklahoma, begins operating.

1977 — Before leaving Mercury to become president and COO of Brunswick, Reichert reconciles Carl Kiekhaefer and Mercury Marine.

1975 — More than 3,200 workers strike for seven weeks.

as Latin America, Singapore, Malaysia, Japan, and New Zealand.

Demand overseas for Mercury engines grew slowly because doing business in foreign countries was extraordinarily difficult for any industry. The absence of quick transport, reliable phone connections, and the expense involved in sending cablegrams made selling in Europe an enormous hassle. Previously, Kiekhaefer simply had sold engines to an import/export company which, in turn, sold them in Europe. Service was, in a word, lousy because Kiekhaefer and the customer dealt with a middleman. In 1960, with air travel and communications becoming cheaper and more common, European dealers approached Kiekhaefer to see if they could buy directly from the company. That year saw the birth of International Mercury Outboards Limited, with Hauser its first executive.[6]

Two men, Reini Schniebner and Ted Tenner, spent the vast majority of their time traveling the world to set up distribution networks and service organizations. Between them they spoke French, German, Spanish, and even a little Swahili (which came in handy at one point), along with English. Tenner conducted local training seminars with

International Mercury Outboards Limited grew from the effort and frequent trips of only a few people. Below is a 1992 photo of Mercury's first European plant in Belgium, which began production in 1972.

mechanics, crude when compared with those today but effective nonetheless.[7]

Mercury's expansion overseas resembled its entry into Walt Disney World. Gradually, the company's presence expanded as opportunities presented themselves or were sought out. But not all of the opportunities would pan out as planned, including the joint venture with Yamaha that ultimately resulted in the Mariner outboard—and established Yamaha as a formidable competitor in North America.

The Best Laid Plans …

In 1972 (a year that proved extraordinarily busy for Mercury), Brunswick bought a minority interest in Yamaha manufacturing. The plan was to diversify distribution in the United States by adding another brand of outboard engine to cover the market. At the time, Mercury and OMC (with Johnson and Evinrude products) each maintained about 30 percent of the market. The second-brand strategy was meant to give Mercury another bite of the same apple, even though Mariner would, in effect, compete against Mercury engines.[8]

According to the terms of the agreement, Mercury provided Yamaha with second-generation blueprints and taught the Japanese manufacturer how to build quality engines, including methods to reduce corrosion and other metallurgical technology.[9] Under the joint venture, Yamaha and Brunswick owned equal shares in a Yamaha subsidiary, Sanshin Kogyo Company, manufacturer

Mariner was originally launched as a joint venture with a Yamaha-owned subsidiary.

MARINER® **OUTBOARDS**
A BRUNSWICK COMPANY

of outboard motors. The subsidiary sold all its outboards to Yamaha, which in turn sold the motors to Brunswick, which then marketed the motors under the Mariner name. For Brunswick, the new outboard was called Mariner to offer, according to Reichert, "an image different than that of the high-performance image of Mercury, using the idea of the 'ancient mariner' of reliability and durability."[10]

The first Mariner outboards were introduced to the Australian market in 1974 and to the United States and Europe in 1976, with worldwide sales and service headquartered in Fond du Lac. Charlie Alexander, who was vice president of Mercury engineering at the time, discussed the testing of engines in Australia:

We had Yamaha make some engines, and we put the Mariner label on them and painted them to our colors, and then we set up dealers in Australia. The question was—was it going to take more away from OMC or from Mercury? Well the test indicated that Mariner was a good idea and would help Mercury against OMC in the outboard end of the business.[11]

To help market the engine in the United States, Brunswick sponsored a fleet of three boats powered by Mariner to travel 4,500 miles up the Mississippi River. Mercury Marine next established a new business division in Fond du Lac called the Mercury Marine International Company (the successor to International Mercury Outboards Limited), headed by R. C. Anderegg under the supervision of Reichert himself.

The US Federal Trade Commission eventually ruled that the agreement hindered competition, ordering Brunswick to sell its shares to Yamaha to allow the Japanese company a foothold in the US market. By 1982, Mercury had become the second-largest seller of outboard motors in the United States, prompting the FTC to rule that as a North American competitor, Yamaha (prohibited from selling under its own name under the terms of the agreement) would increase competition and drive down prices.

Ironically, the reverse actually occurred, explained Jim Schenk, Brunswick vice president in charge of acquisitions in 1998:

Because Mariner, in effect, competed against Mercury, Mariner could not be sold through Mercury dealerships. Mariner was sold to second-tier dealerships as a higher-quality Japanese product made by Yamaha. So we really conditioned the market not only by virtue of having a competitive product from a design standpoint, but the dealers were conditioned to believe that Yamaha was a superior product.[12]

When the FTC forced Brunswick to sell off its interests in the Yamaha subsidiary in the early 1980s, Yamaha was able to raise prices on its Sanshin-brand outboards because they were considered premium.

The MerCruiser Explosion

Early in the decade, Mercury developed bigger, better, and more powerful engines for boating in all areas, including recreation, commercial applications, and racing. The company's crowning achievement in 1970 was the introduction of the first production six-cylinder outboard engines, the Merc 1150 and Merc 1350. Both carried a displacement of 99.8 cubic inches and a rating of 135 horsepower.

The next year MerCruiser added a ninth engine, the MerCruiser 888, to its line of sterndrive power packages. This package featured a 188-horsepower, 302-cubic-inch displacement (cid), V8 engine, a jet prop exhaust, and a power trim to adjust the trim angle for optimum performance.

Mercury again entered new territory by introducing its first jet drive. The MerCruiser Jet 400 utilized a 454-cid, V8 marine jet drive engine, which produced a strong 375 horsepower. The following year, MerCruiser introduced its Blue Water Inboard line, which it later dubbed the Blue Water In-Line engines, for use in offshore boating. These

Workhorse that thrives on deep blue water.

MERC 1150

Plenty of muscle here. Merc 1150 is the only 6-cylinder production outboard in the 115-hp class. Those two extra cylinders make a terrific difference in workpower, in wallop. Compare it for low-end torque. And for whooshing acceleration. Give it the gun. Watch what the starting bite does for a gang of skiers.

Dependability starts with the way it starts. Thunderbolt ignition and Perma Gap spark plugs snap this brawny Merc into life at the turn of the key. Direct Charge induction and "pulse-tuned" exhaust deliver more go per gallon. Like its big brother, the 1500—Merc 1150 has "cam-turned" pistons, huskier new driveshaft housing, and plenty more performance features. Plus extensive use of stainless steel for protection against corrosion.

For pushbutton control of the drive angle, get optional Power Trim. Trim in for more dig. Level out for more speed. Get instant adjustment for boat load and water conditions. And full tilt-up for beaching, launching, trailering. For great fun or heavy work, sign on the Merc 1150.

12

Left: The Merc 1150 was the first production six-cylinder outboard in the 115-horsepower class.

Below: Brochures offered a huge list of Quicksilver's accessories. A 300,000-square-foot facility was built to distribute the multiple product lines.

typewriter," she said. "When my boss arrived, he asked me to knock out a letter for him. I said, 'Well, I have a desk and a phone.' He just said, 'Never mind.'"[13] The plant started out as a small die-cast facility that later added lower drive unit assembly, explained Barry Eller, president of the MerCruiser Business Unit. With a cross-functional team, Stillwater had grown by 1998 to include research and development, engineering, die-casting, machining, assembly and painting, distribution, sales, and marketing—all contained in more than 750,000 square feet of space located on 250 acres with more than 1,100 workers.[14] (In the 1990s, Stillwater would become the test case for the business unit concept that eventually

engines offered superior dependability and performance for both recreational enthusiasts and commercial boaters who wished to risk the high seas. Initially, MerCruiser offered four models, the 198, 228, 255, and 330, which ranged from 198 to 330 in horsepower, and from 305 to 454 cid.

MerCruiser's popularity led to the construction of a plant dedicated to MerCruiser production. The construction of the new manufacturing facility in Stillwater, Oklahoma, was the most ambitious undertaking of the decade. "Reichert wanted to set up a plant down in the South someplace," recalled Alexander. "An independent, stand-alone facility that would be more manageable than a huge facility and one that was dedicated to MerCruiser. And that's how Stillwater got going."

The Stillwater operation officially opened in 1974 with Lois Cutburth, its sole employee, sitting in a downtown office while the plant was under construction. Cutburth remembered when all she had was a desk and a phone. "Not even a

permeated Mercury's structure throughout the decade.)

An additional factory and three distribution centers were acquired in Canada to serve markets north of the border, thus expanding dealer organizations and increasing the range of markets. The first of these was in Mississauga, Ontario, and others followed in Vancouver, British Columbia, and Winnipeg, Manitoba.

Mercury grew back home as well. A 300,000-square-foot, $3.5 million worldwide distribution center in Fond du Lac was built in 1973 for the storage and distribution of Quicksilver parts and accessories. The facility used a new computerized inventory system, warehousing, and an order-pulling system that greatly increased the efficiency of the distribution to other distribution centers, boatbuilders, and dealers throughout North America and the world.

That same year, both the Fond du Lac and Oshkosh facilities were expanded and improved. Fond du Lac saw the addition of a 74,400-square-foot warehouse at Plant 4 to store die castings and forgings. By 1974, Oshkosh Plant 5 had become the largest producer of propellers in the world at a rate of 500,000 a year. Likewise, Plant 5A, an addition adjacent to Plant 5, was the largest producer of outboard aluminum cowlings in the world and produced most of the machined hydraulic parts used by Mercury. A new 19,200-square-foot engineering test facility was also added to Plant 5.[15]

Healing Wounds

Reichert became president of Mercury at a time when the American economy was beginning to flounder from the dual effects of recession and inflation. Three months after Reichert took over as president, the federal government froze wages

and prices for 90 days, a move that brought no relief.

Reichert navigated these crises with skill. By 1977, the year Reichert became Brunswick's president and chief operating officer, sales had doubled from $168 million to $300 million.[16] In Fond du Lac, the company employed 6,000 people—one-fifth of Fond du Lac's population. Heady with success, Mercury prepared to unveil a new line of V6 engines. The product's introduction, however, sparked the strike of 1975, when 3,200 workers walked off the line.

The dispute stands out because it contrasts with Mercury's long history of good labor relations. Essentially, the disagreement erupted over the definition of what constituted a new product. Mercury's V6 engine was its first such product. As such, the company wanted to institute a new pay scale for workers as provided for under the labor agreement. The union, on the other hand, wanted to maintain the old individual incentive pay scale, maintaining that the V6 should not be considered a new product. Both sides dug in their heels. For seven weeks, workers from Cedarburg, Fond du Lac, and Oshkosh picketed in front of the plants. "One thing led to another, and the next thing you know everyone was on strike," remembered Dave Martin, public relations coordinator in Placida, Florida.

The strike quickly turned nasty. The test center in Florida was shut down because Florida-based personnel were sent to Wisconsin to turn out

Above: Jack F. Reichert brought a marketing focus to Mercury throughout the 1970s.

Right: A dispute over what constituted a new product led to the strike of 3,200 workers in 1975.

ACTING LOCALLY

IN THE 1970S, ENVIRONMENTAL CONSERVATION surfaced as a national issue. Environmental awareness had taken root in the 1960s, and during his first term, President Richard Nixon had established the Environmental Protection Agency. California became the first state to require emission reduction equipment in pas-

senger cars, when it enacted legislation in 1971. At the same time, Arab members of OPEC began threatening to use "the oil weapon"—the threat of embargo—to influence world opinion and politics. The 1973 oil embargo brought home the fact that fossil fuels were not infinite in supply.

Mercury had been involved in developing engines more efficient and friendly to the environment for some time. The company had made several developments that increased fuel efficiency by 50 percent between 1961 and 1971.[1] Mercury was the first to eliminate overboard oil drainage by returning crankcase oil to the combustion chamber, where it was mixed and burned with existing fuel.

Other innovations included the Perma-Gap spark plug, designed specifically for use in two-cycle marine engines, which ran dirtier than four-cycle automobile engines and were much more prone to fouling. The Perma-Gap, unlike conventional spark plugs, used a center electrode made of a tungsten alloy that greatly reduced corrosion, giving it a much longer life. The Perma-Gap, along with the existing Thunderbolt fast-voltage ignition, virtually eliminated fouling and preignition.[2]

The company also developed the Direct Charging system in 1970. This breather system precisely controlled the fuel-air induction into the cylinder and the removal of the burned charge through a unique design of transfer passage, ports, and piston timing. The design created a much more efficient intake of burn and exhaust, yielding greater fuel economy and producing more power from the same size engine.[3]

Noise pollution was another concern for Mercury in the 1970s. Focusing on sound reduction, the company developed in 1971 what was known as the "dead room," a special chamber constructed in Mercury's research headquarters in Fond du Lac. This 28-by-31-foot room was designed to absorb sounds from Mercury engines from both internal and external sources.[4]

Mercury also became involved in several studies to examine the effect of engine exhaust on marine life and ecosystems. Beginning in the late 1960s, first at the famous Lake X and later at MerCabo, near Placida, Florida, and the Fox River Testing site in Oshkosh, Mercury helped to create the Marine Exhaust Research Council to seriously investigate this issue.

To closely monitor the effects of the manufacture of marine engines on the environment, Mercury designed an internal housekeeping program to regulate operations and monitor possible causes of pollution. Internal Mercury Action Group on Environment (IMAGE) researched and developed a system of pollution control throughout its manufacturing, distribution, and testing facilities.

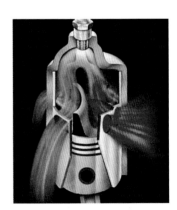

Left: With tungsten center electrodes, Perma-Gap plugs resist corrosion when fired.

Right: The Direct Charging induction systems improved fuel efficiency and horsepower.

engines, a move that didn't sit well with the striking workers. Mercury staffed the production line with virtually every available hand, including clerical and middle management, to turn out engines. "I remember some cars were sabotaged," Martin said. "Two guys would walk across the parking lot, one with a hole in his pocket filled with nails that would fall out. The other guy walked behind him, trying to stand the nails up. Someone from Mercury would then come out with a magnetic sweeper and try to pick them up."[17] The tense situation lasted seven weeks, but Reichert regularly and directly met with workers, answering their questions as completely as he could. The strike was settled on October 9, 1975, and relations eventually improved.

The V6 engine had a number of "firsts" built into it. It was, for instance, the first to use "power porting," a piston design that provided an additional source of fuel and air that significantly increased horsepower without the expense of research and development, retooling, testing, and design of additional new parts. Beginning initially as a racing innovation, power porting wasn't offered to the public until 1976 as the 175-horsepower Merc 1750, later dubbed the Black Max. It was referred to in a 1976 product brochure as "the meanest, toughest, most beautiful machine we've ever built."[18] By 1978, Mercury was producing an entire line of the Black Max engines, ranging from 150 to 200 horsepower.

The ability to understand and communicate with people had always been one of Reichert's particular strengths, as Mercury's relations with its dealers demonstrated during this period. He attended dealer functions on a regular basis and was instrumental, of course, in attracting dealers to the Mariner outboard. In 1977, Abernathy promoted Reichert to president and chief operating officer for the entire Brunswick organization.

Before he left for his new job, however, Reichert had one more task he wanted to accomplish—healing the rift between Kiekhaefer and Mercury Marine. This he did, using a technique similar to the one used by Henry Kissinger in 1973 to resolve the Arab-Israeli wars: shuttle diplomacy.

Rose Smiljanic, Kiekhaefer's long-time secretary and confidant, had remained friends with Sharon L. Trescott, who in 1977 was the executive secretary to Reichert and who had

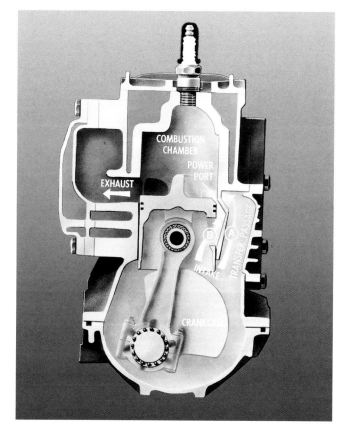

Above: Mercury's power porting, shown in this drawing, delivered more air/fuel supply and compressed the vaporized fuel for the ignition spark, resulting in even better performance.

Below: The logo for the 1976 Black Max 175-horsepower outboard, "the meanest, toughest, most beautiful machine we've ever built."

been Kiekhaefer's dictation secretary for many years. Kiekhaefer had to visit Florida on business, and Smiljanic spoke about his trip with Trescott, who in turn mentioned Kiekhaefer's need to go to Florida to Reichert. The quick-thinking Reichert recognized a golden opportunity to begin to soothe the injured feelings Kiekhaefer had for his old company. "I said to Sharon," Reichert remembered, " 'I want Mr. Kiekhaefer to fly down on our airplane.' And she said, 'Well, Mr. Reichert, there's no way to do that unless you ask him.' " Within minutes, Reichert and

Trescott were in the car on their way to Kiekhaefer's house on the ledge.

It was Reichert's first trip to Kiekhaefer's house, and as they drove up, Carl and Freda Kiekhaefer were returning from a short walk. "He asked me very gruffly what I wanted," Reichert recalled. "I asked him how he was feeling, and he said, 'I'm fine. I'm feeling all right, very cold. Well, what do you care?' " Reichert explained that he had driven up to offer him the Brunswick jet for his flight to Florida, mentioning how much easier it would be for him than a commercial flight:

And he said, "No!" And I said something charming like, "Goddammit Carl! Stop being such a stubborn German! For your information, I'm a German from Wisconsin, too, and I can be just as stubborn as you can." Well, I guess that kind of shocked him, because Carl was used to people caving in, I guess. So Mrs. Kiekhaefer said, "Carl, stop being such a jerk," or worse, and "Why don't you see what this young man is all about?" So, because of her, he said, "Okay."[19]

Kiekhaefer was confused over Reichert's generosity and apparent concern. Shortly after his flight to Florida on the Brunswick Sabreliner, Kiekhaefer said, "The most confounding experience of the whole thing was Reichert driving up to my house and insisting on flying me to Lake X in a company jet. This happened within three hours after I made reservations on a commercial flight, which would have been just as practical. Of course, it was a nice gesture, but I can't for the life of me see them doing any favors suddenly, seven years after my resignation."[20] Kiekhaefer eventually realized, somewhat to his embarrassment, that Reichert was sincere, and wrote, "You are the first officer of Brunswick who has shown any such compassion or kindness since my resignation in 1970, when I thought I had left in good standing."[21]

Reichert continued to convince Kiekhaefer of his sincerity. When Kiekhaefer returned from Florida, Reichert surprised him with a phone call that solidified their trust and friendship. Mercury had prepared a special pictorial montage of its history, which included an image of Kiekhaefer and his early engines and accomplishments, and Reichert wanted him to have a special copy.

Kiekhaefer met with Reichert in his office at Mercury for over an hour, and although the conversation began as a tirade on Brunswick, from that day on, the two men were good friends. Within months of that meeting, in May 1977, Reichert was appointed president of Brunswick and Alexander became president of Mercury Marine. Kiekhaefer was proud that Reichert had asked his advice about who should be the next president of Mercury. "I naturally recommended Charlie Alexander," Kiekhaefer said. Reichert also recognized a good opportunity. He made sure that Kiekhaefer Aeromarine Motors, Kiekhaefer's newest endeavor, would get some component manufacturing business from Mercury.

The following year, when Mercury was hosting an open house, Reichert and Alexander surprised Kiekhaefer by inviting him to a special guided tour of the plant. "We put him on a golf cart," Reichert said,

Opposite page: Carl and Fred Kiekhaefer break down the high-performance engine that won the APBA championship in 1973.

Below: Mercury's 1974 outboard line, from the punchy Merc 40 (far right) to the brawny Merc 1500 (far left).

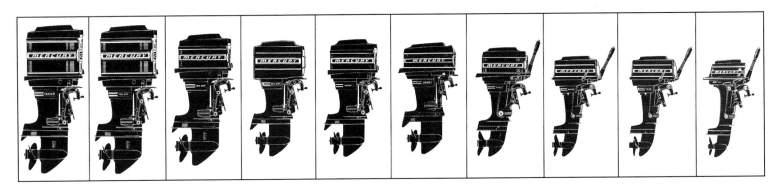

new products. All the while, he was courting the long-term buyers of high-performance marine accessories and opened markets with both large and independent boatbuilders throughout the country. Foremost among his new approaches to race-proven products for the sport boat market were the K-Plane, a line of hydraulic trim-tabs for medium to large sportboats, and a family of high-performance throttle and shifting controls, which would eventually be known as Zero Effort Controls. Fred Kiekhaefer also introduced a new line of high-efficiency propellers, based on the successful designs evolved from competition.

Then Fred was recruited by Price Waterhouse, the nationally acclaimed business consulting firm, which recognized a great potential in his unique background and education. Even though his starting salary wasn't up to his expectations, he realized that the new challenge, located in Boston, would be "in the very worst case, a funded graduate school where I could pull away a lot of the things that I felt I still needed to know." He was a hard worker, and yet in some ways still had to prove himself because of his famous father.

When Fred drove away from the company in the summer of 1978, it marked the beginning of a long and slow decline in the health and fortunes of his father. For Kiekhaefer, not having a son to rely on in times of business stress or to share the dreams and vision of better days ahead for the business meant a feeling of working toward no special purpose. The objective all along, or so he would say to just about everyone except Fred, was to create a strong and durable legacy for his son, to carry on the industrial tradition of Kiekhaefer innovation and excellence for another generation.

Fred eventually would carry on the tradition, right back at the company his father had founded. But Mercury Marine and the entire marine industry were about to face one of the cyclical downturns that had thinned the weaker competitors from the herd.

"and we took him through the plant, and it was like he had died and gone to heaven. And the people were so happy to see Carl, it was unbelievable."[22]

Years later, Reichert considered "bringing back the old man" as one of his greatest accomplishments. "I think that my helping to bring Carl Kiekhaefer back into the company was the best thing I did," Reichert said.[23]

A Sunset Glow

Things were even looking up for Kiekhaefer's enterprise, Kiekhaefer Aeromarine Motors. His son, Fred Kiekhaefer, had become the new executive vice president of Kiekhaefer Aeromarine Motors with the gusto and enthusiasm of youth. He began to cut wasteful engineering programs, streamline accounting procedures, and develop and refine

Reliable engines and accessories have made Mercury synonymous with fishing.

CHAPTER TWELVE

SURVIVAL THROUGH INNOVATION

It was hell.

—Jack Reichert, describing the 1988–1992 recession
in the marine industry[1]

CHARLIE ALEXANDER'S ENGINEERING talents had been honed by Carl Kiekhaefer's relentless drive and unwillingness to admit defeat. In his 26 years at Kiekhaefer Mercury, Alexander helped bring many innovations to market, such as the tilt-up shock absorber and the Jet Prop underwater exhaust. In 1977, an engineer once again assumed the helm when Alexander was named president of Mercury.

Alexander had a special ability to explain technical subjects in understandable terms, and many engineers cut their teeth under his tutelage. With sales brisk in the 1970s, Alexander's knack for innovation promised to make available a slew of new products. Unfortunately, however, his promotion coincided with another recession. By 1979, interest rates had reached a crushing 18 percent, unemployment had risen to 10 percent, and a looming threat of another Mideast oil embargo led President Jimmy Carter to consider banning weekend boating. The proposal was never enacted, but the public discussion of such an act dampened sales across the industry. By the end of 1980, Mercury Marine had lost $11.2 million.

Alexander moved quickly to cut costs. He implemented strict controls of inventory and closed four feeder plants in Cedarburg and Oshkosh, Wisconsin, and instead opened a modern, efficient component parts plant in Juárez, Mexico. He also made a particularly painful decision.

"In June of 1980, we were suddenly out of racing," recalled Fred Hauenstein, director of the Hi-Performance Group. Hauenstein continued:

Alex said, "We're not spending that kind of money because we don't have that kind of money to spend." For the rest of that season, OMC kept sending out their team engines to their team guys, and we, in essence, had the plug pulled well enough that we couldn't afford to send our engines out.[2]

Sterndrive and inboard production was transferred to Stillwater, Oklahoma, and the workforce was reduced by more than 3,000. A fourth plant, the original dairy barn converted by Kiekhaefer, was destined for shutdown in 1981. "It had served well for 35 years," noted Alexander, "but this year it was consolidated into the large complex in Fond du Lac to reduce overall costs."[3]

Alexander's efforts paid off. By 1981, Mercury Marine had returned to profitability, with earnings of $38.2 million on $461 million in revenue. A new

---

A Quicksilver speedometer. Mercury's own speed of growth was interrupted by a recession and the threat of another Mideast oil embargo.

computerized system called Material Requirements Planning aided the cost-cutting measures, feeding the company millions of dollars previously tied up in inventory. The money saved was used to purchase new machine tools and to consolidate and build new factories. The company also set up a task force to purchase and connect computer terminals to Mercury's IBM 360 mainframe, the first of a series of computer control systems for manufacturing.

Though the national economy bottomed out in 1982, Mercury's market share grew, particularly in the bass boat market. The revamped 60-degree, V6 loop-charged Black Max was upgraded from a 175-horsepower, 2.0-liter engine to a rating of 200 horsepower and 2.5 liters. Eventually, the Black Max would be upgraded to produce 300 horsepower.

Meanwhile, Mariner expanded overseas, thanks to a sudden decision by OMC to terminate its relationship with distributors. OMC sent a letter out to its distributors in 1976 telling them, in the words of Roger Miller, retired senior vice president of Mercury International:

> *Adios. Next year OMC is selling direct to dealers in Europe. The method by which they did this absolutely infuriated their customers because some of them had been long term—40 to 50 years. Virtually overnight they were told they were out. Their anger turned vengeful, and the best way to get back at OMC was to take the Mariner product line and do everything in their power to stick it to OMC.*[4]

Mercury knew it would eventually have to move toward direct distribution as well to stay competitive. When the time came to begin phasing out distributors, however, executives chose a slower, more sensitive schedule. Attrition made the task easier because several distributors had grown older and wanted out of the business, particularly in the 1970s when a vicious price war wreaked havoc on profit margins.[5]

With demand on the upswing, more assembly lines were added at Fond du Lac so the company could produce every popular model each week. The goal was to increase the availability of all models when demand for a particular model grew. This would help Mercury avoid the high cost of storing a lot of inventory. But high inventory wasn't a problem at this time because Mercury's factories could barely keep up with the orders. From the early 1980s until the start of the next downturn, in 1988, Mercury ran at full capacity with plenty of overtime.

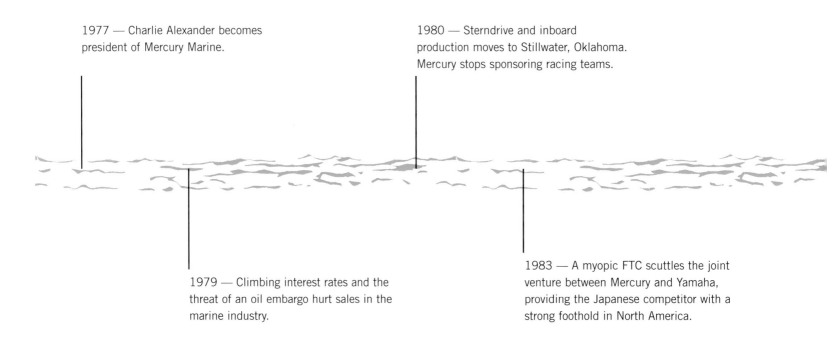

1977 — Charlie Alexander becomes president of Mercury Marine.

1980 — Sterndrive and inboard production moves to Stillwater, Oklahoma. Mercury stops sponsoring racing teams.

1979 — Climbing interest rates and the threat of an oil embargo hurt sales in the marine industry.

1983 — A myopic FTC scuttles the joint venture between Mercury and Yamaha, providing the Japanese competitor with a strong foothold in North America.

A New Organization

Stronger competition was coming from Yamaha Motor Company, which had entered into a joint venture with Mercury Marine in 1972. The FTC order that compelled Brunswick to sell its shares in Yamaha (after Mercury helped establish Yamaha's reputation in the United States) coincided with a monetary exchange rate that benefited the Japanese. With Yamaha entering the picture as a competitor, the Mariner and Mercury lines moved closer together in terms of sales and engineering. When fuel-injected Mercury engines were introduced in 1983, for example, the innovation was also included in Mariner.

"It was a big change when we decided to move Mercury and Mariner closer together," said Denny Sheller, who started in 1983 as a Mariner salesman before becoming vice president of sales, marketing, and service for MerCruiser.[6] Alexander agreed. "Mariner was a good idea and helped Mercury against OMC in the outboard end of the business,"

Alexander said in a 1998 interview. "Now, of course, it's worldwide, and although it never achieved the volume of Mercury, it's been a strong addition to the business. And it's certainly taken business from our competitors."[7]

The streamlining continued—and not only for Mercury. In 1982, the Whittaker Corporation, a conglomerate involved in healthcare, energy, aerospace, marine, and specialty chemical markets, mounted a serious challenge to Brunswick's 138 years of independence by trying to buy the company. Whittaker had its eye mainly on Brunswick's Sherwood Medical Industries, a highly touted subsidiary that accounted for a third of Brunswick's earnings. Brunswick Corporation knew that Whittaker would most likely sell off most of the rest of Brunswick to pay down its debt—a maneuver that was definitely not in Brunswick's best interests—so it

The FTC tore up the joint venture between Mercury and Yamaha to spur competition in the marine industry.

1983 — Kiekhaefer dies and is buried at St. Charles Cemetery in Fond du Lac.

1986 — Brunswick buys the two largest boat companies in the world, Sea Ray and Bayliner.

1985 — Richard Jordan becomes president of Mercury. The Marine Power Group is consolidated under one organization.

1989 — A full-blown recession pummels the marine industry. David Jones is named president of Mercury.

responded to the hostile takeover by selling Sherwood Medical, the very asset that Whittaker desired most.[8]

Brunswick was successful in staving off the takeover, but at a high cost. Jack Reichert who took over as CEO in 1982 following the retirement of Abernathy, made a pivotal decision to decentralize operations and restructure the entire company, noted the *Chicago Tribune*:

Charles Alexander (left) handed over control of Mercury to Richard Jordan.

Burdened with excess manufacturing capacity, Mercury could follow the lead of archrival, Outboard Marine Corp., by closing high-cost Northern plants and moving the bulk of its manufacturing to new, mostly non-union operations in the South. But ... a full-time task force of a dozen key managers from a variety of disciplines decided on a radically different approach: redoing the company's sprawling outboard-motor plant in Fond du Lac, without interrupting production. Mercury ... bet that it would be able to improve productivity and quality by increasing the flexibility of man and machine.[9]

Decentralizing operations was probably the least controversial move Reichert made in light of the prevailing advice he kept getting—sell off Mercury and the rest of the recreational business. "People were telling me that Sherwood had been our only good operation," Reichert was quoted as saying in the book, *Brunswick: The Story of an American Company.* "I couldn't accept that opinion. Because of the trauma at the time—there's no doubt we were an injured company—many people lost sight of the fact that we were in good businesses and that we had leadership positions in some of them."[10]

By this time, Alexander had handed leadership of Mercury over to Richard Jordan. He remained a vice president reporting to Reichert, however, and continued to work on special technical assignments.

Under Jordan, the four divisions of the Marine Power Group—Mercury, Mariner, MerCruiser, and Quicksilver—were consolidated into one organization consisting of engineering, sales and service, marketing, manufacturing, human resources, finance, quality, international distribution, and legal and industrial affairs.[11] The rationale behind the consolidation was, according to Jordan, "to improve efficiency and become more responsive to customer needs."[12]

QUEST

Jordan was only partially successful in his initiatives. He began the QUEST program after the Mariner line was transferred to Fond du Lac and after the FTC scuttled the joint venture with Yamaha. QUEST, an acronym for Quality by United Effort Secures Tomorrow, was originally devised to improve the efficiency of the entire subsidiary, but it never went beyond the manufacturing segment. The prospect of these changes made European customers nervous. Roger Miller recalled, "The guy who distributed Mariner in Europe had always been delighted, and all of a sudden he found out his engines were going to be built by Mercury Marine. His perception was that he liked the Yamaha engines."[13]

The QUEST program had many facets. It acquired new equipment and upgraded the old. It provided new and ongoing supplemental training for employees. It also reorganized production lines into cell manufacturing and U-lines. And it implemented the just-in-time (JIT) inventory control and other practices to attain flexibility in manufacturing.

The QUEST Modular Plant dedicated specific areas of the Fond du Lac plant, called modules, to manufacturing one specific product. These modules were separated into the power head, gearcase, and driveshaft housing modules. At the same time, the JIT system provided a continuous line of what were called trim cells—small, highly organized areas of dedicated manufacture that greatly improved efficiency and reduced the number of workers. JIT also provided for immediate feedback on quality control.

Mercury Marine's drive to slim down its manufacturing was dubbed "the possible dream." The Marine Retailers Association of America recognized the company's achievement by naming Mercury "Manufacturer of the Year" for 1984. But the full potential of QUEST was never realized because strong demand lessened the sense of urgency.

Jordan's forte was production, but he also helped bring marketing and engineering closer together. Under Kiekhaefer, engineering led the company with nifty new engines, leaving it up to marketing and sales to persuade customers to buy them. Gradually, the focus shifted so that marketing found the niche and then worked with engineering to fill that niche.

A Wave of Consolidation

Prior to the 1980s, the industry had several clearly defined players. Companies such as Mercury and OMC made engines, while companies such as Sea Ray and Bayliner made boats. "Back in the good old days, there were engine companies and there were boat companies, and the two didn't mix," said Mike Gyorog, vice president of marketing for the Quicksilver unit in 1998. "Lots

of things have happened between those relationships. What's happened is boat companies and engine companies have become aligned with one another out of ownership, out of equity investments, out of long-term supply agreements, or whatever the nature might be. It's made the industry much more complicated."[14]

Reichert began exploring the idea of consolidation in the marine industry in 1984. The concept was called BMT, short for Boat, Motor, Trailer. Under the concept, Mercury—and not the dealers—would package the three elements and sell them to the consumer. Two years later, Reichert and Jordan worked out a plan to buy Bayliner Marine Corporation and Sea Ray. The acquisitions were completed at a cost of $775 million, and shortly thereafter, OMC purchased five small boat companies, including Four Winns and Hydrasport. Reichert's foresight, however, had let Brunswick acquire the leading boatbuilders in a very short amount of time, surprising many who thought personalities would clash during the dealmaking.

The clashes would come later. Brunswick entered the boat market when credit was relatively easy to obtain and the interest on mortgages for such items as boats could be tax deductible. Both boat companies added new attractions to their lines. Bayliner unveiled the Maxum line of pleasure boats, and Sea Ray was getting ready to bring out four new models in 1988, bringing its product line to 50.

Mercury products in the 1980s reflected the industry's movement to customer-friendly boating. People wanted boats that ran seamlessly, started effortlessly, and spent as little time in dry dock as possible. Accordingly, one of the most significant innovations of the period was the fuel-injected V6 outboard with a key-start. "Customers liked it," said engineer Rick Davis. "They were often rated at the same power level as a carbureted model, but it had the fuel-injection system on it that was nice to start, and it ran nicely."[15]

The unit automatically mixed oil and gas through the fuel pump, which eliminated the

The QUEST program improved manufacturing and quality, but it was never implemented on a company-wide scale.

hassle of pre-measuring—or guessing—to obtain the proper mixture. This process delivered oil to the engine only when needed and automatically adjusted the oil level as the motor reached higher rpms.

Around the same time, the company developed the first throttle and shift tiller that offered steering control, speed, and stop buttons—plus forward, neutral, and reverse—all in a single control that could be operated by one hand. This not only increased the ease of operation but greatly reduced the risk of changing gears at the incorrect speed.

Driven by the new technology and rising expectation for hassle-free boating, Mercury's newer engines blended the company's passion for speed with the changing market. Three new fishing models were introduced (3.6, 18, and 25 horsepower), as well as two new V6s, one 225 horsepower and one 300 horsepower. The latter was an extremely powerful outboard that weighed about 700 pounds less than a comparable inboard or sterndrive, accounting for a significant decrease in fuel consumption. It also offered a new option for Hydrasteer, a power steering that provided a steering fin on the gearcase, thus greatly easing the process of steering an outboard. Mercury also offered two new outboards in 1989 for use in offshore fishing—the 250- and 275-horsepower V6 models.

The Thruster line of electric motors was expanded by the Thruster Plus, delivering 28 pounds of thrust on 32.5 amperes. This allowed the user the new option of acquiring an electric motor on a larger boat. Thrusters were offered in three versions: remote controlled, deck manual controlled, and transom mounted controlled.

To complement the Thruster line of electric motors, Mariner soon expanded into the fishing market with the Stalker 12- and 24-volt electric trolling motors, which offered the almost silent

Fishermen on their way out in a Sea Ray, powered by a Mariner engine. Brunswick acquired Sea Ray and Bayliner.

The Thruster line of electric motors gave fishermen more control to get in and out of tight spots.

Whisper Drive. These motors offered 21- and 28-pound thrust from the 12- and 24-volt models, respectively. They also offered the machete propeller, engineered for easy operation in heavily weeded back areas of lakes and rivers.

In 1988, Quicksilver introduced a line of marine generators in 4-, 6.5-, and 8-kilowatt gas generators, plus a new 8-kilowatt diesel model. These generators were designed to be used as auxiliary power units on boats, either at dock or at sea.

The next year, Quicksilver entered new territory by introducing a line of inflatable boats capable of handling a Mercury or Mariner outboard. Manufactured by a firm in Korea, the Quicksilver boats quickly became a profit center for Mercury. "We've really tried to utilize the notion of making this fun craft available at an affordable price," noted Gyorog. "It's generally used as a dinghy or tender, but we try to promote the fun of boating and the fun that's specifically associated with an inflatable boat."[16]

Production agreements with foreign manufacturers helped Mercury expand its presence around the world. One such agreement took place in 1982, when Brunswick and Escorts, Ltd., of Delhi, India, decided to produce Mercury outboards for local distribution. The agreement was described by Mercury President Richard Jordan as "the best opportunity we have had to supply Mercury products to this potentially vast market."[17]

Likewise, Mercury entered into a contractual relationship with Orbital Engine Corporation, Ltd., of Perth, Australia, in 1987 to further develop an idea Orbital had been working on. Orbital was working to create a unique two-stroke engine design that used a direct fuel-injection process. High-pressure air injected the fuel mixture directly into the cylinder after the exhaust ports had closed. This design would offer boating markets a two-cycle outboard engine that would burn significantly cleaner and more efficiently than traditional two-cycle designs. "We were dealing with a technology that was on the cutting edge relative to invention," said Dennis Banks, head of engineering in 1998. "Orbital had a lot of skills that, in a particularly narrow segment, were ahead of others in the industry."[18]

The company signed a second agreement for the joint development of Mercury products overseas in 1988 with the Tohatsu Corporation of Tokyo. The deal called for Tohatsu to manufacture and market outboard motors for the United States and world markets. In another joint venture with a foreign company that year, Mercury signed a five-year agreement with Wei Min Machinery Factory to produce and distribute outboards in China. The new company under the joint venture was called Jiangxi Marine Company, Ltd., in Leping, and would share Mercury's technology and the existing facility to produce a selection of outboards for use in China and South Asia.

Gathering Storm Clouds

Mercury's outstanding sales volume had a dark side; however, fear of competition and the principle of listening to the customer became "a little tarnished," noted Jim Hubbard, senior vice president and chief of staff for Mercury. "With all the success we were enjoying, it was easy to adopt the point of

REELING IN THE MARKET

D AWN CASTS A PURPLE HAZE IN THE SKY AS THREE men move their gleaming Ranger bass boat down the ramp to the water. They fire up the Mercury outboard and power their way to the first fishing spot of the day, trading stories from countless other fishing trips.

Mercury outboards and fishing is a relationship forged with the common purpose of moving from spot to spot quickly and returning under reliable power so the ritual of bragging can begin. This seemingly simple goal can be thwarted if the engine has a history of ill use or spotty maintenance. A breakdown during a weekend walleye or bass fishing trip is bad enough. Engine failure during a tournament, when the fishing community has its eyes on an angler's prowess, is heartbreaking. "The one thing tournament fishermen can't tolerate is equipment failure," Clem Koehler observed. "So having our service teams at tournaments cemented loyalty to our brands among the top pros."[1] It occurred to Ham Hamberger, then vice president of marketing, and Atlanta branch manager Chic Morris that they ought to send a few mechanics to tournaments. The mechanics found themselves inundated with people who needed help.

Mercury started out with a modest remuneration for several of the top pros and soon developed solid relationships with such bass legends as Ricky Clunn, Roland Martin, Tommy Martin, and Hank Parker, all of whom wield a tremendous amount of influence. Those aspiring to greatness upgrade their equipment on a regular basis by taking their cue from the pros.[2] Eventually, Mercury Marine became a key tournament sponsor for the Bass Anglers Sportsman's Society (B.A.S.S.), the premier bass fishing organization in the United States, until 1988, when Mercury Marine ceased sponsorship. Mercury returned to leadership of B.A.S.S. sponsorship in 1998.

Jim Kalkofen and Ed Huck helped repeat this performance for Mercury in the walleye arena. The walleye is a freshwater fish that was clearly gaining strength and popularity in the Great Lakes region and in the western reservoirs of the Missouri River in the early and mid-1980s. Like the bass in the southern United States, the walleye is a four-season fish and one that's good for the table (especially fried, with just a hint of dill, lemon, or pepper). Working with top pros and guides such as Al Linder, Mike McClelland, and Gary Parsons, Mercury launched its own walleye tour and sponsored a number of independent tournaments at the same time. "We wanted to identify Mariner with the folks who were out there fishing every month for the whole year, the hardcore anglers who worked hard on the water," Kalkofen explained. Kalkofen proposed, and Koehler endorsed, the start of the Mariner Walleye Classics series in 1985. Mercury provided service support while walleye professionals, under contract with the company, served

Fishing in the wind can be very productive if one knows what the wind does to walleye feeding patterns. Control over the boat at these times, however, is crucial to success.

Mercury's commitment to the walleye and bass sports meant more to participants than just a marketing scheme. "You can't miss a day or even half a day when you're fishing competitively against the top anglers in the world," Kalkofen noted.[3] He continued:

Mercury recognized that from day one. We held special seminars on service, and on how to maintain engines, what to look for, and what to do if something happens during an event. The fishermen appreciated the attention shown them by Mercury, and I was fortunate enough to be there to direct a lot of those activities. The foresight and willingness of Clem Koehler and Ed Huck to budget these activities still shows results today.[4]

Left: A top walleye guide and competitor, Mike McClelland is also author of several books, including the one shown here.

Below: Mariner is heavily involved in the Manufacturers Walleye Circuit Tournament Trail. Pictured here is the 1986 tournament held in Spring Valley, Illinois. Left to right: Jim Kalkofen, Bob Propst, Mike McClelland, and Bob Kaczkowski.

as emcees to the no-entry fee events. Interest in walleye skyrocketed. In a decade, participation in the sport had doubled from 4 million to more than 8 million.

Mercury developed products specifically for the walleye market. Walleyes are much more skittish than bass. While bass will attack bait bigger than itself, walleyes will run from an engine's sound and turbulence. The size of boats grew, as did the engines that powered them, beginning with a 45-horsepower engine, and then a four-cylinder, 50-horsepower engine. They proved extremely helpful for backtrolling through the waves, staying on the exact spot, and keeping the bait at the same depth. The company continued to modify its mid-range outboards as boats grew bigger.

executives wanted to put their dealers in a competitive position in the fishing boat markets and arranged a special marketing agreement with dealers to compete directly with Tracker. Mercury Powerboats became its own organization with its own management.

But purchasing and organizing such a diverse mix of boatbuilders was one thing; managing this array of competing cultures proved quite another. A lot of time and money would be spent trying to make Mercury Powerboats operate as originally planned. Futhermore, Mercury's relationship with other boatbuilders wasn't helped by the fact that it owned its own boat manufacturers. Some boatbuilding customers felt that Mercury Marine, by getting into the boat manufacturing business, had become a direct competitor. A realignment of some boat brands and some engine brands also complicated matters.

Left: Mercury expanded its presence and its product lines all over the world, particularly in Australia, where the company had entered into a joint venture with Orbital Engine Corporation to develop a two-stroke engine.

Below: Boats such as this Fisher were popular and easy to obtain, but the federal government changed the tax laws in the late 1980s. People could no longer write off interest on consumer loans and credit cards.

view, 'Why should we be too concerned since we are selling everything we can make?' "[19] The problem, Mercury executives have candidly acknowledged, was a belief that an engine with the label "Mercury" would sell itself. Tracker Marine shattered this notion when its president and founder, Johnny Morris, signed a five-year agreement to buy engines from OMC. Tracker had been Mercury's largest customer, buying more than 16,000 engines a year.

Brunswick purchased several more boat companies to make up for lost volume: Marine Group, Inc., of Murfreesboro, Tennessee, which manufactured fiberglass fishing boats; Mon Ark Boat Company of Monticello, Arkansas, which manufactured aluminum fishing boats and pontoon boats; Fisher Marine, Inc., of West Point, Mississippi, a private manufacturer of aluminum fishing boats; and StarCraft Power Boats Corporation of Topeka, Indiana, manufacturers of aluminum and fiberglass fishing, pleasure, and pontoon boats.

The companies were organized under their own division known as Mercury Powerboats. Mercury

Mon Ark was one of four boat companies purchased by Brunswick to make up the volume of engine sales lost when dealers switched from Mercury to competitors.

Events out of the control of the marine industry, however, were about to knock the bottom out of the market.

Mercury Marine was working in high gear to keep up with seemingly endless demand, but the era of good feeling came to an abrupt end with the onset of another recession—and an unexpected stab to the heart inflicted by the federal government. In 1990, a luxury tax looked like a politically acceptable way to reduce the federal deficit, a growing sore that was reported on almost daily. Items such as boats priced over $100,000 were subject to a 10 percent tax because, as one columnist put it, "there's no changing the perception that boaters are rich and so somehow deserve to be whacked."[20]

With the presidential election cycle beginning, wealth became a political issue along with the huge federal deficit. The tax was enacted January 1, 1991, the worst possible timing because the economy had already gone soft and was widely blamed for the 73 percent drop in boat sales as compared to peak levels in 1988.

But there was a more insidious reason behind the marine industry's rapid slide into recession. Beginning in 1988, the Internal Revenue Service no longer allowed people to deduct the interest on car loans, boat mortgages, or credit cards. The change was made quietly, but the effect was immediate because consumer purchasing stopped cold, taking industries across the board by surprise.

Between 1989 and 1991, Mercury Marine watched its revenues fall by half a billion dollars. The layoffs implemented to staunch the flow of red ink were unprecedented, the most severe taking place between May and September of 1989, when Mercury laid off almost 1,000 employees, reducing its workforce to less than 2,700 in Fond du Lac.

Jordan was replaced by Tom Weigt that year, but Weigt's initiatives failed to turn the company around. It was hardly comforting to know that the entire industry was suffering. Prior to the luxury tax, the National Marine Manufacturers Association estimated that more than 8,000 workers in the industry would lose their jobs as a direct result of its enactment.[21] (The combination of the IRS action and the tax actually cost more than 20,000 jobs in the marine industry by 1992, according to the organization's estimates.)[22] Sales dropped almost 60 percent, and the number of boats sold fell from 520,000 in 1988 to 260,000 in 1990. As Reichert described the situation, "It was hell."[23]

Mercury Marine was in the midst of an economic tailspin—the worst it had ever navigated. The company had gone from a record of technological innovation and booming sales at the decade's beginning to economic turmoil and near disaster by the end. The 1990s offered Mercury and Brunswick a dubious prognosis at best, and it would take all of the company's perseverance to bring it back to its former glory.

A new leader with a new approach was needed. At the end of 1989, David Jones was given the opportunity to turn Mercury Marine around.

Death of a Pioneer

Carl Kiekhaefer did not live to see his beloved marine industry torn apart. Ever since his bypass operation in 1977, Kiekhaefer had scheduled check-ups at the Mayo Clinic, and for a few years, doctors gave him cause for optimism and peace of mind. However, he was later diagnosed with lymphoma, and by March 1983, tests performed at the Fond du Lac Clinic confirmed that Kiekhaefer's lymphoma needed immediate treatment.[24] By May, Kiekhaefer was prohibited from travel, and he began to prepare for the inevitable.

The acquisition of StarCraft Power Boat Corporation gave Brunswick a line of products that included fishing, pleasure, and pontoon boats.

Mercury paid tribute to its founder, lauding Kiekhaefer as a "man of imagination, an engineering genius, a gifted and energetic pioneer constantly searching for better ways to do things."

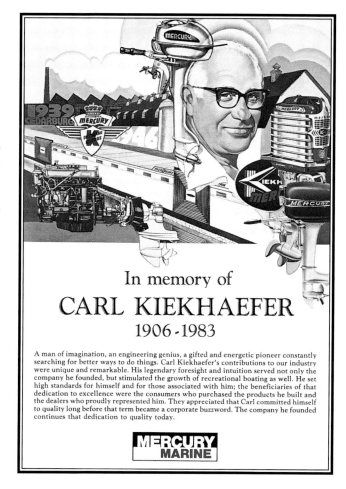

In memory of
CARL KIEKHAEFER
1906 - 1983

A man of imagination, an engineering genius, a gifted and energetic pioneer constantly searching for better ways to do things. Carl Kiekhaefer's contributions to our industry were unique and remarkable. His legendary foresight and intuition served not only the company he founded, but stimulated the growth of recreational boating as well. He set high standards for himself and for those associated with him; the beneficiaries of that dedication to excellence were the consumers who purchased the products he built and the dealers who proudly represented him. They appreciated that Carl committed himself to quality long before that term became a corporate buzzword. The company he founded continues that dedication to quality today.

MERCURY MARINE

In July 1983, Reichert notified Kiekhaefer that the Brunswick Foundation was establishing a $50,000 scholarship in Kiekhaefer's name in recognition of his outstanding contributions to both the industry and the community. This was an honor usually reserved for retiring chief executive officers of the corporation, but Reichert felt that Kiekhaefer's special place in Brunswick history warranted the special consideration. But Kiekhaefer turned the honor down. In a letter to the newly installed general manager of Mercury, Jordan, Kiekhaefer wrote: "As much as I appreciated your considering honoring me in this way, it is my feeling that I would not have any control on how my name would be used, as well as not knowing in advance of other details regarding the issuance of this award. It would be almost like putting my name on something 'carte blanche.'"[25]

Kiekhaefer was admitted to the hospital a number of times before he died on October 5, 1983. Moments before he died, at 6:27 a.m., he gently squeezed the hand of the nurse who was at his side, and the old engineer issued his last order: "Tell Charlie to forgive me." His final words acknowledged the suffering he had caused Charlie Strang, not only by selling Mercury to Brunswick in the first place, but by turning his back on his great and loyal friend when he wrongly accused him of betrayal. Kiekhaefer had spelled it out in a letter to Strang years earlier: "No one need ever remind me of the great

mistake I made in my lifetime. Thank goodness you were young enough to recover, but it's too late for me to start over."[26]

Kiekhaefer was buried at St. Charles Cemetery, within view of the plant he had built on the ledge above Fond du Lac. Once, while reflecting on his own mortality, Kiekhaefer had said, "Wherever I'm going, heaven or hell, I do hope they have an engineering department."

Mercury Marine powered the fleet of 125 event support boats at the yachting, rowing, canoeing, and kayaking competitions during the 1996 Olympics.

CHAPTER THIRTEEN

NEW CHALLENGES

Mercury has that rare mix: the courage to grow but the discipline to contain. We have enthusiasm for innovation yet control of the bottom line. It's taken many decades to achieve both in just the right quantities. There's going to be a new legend here. And so the Mercury mystique continues.

—George W. Buckley, Mercury Marine president, 1998[1]

FROM THE MOMENT TRACKER MARINE SIGNED its five-year agreement with OMC in 1987, Brunswick CEO and Chairman Jack Reichert and his executive team had committed themselves to getting Mercury's biggest customer back. They made the effort quietly and without Mercury's knowledge.

Mercury, meanwhile, had been struggling with high turnover in leadership until David Jones became president at the end of 1989. Morale had ebbed almost as low as sales. Mercury had to lay off 20 percent of its workforce as the entire industry went from selling 419,000 outboards at retail in 1988 to about 220,000 in 1990. The struggle to make the different boat companies function together with the outboard business just wasn't working. Boatbuilders not part of Mercury Marine resented buying motors from a perceived competitor; at the same time, the boatbuilders Mercury did own did not appreciate the engine package deals they had to implement. The recession made an already tense situation untenable.

Not long after Jones became president, Mercury Powerboats was disengaged from Mercury to become Brunswick Fishing Boats, a move designed to give it a separate personality. The new Brunswick division now had to face the marketplace on its own, leaving Mercury to concentrate on its own task of improving its marine propulsion business. "The happiest day of my professional life," reminisced Roger Patterson, "was the day they left. The cultures were so different we could not make them work."[2]

By 1991, the bottom had dropped out for the Brunswick Marine Group, with sales plunging 60 percent compared to the previous year and losses exceeding $30.5 million on sales of $1.4 billion.[3] Reichert was forced to make the painful but necessary decision to lay off a total of 8,000 people— more than 40 percent of the workforce— from the marine businesses. Recounting these gloomy days in the book *Brunswick: The Story of an American Company*, Reichert said, "Too often in business one looks only at the financial numbers in a crisis. But in any calamity such as this, those who suffer most are people. And many were unavoidably hurt by what had to be done."[4]

Mercury was stuck with high inventory, trying to sell to dealers and boatbuilders who were no longer on the most friendly of terms with the company. From the moment he stepped through the

A microprocessor in the Mercury DFI 200 injects the optimum mixture of fuel and air into a carefully designed cylinder. The engine burns as much as 80 percent cleaner than standard two-stroke engines.

door, Jones was determined to steer the company's personnel—on every level and in every way—back in touch with the customer's needs. His first three years as president would be marked by frequent field trips, accompanied by his staff, to customers to get to know them again and to understand their goals and concerns. "David was a master at that," recalled Roger Patterson.

He was totally focused on getting us out there to re-establish relationships that had been lost in the late 1980s because of our acquisition of the boat companies, and even because of our arrogance towards our approach to the dealer. David said that wasn't going to be how we work. We formed dealer councils, bringing our customers into the decision-making process.[5]

Left: A Force 25 outboard engine.

Above right: The Force Outboards logo. Force Outboards was consolidated in 1991, when operations moved from Hartford to Fond du Lac.

Jones sent every vice president and every director to meet the dealers, recalled Gerald Neisen, a former director of engineering. "Not only that, he told them to write up a report on each visit—who was happy and who wasn't. He told them to get together in the auditorium and share notes. It was a great learning experience."[6]

Jones began his career at Mercury as a product manager for the MerCruiser line and advanced quickly to become director of marketing. He helped expand MerCruiser until it boasted the broadest sterndrive line in the industry. Jones left Mercury in 1984 and eventually went to work for US Marine Corporation as

1990 — Mercury Powerboats becomes Brunswick Fishing Boats.

1991 — Sales for the entire Marine Group fall 60 percent, and more than 8,000 people are laid off.

1990 — Fred Kiekhaefer joins Mercury's Hi-Performance department as David Jones institutes programs to increase customer satisfaction.

1992 — Mercury is divided into five business units.

David Jones served as president of Mercury for eight years, second only to Carl Kiekhaefer in length of time.

head of what would later be called the Force Outboard operations. He repeated his success with Force Outboards, which was purchased by Brunswick as part of the US Marine/Bayliner acquisition of the 1980s. After his circular route back to Brunswick, Jones watched his company's fortunes decline. He volunteered to try to lead Mercury out of the hole in which it found itself. Brunswick listened to Jones' ideas to restore Mercury's position as industry leader and gave him the chance to implement them.

The philosophy of "the customer is always right" was only part of the strategy. Jones had to restore morale among the workers; otherwise the company-wide mission would be dismissed as typical corporate jargon. A holder of a PhD in mechanical engineering, Jones advocated

intense employee development and training, critical if workers were to compete on a global scale. His first year as president was marked by more training programs implemented than ever before. Executives took one-week annual training courses to learn how to reduce defect and cycle time.[7]

At the depth of the marine industry's downturn in 1993, Mercury Marine demonstrated its commitment to workers by providing benefits such as the Mercury Marine Family Medical Center. This 8,200-square-foot facility, equipped with examination rooms, lab and x-ray facilities, as well as an on-site pharmacy, was designed to meet the primary care medical needs of Mercury employees, retirees, and dependents.[8] It proved so successful that in 1997, the MerCruiser plant in Stillwater, Oklahoma, contracted with MediCenter to build and manage a medical facility to serve its 1,100 employees. The Stillwater clinic opened for patients in early 1998.[9]

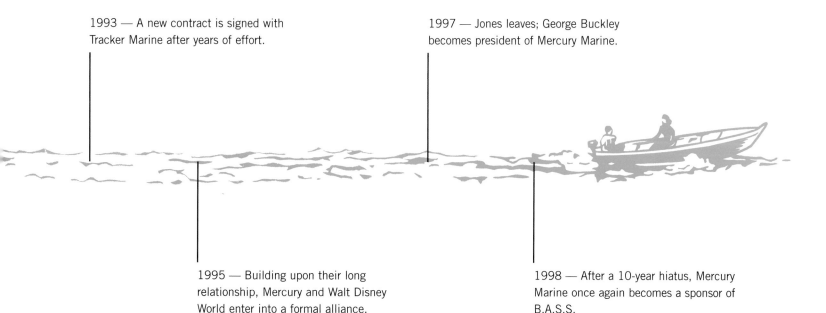

1993 — A new contract is signed with Tracker Marine after years of effort.

1997 — Jones leaves; George Buckley becomes president of Mercury Marine.

1995 — Building upon their long relationship, Mercury and Walt Disney World enter into a formal alliance.

1998 — After a 10-year hiatus, Mercury Marine once again becomes a sponsor of B.A.S.S.

The clinic was part of a three-point health, wellness, and prevention program. The program screened for potential health problems and established preventative measures such as diet and exercise programs and regular preventative testing. The final element focused on addressing problems such as stress and family management, substance abuse, and other emotional health issues. This service supplemented Mercury's existing health plan.[10]

Other programs were introduced to help employees improve themselves. The Personal Development Center and the Employee Assistance Program gave educational and emotional support to workers. The emphasis on training and education spread to the dealer network with the establishment of Mercury University in 1996. The university consolidated many of the courses offered to dealers under one umbrella, a concept that went far beyond any program offered by competitors. Merc U became part of the strategy to improve overall service and treatment of customers by retail marine dealers. The courses are marine-specific, and Mercury dealers show their value by paying for their employees to attend the classes.[11] "This industry as a whole doesn't deliver the necessary level of service to the customer after he buys a boat," said Denny Sheller, vice president of sales, marketing, and service. "Other leisure industries are vying for the boating dollar these days, so we need to fix that."[12] In its first two-and-a-half years, Merc U had assisted more than 300 individual dealerships and their employees.

Mercury University eventually led to MercuryCare. Research by Mercury showed that for too many boaters, the happiest two days are the day their boat is bought and the day it is sold. MercuryCare was launched to counter this with a more positive tag line, explained Senior Vice President Jim Hubbard. "We're going to make the best two days of a boater's life Saturday and Sunday."[13] Initiated in 1999, the program worked through dealers by giving them incentives to provide five-star service levels. As one brochure explained: "When we allow ourselves to let the focus of the discussion slip back to product alone and disregard the consumer's desired experience, we cheapen the relationship. That's why we focus on including the MercuryCare branded services in the package price of the boat in all our advertising, training materials, and consulting sessions."[14]

An Independent Spirit

The frequent visits with dealers and the emphasis on individual improvement on all fronts were actually a reflection of what was happening within

Mercury Marine's Family Medical Center opened in 1993 and was designed to meet the primary care medical needs of Mercury employees.

Fred Kiekhaefer, son of the "Old Man," Carl Kiekhaefer, became president of the Hi-Performance unit of Mercury Marine.

Mercury Marine. Old habits and beliefs changed dramatically because Mercury Marine was reorganized into individual business units. Each unit—and each unit president—would be held accountable for performance. Prior to 1990, Mercury had been a functional company in which the whole entity could be divided up into broad categories, such as finance, marketing, engineering, sales, and manufacturing. The business units were organized along product rather than relationship lines. In other words, a boat company or marine retailer that bought outboards and sterndrives (each its own business unit) could count on support from individual managers from both units. This permitted experts to focus on certain goals, such as lowering emissions in outboards.

But before fully committing all of Mercury to this new, more independent structure, the concept was first tested on what was then known as the Performance Products Division, headed by none other than Fred Kiekhaefer, son of founder Carl Kiekhaefer. The Kiekhaefer name returned to Mercury Marine in July 1990, when the company merged Kiekhaefer Aeromarine Motors with Mercury Performance Products.

Fred learned the business at his father's knee, and when Carl needed a coronary bypass in 1977, Fred ran Kiekhaefer Aeromarine Motors. As the executive vice president of Kiekhaefer Aeromarine, he needed only a year to turn a loss to a modest 12 percent profit. Fred also restructured the company to take advantage of its strong image and good reputation over the long term rather than build a few very expensive offshore engines for a small and volatile market.

Fred left Kiekhaefer Aeromarine Motors to work for Price Waterhouse, the nationally acclaimed business consulting firm. Following his father's death, Fred bought out Kiekhaefer Aeromarine Motors and became its president. A new generation of sterndrives introduced in 1988 was among the enticements that attracted Reichert and Brunswick to Kiekhaefer Aeromarine, besides the obvious advantage of Fred Kiekhaefer's engineering and entrepreneurial skills. Following their introduction, the

sterndrives won four national and five world championship offshore titles. The first time these new drives were used in competition resulted in a world championship at the 1988 Offshore World Cup Races, held in Key West, Florida. The sterndrive that helped win the victory was renamed the MerCruiser 6, one of a number of innovations including the Mercury Pro Max Series, the Mariner Super Magnum Series, the MerCruiser Hi-Performance Series, the Sport Master Gearcase, and the Kiekhaefer Zero Effort Controls.

When he took over Performance Products, the business was more of a "cost center," Kiekhaefer said in a 1998 interview:

It was not genuinely a business. Its primary role was promotion, enhancing the brand image, without losing too much money. It was done for the greater good of Mercury brands. In my mind, it was a strategically conceived but tactically implemented combination. I was told, "Do what you want with this Kiekhaefer group, but you must combine Mercury's

Performance Products business with the Kiekhaefer product line." David Jones was only six months in the saddle, and he had his hands full with bigger issues.[15]

MerCruiser was the next line that was turned into a business unit. Barry Eller was recruited as general manager, and in 1990 all functions except

marketing were relocated to Stillwater, Oklahoma. The only way to improve product quality and speed up product improvement, according to the management philosophy, was to locate the engineering and marketing staffs close to each other. Communication between the groups immediately improved. Meanwhile, the business unit concept gave employees a sense of ownership and personal pride in their product line. Of course, there was the natural danger of each unit becoming too independent and acting in its own interest instead of the interest of Mercury, so business unit leaders and upper management continually reviewed the structure to prevent this from occurring.

The new structure ended the historical separation of the Oshkosh-based product engineering for outboards and MerCruiser from the manufacturing sites. Outboard product engineering was moved into a new area at Plant 15, and the product engineering for MerCruiser and its engineering staff were moved to Stillwater.

By 1992, Jones oversaw five distinct business units—Outboards, MerCruiser, International, Quicksilver, and Hi-Performance. He directed Kiekhaefer to find a way to turn Hi-Performance into a true profit center, with public relations and media exposure as a beneficial side effect. Kiekhaefer was given a free hand to turn the unit around. That year, Kiekhaefer made an important and controversial decision: "We had to stop being the sugar daddy promoter for all competitive marine water sports." He continued:

We had hooked our constituents by sponsoring their race circuits and subsidizing their engine programs, and then stopped sponsoring racing. We stopped

Decisions on whether to fund promotion or engine development in the Hi-Performance unit had to be made. Engine development won.

being spokesmen, paying for special events, and we put the emphasis on getting the magazine publicity through product placement.[16]

Kiekhaefer said many offshore racing enthusiasts "are still mad at me," but that difficult choices had to be made about whether to fund a racer or an outboard development project.

The Payoff

The revolution inside Mercury continued with the decision to sell outboards to independent boatbuilders in 1992. Jones sought out boatbuilders interested in selling boat/motor/trailer packages to their dealers and then sold them Mercury, Mariner, or Force (which later became known as Mercury Classics) engines to be installed or packaged at the boat factory before shipment to dealers. Learning from the past, executives made sure the plan was sensitive to existing customers. In fact, Reichert personally met with several longtime Mercury dealers, all of whom knew Reichert from his days as company president, prior to the plan's implementation. A provision was made to ensure that boatbuilders seeking to buy outboards had to agree to sell BMTs only through authorized dealers. Some of the boatbuilders had quality retail dealers that did not sell Mercury or Mariner engines. This strategy gave Mercury a chance to expand its dealer network.

The seemingly endless string of difficult choices made and hard miles traveled by Mercury and Brunswick executives finally began to crack the pall that had hung over the company in the early 1990s. Fred Kiekhaefer had succeeded in his mission to turn Hi-Performance into a profitable business. "We went from a losing operation five years ago to the company's biggest gainer in percentage terms," said Tom Mielke, who started marketing in the Hi-Performance Division in 1994. He continued:

The marketplace is becoming much more mature. You've got mature boaters who are buying higher-end equipment, and you have newcomers who look like they are mature boaters. ... If they're going to get a boat, dammit, they're going to get a good one ... a high-performance power set.[17]

A Challenging Environment

Mercury engineers fielded another technical curve ball when the US Environmental Protection Agency instituted tough standards for powerboat engines that many in the industry protested as too stringent. The EPA, however, was only mirroring public concern and awareness worldwide as regulations and requirements tightened around the globe. "People used to be content starting an outboard and having a huge, blue cloud of smoke. Those days are gone," noted Rick Davis, vice president of outboard engineering. Davis continued:

You get that big cloud, and it's an embarrassment to the customer. He's looking for a cleaner product, a better-running product, an environmentally responsible product. And that's going to continue and even grow stronger. The customers are growing up, and we're going to

Top: The MerCruiser Bravo Three drive, which was wildly successful in the market.

Mercury Marine Propeller Company made high-performance propellers such as the Typhoon (left) and the High Five (above) props.

work on maintaining a sophistication level to satisfy them.[18]

In 1993, Mercury entered into an agreement to co-develop a four-stroke power head for outboard motors with its former partner, Yamaha Motor Company, Ltd. The motors were manufactured separately and independently marketed by each company. This expanded variety, but more importantly, developed low-emission four-stroke engines as an alternative to standard two-stroke outboards.[19]

That year, Mercury introduced the Sport Jet 90, the first of a successful and ever more powerful line of engines. Developed at the request of Bayliner for use on its new "Jazz" Jet Boat, as well as the Sea Ray "Sea Rayder," the original Sport Jet used a 6.43-inch mixed flow, single-stage jet pump with four-blade aluminum impeller.[20] It produced 650 pounds of thrust, was rated at 90 horsepower, and was designed primarily for entry-level mini-boats needing shallow running clearance.[21] The line was later expanded to include the Sport Jet 120, 95 XR, and 120 XR, with such refinements as larger jet nozzle and tapered impeller thrust to provide better acceleration, greater top speed, and improved low-end thrust.[22]

The market found a place for jet-powered boats, and customer demand soon led to a series of upgrades. A V6 175-horsepower model was developed, followed by 210 and 240 horsepower engines, which led Bombardier, Inc., in 1999, to choose the Sport Jet to power its line of SeaDoo jet boats.[23]

Innovation in 1993 wasn't confined to the Sport Jet, as MerCruiser introduced its first twin-propeller sterndrive, called the Bravo Three.[24]

Old Friends, New Relationships

In 1993, Reichert announced that a new contract had been hammered out with Tracker Marine. The news was an important shot in the arm because it allowed Mercury to restore and strengthen relationships

with dealers and fishing enthusiasts, particularly in the Midwest.

Tracker had grown from a small company specializing in bass fishing gear, called Bass Pro Shop, in the 1970s to become one of the nation's best-known boatbuilders. Its founder, Johnny Morris, credits his father with the idea that the bass boat had evolved from the old john boat into a high-performance fiberglass boat. During this period, Mercury's Ham Hamberger visited with Morris frequently and was responsible for setting Tracker up as a Mercury dealership, which was the genesis of the boat/motor/trailer concept. "Ham sensed that what we were doing might be a good thing for Mercury and a good thing for the industry," Morris commented. "He saw we were deeply committed to fishing."[25] Although the decision to set Tracker up as a dealer was not popular with existing Mercury dealers, the BMT package made boating more affordable, encouraging many first-time buyers. Hamberger, who eventually joined the Tracker organization and became its president for six years, was one of the men who

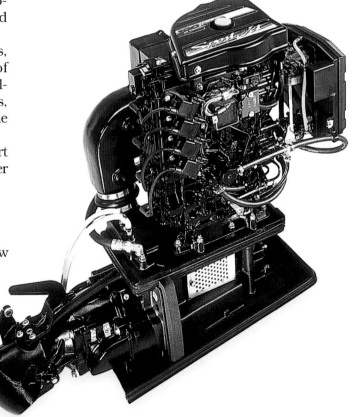

The Sport Jet 120 used a 120-horsepower outboard power head.

established Mercury as the engine of choice for bass fishermen.

The Tracker deal meant more than just volume and revenue; it marked a significant shift in the relationship between Mercury Marine and its parent, Brunswick Corporation. Customers, known on a first-name basis by people in both Brunswick and Mercury, could now call either organization. "Unlike a lot of large companies, we're really working with our divisions at a customer level," noted BC executive Jim Schenk. He explained:

It's interchangeable in terms of working as a team to put our customer teams together. I'm on a first-name basis with most of Mercury's accounts and work in tandem. This is part of Brunswick's strength now, which is the irony of it all, that Carl Kiekhaefer hated Brunswick and tried to keep them out.[26]

In 1995, the team concept extended to the longstanding relationship between Mercury and Walt Disney World in Orlando, Florida, to include Brunswick's boat companies and outdoor recreational products. Since 1972, Mercury has supplied engines, parts, and expertise to the world-renowned family recreational park. Mercs powered everything on the water, from the large barges that launched fireworks to the small, sturdy, and safe Water Sprites. In fact, these small craft gave Mercury an opportunity to test its engines under the most engine-rattling conditions. Joe Wisner, director of sports and recreation at Walt Disney World, said the average Mercury engine at Disney gets between 1,000 and 2,000 hours of use each year, the equivalent of 10 or 20 years of normal usage. Wisner said Mercury was hired to operate Disney's dry dock facilities. Today, nine Mercury technicians service Disney's fleet of more than 300 marine engines. "We've got a fairly major contract with them," Wisner said. "It works to our advantage because we concentrate on our business, and they provide us with a model of a state-of-the-art service center, where they can try new techniques and products. Mercury has taken the partnership with us and, I think, improved upon it."[27]

Mercury also participated in the development of the next generation of small powerboats to replace the aging fleet of Water Sprites and other craft. Disney happily gave the production of the new craft,

called the Water Mouse, to Mercury. Later, the Water Mouse boats were replaced by the Sea Raycer boat designed by Sea Ray and manufactured by Boston Whaler. Mercury continues to maintain a fleet of 170 Sea Raycer boats at Walt Disney World. "They were pretty innovative in the way they developed these things," Wisner noted. He continued:

For our application, you almost have to have a bullet-proof craft because of the wear and tear. We try to get the craft to perform to a very tight spec. Running on a 9.9 Merc, it has to take up to 300 pounds, and the hull is designed to break the plane and run between 22 and 23 miles an hour. The boat was also designed not to go faster than that when it has about 100 pounds in it, so the craft doesn't shoot up to 30 or 35 miles an hour when younger kids are in it.[28]

It was Mercury's entry into Walt Disney World that enabled Brunswick Corporation to forge an even stronger partnership by becoming the Outdoor Recreation Partner of the Walt Disney World Resort in 1998. "Disney chooses its partners carefully," noted Adrian Sakowicz, Brunswick's director of marketing services. "Clearly, Disney was impressed with the product quality and professionalism that Mercury Marine brought to the table and wanted to expand upon it."

Besides Mercury's distinction as the Official Marine Power of Walt Disney World, Brunswick was able to expand the partnership to include products from other areas of the corporation. Sea Ray and Bayliner comprise Disney's Official Boats, and Boston Whalers serve as Official Patrol Boats. Brunswick also supplied Roadmaster bicycles, Zebco fishing equipment, American Camper camping equipment, and Igloo coolers.

In 1995, Mercury saw the fruition of another long and successful partnership, this one with Orbital Engine Corporation, Ltd., of Perth, Australia. The two companies consummated the relationship by signing a joint venture agreement to design, manufacture, and market fuel systems for low-emission, two-cycle engines. These new fuel systems used Orbital direct injection technology and were capable of outperforming the 2006 proposed emissions standards. The system works by injecting fuel directly into the cylinder using a fine blast combined with air after the exhaust ports are closed. The system reduces emissions by 80 percent.

With the first success behind it, the relationship took a further step in 1995, when Mercury introduced a line of engines known as DFI, or Direct Fuel Injection. The engines rely on a microprocessor to inject fuel and air into a specially shaped cylinder precisely when the exhaust valves are closed, thus burning as much as 80 percent cleaner than the standard two-stroke engine. Engine temperature, barometric pressure, engine speed, and exhaust pressure were also monitored. Mercury offered these engines (later released as the OptiMax series) rated at 200 horsepower initially, then later at 135, 150, and 225 horsepower. The first production models rolled off the assembly lines on January 22, 1996, and were ready for dealers by March. Two years later, OptiMax had achieved the pre-eminent market share position in high horsepower, low-emission categories.

"We've always been a pleasure craft supplier, and our true immediate growth opportunities are to look at commercial applications," said Sean Cummings, then vice president of marketing/outboards and general manager of Canadian operations. "Of course, with the strength of the Latin American and Asian markets, there's still tremendous opportunity in the pleasure side there as well."

On the World Market

The opportunities Cummings alluded to span the world, but to compete effectively on a global basis required additional training. For decades, Mercury Marine met the demand of international recreational boaters who enjoyed sport fishing, waterskiing, and cruising. Employees now had to redesign products to handle the rigors of the international commercial market. Engineers traveled to the corners of the earth to experience first-hand some of the most

In 1995, Mercury Marine and Walt Disney World entered into a formal alliance. As part of the agreement, Mercury supplies the family-friendly Water Mouse, the successor to the Water Sprite.

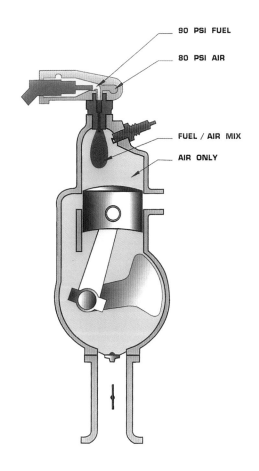

90 PSI FUEL

80 PSI AIR

FUEL / AIR MIX

AIR ONLY

Introduced in 1995, Direct Fuel Injection increased efficiency and reduced exhaust emissions.

abominable weather on the planet, from the ice-cold waters off Norway to the corrosive summer heat of the Yucatan peninsula in Mexico. Though the weather is dissimilar, the expectations of the fishermen remain the same. Day after freezing or scorching day fishermen brave the elements to do their work; they need an engine that will do the same.

The engineers learned how the engines were used and in what conditions. The resulting designs vastly improved the durability and reliability of the engines that would see these fishermen safely home. With improved products, Mercury's international sales grew.

Retired vice president Roger Miller dedicated his 30 years with Mercury to building an international network of distribution. His overall approach was to start in new markets using established distributors

in the area. The Mercury subsidiary International Mercury Outboards Limited would acquire the distributor in markets or regions showing impressive growth and sell directly to the dealer. OMC inadvertently helped this strategy in the 1970s, when it abruptly decided to terminate its distributor relationships, many of them long-standing. Mercury moved in to fill the gap. At the same time, Mercury has, where appropriate, phased out distributors in a more gentle manner, preserving relationships while methodically reaching the same goal. This sequence was repeated throughout Europe. Today, one finds dealer-direct relationships in Sweden, Norway, Denmark, Germany, Holland, France, Belgium, and Italy.

In 1995, Theo Wiggill succeeded Roger Miller as president of International. Wiggill was general manager of the Australia, Asia/Pacific Business Unit (known within Mercury as AAP) before he accepted the challenge to direct all international efforts.

AAP was the pioneer behind several initiatives that have helped make Mercury Marine one of the largest unit seller of boats—about 25,000 boats a year, including fiberglass, aluminum, and inflatable—in the world. One of these initiatives is the reverse-OEM (short for original equipment manufacturer) concept. Under reverse-OEM, Mercury buys boats made by contracted manufacturers. These boats are labeled with Mercury brands and are packaged with Mercury engines and sold through the company's dealership network. (In the United States, engines are sold to boat companies, which then sell the product through their own dealer networks.) The concept of reverse-OEM has spread to all other international regions.[29]

In Australia and New Zealand, Mercury goes dealer-direct. In Southeast Asian nations served by AAP, such as India, Korea, and Vietnam, among others, Mercury relies on a network of quality marine distributors.

The Asia/Pacific unit was instrumental in making Mercury one of the first marine companies to open in China. In 1998, Mercury established the Suzhou Taihu Mercury Club and Marina. The club is located in an area reserved for recreation by the Chinese government, where boats are sold, leased, rented, and serviced. Next to the marina, the club serves food and beverages to members, Chinese nationals, and international businesspeople. A distribution center, also next to the marina, serves the growing markets throughout China that are currently handled by a mix of dealers and distributors.[30]

Suzhou is just one of 11 such areas designated as "vacation zones," and Brunswick Corporation is committed to investing capital in this unique joint venture. If the vacation zone concept proves successful, Mercury is in an ideal position to develop other water-related recreational facilities in future zones.

On the other side of the globe, in Europe, Mercury consolidated all of its logistical and distribution capability under a single multilingual Customer Call Center and Distribution facility in Belgium. The center operated under the Marine Power Europe Business Unit (MPE), which also adopted the reverse-OEM strategy with great success. Acquisitions, moreover, have strengthened Mercury's boat-building position. The company purchased all of the stock of two Swedish boatbuilders, Uttern and Ornvik, as well as St. Cast

of France. The St. Cast acquisition, which produced the Armor and Arvor brands of boats, put MPE into the sailboat market for a short time.

Mercury also acquired equity in a Finnish boat company called Askaladden and a specialized large inflatable boat company called Valiant in Portugal.

Toward the end of the 1990s, Mercury Marine expanded its international distribution, service, and sales offices in Canada, Europe, the Andean region of South America, Brazil, Australia, New Zealand, Singapore, Malaysia, China, and Japan. The company sold outboards, sterndrives, and boats that exceeded more than 20 percent of the total sales worldwide for Mercury.

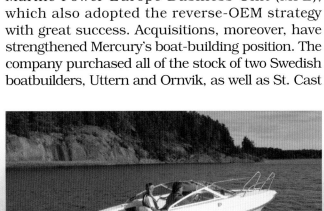

Mercury Marine is one of the largest unit seller of boats in the world, selling more than 25,000 fiberglass, aluminum, and inflatable boats each year. In 1999, the company acquired a number of international boatbuilders, including Sweden-based Uttern (left) and Portugal-based Valiant (above).

Below: This modern and cost-efficient plant opened in 1979 in Juárez, Mexico.

Passing the Reins

Jones' tenure as president of Mercury Marine has so far proved the second longest, after that of Carl Kiekhaefer himself. Jones stepped down from the position in 1997, after eight years as president. Peter Larson, who took over Brunswick from Jack Reichert two years earlier, commended Jones for leading Mercury back to its position of market preeminence. Jones later became the chairman and CEO of rival OMC, in another example of the leadership positions held by former Mercury executives throughout the marine industry.

When George Buckley took over as president at Mercury, he was new to the marine industry but had been an avid boat enthusiast for years.

George Buckley succeeded Jones as president. A native of Sheffield, England, Buckley was a newcomer to the marine industry, having served as president of the Electric Motors Division of Emerson Electric Company. He previously held executive positions with British Railways, GEC Turbine Generators, and Detroit Edison Company.

Buckley's plan called for "denominator management," or, in simpler language, "bottom line protection." Numerator management represents the growth portion of the plan. Buckley said:

Essentially, what you do is provide a stable financial platform for the company for the future. The thing I've been trying to do is bring discipline to the company. When I arrived, expense-tracking was minimal. People were allowed to add resources almost at will. Obviously there was a tacit understanding that that cost you money, but there was no control mechanism in place. So now we are controlling and understanding the costs.[31]

Outboard, for instance, was in a weak profit position when Buckley arrived. He hammered home the idea that Mercury had to be the best cost producer in the industry. "This especially applies in small engines, where you are getting down to near-commodity positions. And that depends on how productive you are, what kind of quality levels you can achieve," Buckley said. "If you can turn out high-quality products that don't require a lot of

service, you have a high customer retention ratio, even though you're not selling as many parts."

Eller said keeping costs down traditionally had been "the rock we've been stepping over all the time. Buckley stumbled on that rock and asked why it was in the way."[32]

"I'm working harder than I've ever worked in my life," commented Fred Brightbill, president and general manager of the Outboard Business Unit. "The amount of information to absorb has been referred to around here as drinking from a fire hose. I think we've accomplished what David Jones' immediate objectives were, and George Buckley has accelerated that by bringing more financial models to the business. We're still absorbing that, but the discipline has been a huge growing experience for the organization."[33]

But Buckley said he isn't interested solely in predictability; he still finds numerator management far more interesting. Millions of dollars that had been squeezed from the cost control initiatives are being used to fund growth programs, so Mercury's earnings won't suffer. He said:

In the old Mercury, if a program or project didn't work, the bottom line would get hit. With this methodology, you don't get that. Even if something doesn't work, you see no margin erosion because you're pumping it out of other things.[34]

Buckley has made the presidents of the business units more accountable for performance. Using a rolling five-year plan, the units can measure their progress on a quarterly basis. And the reports are given by each unit president himself. "In the past, presidents would go to a meeting, chat for awhile, and then the finance guy would step up and talk about finance," Buckley explained. "That's not how I do it. Each business unit president talks

EVOLUTION OF THE LOGO

The Mercury logo evolved as the years passed, often reflecting the events that have shaped the company's history. A new logo (at the bottom of the list) was adopted as the company entered the new millennium. From the top, at left: Mercury's first logo, adopted in 1939. The logo remained unchanged until the 1946 version (on the right) and changed again in 1955 to Kiekhaefer Mercury. The Mercury Marine logo was adopted in 1971, when the company's name changed. The next most recent logo went into effect in 1978 and lasted until 1999, when the new single-word logo of Mercury was adopted.

about the finances and damn well better know this stuff."

The New Millennium

But financial performance and discipline did not overshadow what has made Mercury Marine the most enduring name in the industry—innovation. In 1999, the company introduced the SmartCraft high performance concept, an electronically integrated "customer-helm interface." SmartCraft is an electronic system that links all of the gauges, engines, and electronic controls (helm computer, satellite navigation, engine data, and the like) together to provide the operator with data on all aspects of the boat. SmartCraft also warns of potential damage before it actually occurs with data going far beyond the average "idiot" lights used in automobiles.

Buckley sees technology as the way to keep Mercury's products fresh and unique, which is an inherent part of the Mercury mystique.[35]

To preserve that mystique, Mercury Marine is building upon its own reputation. Force outboards, for instance, have been replaced with the Mercury Classics models. Mariner, however, will continue under that brand because it is a strong presence in international markets, noted Hubbard. "We won't bring it into new markets, but where it already exists, we'll leave it and support it there," he said. In a similar vein, the Hi-Performance Business Unit was changed to Mercury Racing, and Quicksilver has become the Parts and Accessories Business Unit.[36]

Buckley explained that brand management has become more disciplined. "In the old days, people could write our brand names any bloody way they liked. We have a disciplined design manual now in place that goes along with the new iconography."[37]

The Mercury Mystique

If there is one site most associated with Mercury's image, it is Lake X, Carl Kiekhaefer's ultrasecret proving ground. Mercury is building upon the legacy that made Lake X and Mercury a legend on the water. In literature and on the company's website, Lake X has been reborn in Mercury's image. It is a working symbol of

Mercury's leadership and continuing dominance in the marine industry.

Buckley inherited an organization that, in Fred Kiekhaefer's words, "bleeds black." It is a group of individuals dedicated to Mercury Marine that is still infused with Carl Kiekhaefer's relentless energy. "The culture here still goes back, to a considerable degree, to Carl Kiekhaefer," reflected Dennis Banks, senior vice president of engineering and technology, who came to Mercury in 1997. "His ghost is alive and well, and it roams the halls here."[38]

Perhaps it is that ghost that shouts the refrain "Failure is not an option!" in the minds of the people who comprise the Mercury organization. Those who witnessed the frenzied atmosphere of the Carl Kiekhaefer days have passed on the culture of dis-

George W. Buckley (left) with President George H. W. Bush, showing off a dolphin Bush caught off the coast of North Carolina.

cipline that was intolerant of failure. Although the challenges are different than they were in Kiekhaefer's day, the passion remains. "Mercury has that rare mix: the courage to grow, but the discipline to contain," Buckley commented. He continued:

We have enthusiasm for innovation, yet control of the bottom line. It's taken many decades to achieve both in just the right quantities. There's going to be a new legend here. And so the Mercury mystique continues.[39]

When its $10.7 million plant expansion was completed in May 2001, Mercury Marine's Plant 4 in Fond du Lac, Wisconsin, became the only facility in North America capable of high-pressure, lost-foam aluminum casting.

CHAPTER FOURTEEN

INVESTING IN BRAND MERCURY

I don't ever want to put product out in the marketplace until I'm sure it's right. I don't care how long it takes.

—Patrick C. Mackey,
Mercury Marine president
and CEO, 2007[1]

As a marine industry newcomer, George Buckley's initiation as Mercury Marine's president was akin to a baptism by fire. Buckley described the marine industry as being "under siege," attacked by stricter environmental regulations and increasingly savvy competitors.[2] As Buckley reminded employees at the end of 1998, "Yamaha is in the process of increasing their engine production [and] Honda is aggressively pursuing penetration into our US markets with high-quality products."[3] Industry analysts backed up Buckley's concerns. In 1997, US outboard manufacturers lost 7 percent of their market share to Japanese companies—and the trend was continuing in 1998.[4]

Just as worrisome were the stricter environmental regulations on marine engines imposed by the Environmental Protection Agency (EPA) in 1996. The EPA ruled that hydrocarbon emissions from outboards must be reduced by 75 percent before 2006. The cost of engineering and producing these new engines would necessarily drive up the price to the consumer, and many in the industry feared that people would choose to spend their disposable income on recreational pursuits less expensive than boating. Those who were willing to spend their hard-earned dollars on pleasure craft understandably sought a reliable, trouble-free engine. As one industry reporter noted, they wanted boats that were "as easy to drive and care for as the family car."[5]

To overcome these challenges in the marine industry, Buckley embarked on a new era of fiscal responsibility that improved overall profitability. After a detailed look at Mercury's expenditures, Buckley took measures to reduce waste, streamline the manufacturing process, and improve overall quality. By investing dollars to improve product quality (developing new tooling and equipment, for example), Mercury actually saved money in the form of reduced warranty costs.[6]

Different Strokes

Buckley continued to implement better fiscal responsibility, even while promoting innovation and what he called "measured risk taking to produce growth."[7] As Mercury transitioned from one millennium to the next, the company spent millions of research and development (R&D) dollars to develop new models of low-emission

Patrick C. Mackey became president of Mercury Marine in the fall of 2000, after George Buckley's promotion to chairman and CEO of parent company Brunswick Corporation earlier that year.

two-stroke engines that would meet the EPA's stringent new regulations.

For decades, Mercury's two-stroke engines had been the company's bread and butter, but traditional two-stroke engines emitted more hydrocarbon emissions than four-strokes because they cross scavenged with its intake and exhaust ports open at the same time. On the other hand, two-stroke motors tended to be lighter and offered snappier acceleration than four-strokes—important considerations when it came to waterskiing or bass fishing, for example. Unfortunately, many perceived all two-stroke engines as being, by nature, less clean than four-strokes—even though Mercury's revolutionary OptiMax used direct-fuel injection to produce less emissions than many four-stroke motors. During the late 1990s, Mercury continued to turn out new models of OptiMax, which offered (on average) 45 percent better fuel economy than traditional two-strokes, but the company's engineers also began looking at ways to increase the horsepower capability of four-stroke engines.[8]

"In the mid-1990s, we didn't really invest in four-stroke technology," explained Jim Hubbard, a Mercury Marine vice president and the company's chief of staff. "We co-engineered and co-manufac-

Mercury test drivers analyze the company's new 115-horsepower OptiMax engines. Mercury Marine's OptiMax series of two-stroke outboards became immensely popular because they utilized direct-fuel injection rather than a carburetor to create the cleanest burn available in two-stroke engines.

1999 — Mercury Marine becomes the first company to air the "24 Hours of Rouen" endurance race live on the Internet.

2000 — Patrick C. Mackey succeeds George Buckley as president of Mercury Marine.

2000 — Mercury's OptiMax 200XS racing outboard sets course records at Rouen and wins first, second, and fourth place.

2000 — MerCruiser introduces the 454 MAG MPI and the 350 MAG MPI Horizon sterndrive models.

tured four-strokes with Yamaha, but George [Buckley] decided that it wasn't a long-term strategy. If we weren't making it ourselves, we were in trouble."[9]

Traditionally, four-strokes had been used on inboard and sterndrive engines or on outboards with low horsepower. Four-stroke engines tended to have virtually smokeless exhausts because they did not require mixing oil with gas; they were also, traditionally, more fuel-efficient than two-stroke engines. On the other hand, they were more complex and thus weighed more than two-strokes. The heavier weight meant that four-stroke engines needed either turbo-charging of nitrous injection to achieve the same level of horsepower found in two-strokes.[10] Mercury Marine needed to find a way to increase the horsepower of a four-stroke while preserving all of the qualities that made it desirable.

To accomplish this, the company had to bring in new talent. As Hubbard explained, "[Mercury] had always been a two-stroke company, so we didn't

In 1999, Rick Davis became Mercury Marine's vice president of engine development and chief technology officer. He had been with the company since 1990.

know much about engineering four-strokes."[11]

Mercury began hiring engineers who specialized in four-stroke technology (mostly from the automotive industry) and, in 1999, promoted Rick Davis as vice president of engine development and chief technology officer. Davis had been with the company since 1990 in a variety of leadership positions, including vice president of outboard engineering. In his new role, Davis was involved in all technology-related issues at the company.[12]

For model year 1999, Mercury Marine was able to release 75- and 90-horsepower models of four-stroke outboards, but unfortunately that feat was overshadowed by Honda's latest

2000 — The IBBI's antitrust lawsuit against Brunswick is put to rest when a US Court of Appeals rules that the case has no merit, and the US Supreme Court declines the IBBI's request to appeal the verdict.

2001 — Mercury becomes the last surviving US-owned and -operated outboard engine company after the assets of bankrupt OMC are sold off.

2001 — Mackey realigns Mercury Marine around customer categories rather than product lines to make the company more flexible and responsive.

2001 — Mercury introduces its first 115-horsepower four-stroke outboard.

achievement.[13] The Japanese manufacturer, which had long specialized in four-stroke technology, leaped ahead of the competition in 1999 with a 130-horsepower four-stroke outboard.[14]

Best Brand

For the first year of the new millennium, Mercury Marine would muscle its way to the head of the pack with a new line of low-emission, two-stroke outboards, and an expanded line of Mercury four-stroke engines. But before that happened, Buckley's goal to further leverage the intrinsic value of the Mercury name was bearing fruit. Parent company Brunswick's market research had already shown that Mercury was the most widely recognized brand name in the marine industry.[15] Buckley's goal was to establish Mercury as the proven "best brand."[16]

To help consumers better distinguish between competing products, in February 1999, Mercury announced it would discontinue its carbureted two-stroke Force brand in model year 2000 and replace it with the company's "Mercury Classics" series of outboards. Force, a less expensive alternative to the Mercury brand, was dropped to adhere to the EPA's 2006 compliance plan for old-technology two-strokes[17] and because, as Hubbard explained, it was considered "almost a price point rather than a brand."[18]

Also in 1999, Mercury stopped selling the Mariner brand in the United States but continued to sell it internationally, where the name started.[19] "Unlike Force, Mariner was a brand," Hubbard explained. "But after almost 25 years, it still wasn't garnering much market share in the United States and we couldn't get the same price for it as we could for a Mercury."[20]

In the meantime, Mercury's R&D team added a new six-cylinder, 115-horsepower OptiMax model to Mercury's 1999 lineup. This new OptiMax complemented the existing 115-horsepower, four-cylinder carbureted two-stroke and received high acclaim for outperforming all comparable two-stroke outboards.[21]

Prior to the Environmental Protection Agency's 2006 lower-emission standards for outboard motors, Mercury Marine produced a number of carbureted outboards, like this 125-horsepower, two-stroke motor.

Racing Ahead

Mercury also received high acclaim on the race course that year. In May 1999, the Mercury OptiMax 200XS took third place in France's "24 Hours of Rouen" endurance race. As one of the toughest race events in the world, the Rouen race tests both driver and machine, with boats running for 24 hours straight, stopping only to refuel and change drivers. Finishing third place in such a grueling race was no small feat, especially considering that Mercury's low-emission, two-stroke technology was only a few years old.

"That first year we ran the OptiMax [in 1997], the DFI [direct fuel-injected] two-stroke technology was so new that we had to run them in an 'experimental' class," said Fred Kiekhaefer, head of Mercury's Racing division and son of the late company founder, Carl Kiekhaefer. "Although the 200-horsepower OptiMax was considered 'experimental,' it still finished in fourth place. It was pretty impressive."[22]

In 1999, Mercury Marine made history by becoming the first company to broadcast the Rouen race live on the Internet.

As had happened often in the past, the technologies developed in Mercury Racing led to some of Mercury Marine's most enduring and popular engines. "We at Mercury have a real talent ... for taking what we've already done and bringing it to the next level pretty quickly," said Rick Mackie, who started working at Mercury in 1988 and later became senior marketing manager for Mercury Racing. "The XS series came about because of increased competition from Bombardier and Yamaha. Mercury's leaders were looking to us at Mercury Racing to share the technologies that we had been working on, and that led to the OptiMax XS."[23]

The OptiMax 200XS made racing history in 2000, when it set course records at Rouen, paving the way for the future of racing with low-emission, two-stroke engines. The OptiMax 200XS placed first, second, and fourth, beating out higher-horsepower, larger-displacement race engines.[24]

MerCruiser also had its share of successes. In 2000, it released several new MerCruiser Horizon sterndrive models, including the "virtually maintenance free" 454 MAG MPI (multi-point fuel injection) and the 350 MAG MPI. That same year MerCruiser celebrated its 25th anniversary of production in Stillwater, Oklahoma.[25]

Additions to the Family

While the company's engineers worked on pushing the envelope in marine engine technology, Buckley took advantage of some opportunities to enhance the company's international presence through acquisition.

In the summer of 1999, Mercury purchased J. J. Savage & Sons, based in Melbourne, Australia. The family-owned company was founded in 1898 by John Joseph Savage, and when Mercury acquired it, it produced more than 70 models of aluminum and fiberglass boats for the Australian, Japanese, and Pacific markets.[26]

Mercury Marine had been seeking to increase its share of the Asian Pacific market but lacked a manufacturing presence in the area. "Ownership of Savage Boats allows Mercury to further penetrate the mature Australian and New

Zealand markets with Mercury-powered boats, and allows us to gain increased market share in the emerging Asian markets," said Theo Wiggill, president of Mercury International.[27]

In September 1999, Mercury acquired St. Cast Marine. Based in St. Cast, France, St. Cast Marine owned the Arvor and Armor boat brands. In buying the company, Mercury extended its distribution and was able to offer European customers a broader range of boats, which included seven diesel-powered models.[28]

Legal Distractions

The steps Buckley had taken to steer the company in a more profitable direction were clearly paying off, but the progress being made at Mercury Marine was sometimes dampened by a series of antitrust suits against parent company Brunswick —especially a suit filed in 1995 by 22 members of marine purchasing cooperative Independent Boat Builders, Inc. (IBBI).

Lawyers for the IBBI suit claimed that Brunswick had been trying to monopolize the sterndrive industry by purchasing Bayliner and Sea Ray to prevent them from forcing down engine prices. The

Left: The OptiMax 200XS won first and second place at the "24 Hours of Rouen" endurance race in 2000. The two-stroke outboard beat out engines with larger displacement and higher horsepower, proving the durability and efficiency of OptiMax's direct-fuel injection technology.

Above: Fred Kiekhaefer, son of Mercury Marine's late founder, Carl Kiekhaefer, has been president of Mercury's Racing Division since 1990.

Left: In 2000, Mercury Racing took first and second place at the "24 Hours of Rouen" endurance race, proving the durability and efficiency of Mercury's new OptiMax 200XS outboards. Team Mercury X1 finished first, completing a record 837 laps, and Team Mercury X0 wasn't far behind, with 835 laps completed.

Below: The three drivers of Team Mercury X1 celebrate their win at the "24 Hours of Rouen" endurance race in 2000. Rolf Maagne Sunde is driving, Claude Tonella is holding the flowers, and Chris Fairchild is holding the Mercury flag. Their boat was powered by Mercury Marine's OptiMax 200XS, which set new standards for low-emission, two-stroke outboards.

lawyers also charged that Brunswick had forced Yamaha out of the sterndrive market by deliberately "delaying consummation" and ultimately ending a joint venture it had formed with the Japanese company. Furthermore, the plaintiff claimed that Brunswick offered dealers cash and other incentives to persuade them to stop distributing competing sterndrives. Finally, the IBBI lawyers accused Brunswick of trying to "control prices and/or destroy competition" by offering volume discounts to boatbuilders who agreed to buy a certain percentage of engines from Mercury.[29]

After a 10-week trial in June 1998, the court in Little Rock, Arkansas, ruled in favor of the plaintiff and awarded IBBI members more than $133 million. Brunswick appealed, and after reviewing the lower court's ruling, in March 2000, the US Court of Appeals for the Eighth Circuit in St. Louis ruled that the case had no merit and overturned the Little Rock court's verdict. As Brunswick Chairman and CEO Peter Larson noted in a letter to shareholders, the court's "unanimous opinion ... clearly ratified Brunswick's business conduct as entirely lawful." After the opposition requested a review of the appeal verdict, the case went all the way to the US Supreme Court, which denied, without comment, the request to revive the case.[30]

On behalf of Brunswick, Buckley issued a public statement that expressed the company's gratification with the Supreme Court's decision. "With the issue now put to rest, we can fully focus our attention and resources on serving our customers with the quality products and services they've come to expect from Mercury Marine and all of our businesses at Brunswick," Buckley said.[31]

Before the $133 million verdict was overturned, four other suits were filed against Brunswick by various boatbuilders, dealers, and individuals. Each antitrust suit invoked the allegations contained in the IBBI suit. Brunswick chose to settle all of the suits out of court—not because it admitted to any wrongdoing, but because the lawsuits were creating uncertainty among investors and required extensive management attention and resources.

New Leadership

In June 2000, a few months after the St. Louis Appeals Court ruled to overturn the judgment of the IBBI trial, Buckley was promoted from president of Mercury to chairman and CEO of Brunswick Corporation. (Buckley had been serving as Brunswick's president and chief operating officer since May 2000.) During his three years at Mercury's helm, the company's sales increased 14 percent and operating earnings shot up 31 percent. Buckley succeeded Peter Larson, who was retiring after his five-year stint as chairman and CEO.[32]

Patrick C. Mackey came out of retirement in September 2000 to replace Buckley as president of Brunswick's Mercury Marine Group. Like Buckley when he started at Mercury, Mackey was a newcomer to the marine industry but brought with him an abundance of leadership experience and a reputation for operational excellence. Previously, Mackey served as an executive vice president of Witco Corporation, and before that he spent more than 30 years in various operating positions at E. I. DuPont de Nemours & Company. Mackey's background in mechanical engineering made him especially receptive to adopting new technologies and improving Mercury's products.[33]

A Technological Makeover

During his first months at the company, Mackey learned about Mercury Marine "from the outside in," he said. "I talked to dealers, boat-builders, and consumers in virtually every region in the world. I wanted to learn about the company from the customers' view first rather than learning the company from the inside. That way, when I sat down to a serious discussion with Mercury people, I was able to bring more of the customers' perceptions to the table."[34]

From talking to customers, Mackey learned that Mercury had a great reputation but, from an external point of view, it had too much bureaucracy and could sometimes be complacent. He learned that Mercury's customer service needed improvement, and he realized that Mercury had to be more cutting-edge in terms of product development.

Then Mackey started to look at the company from an insiders' perspective and saw that its people were not appropriately aligned around strategic objectives. "Everybody was working extremely hard, but we had a ways to go," Mackey said. "We needed to be better and faster. We needed to improve our processes from design to manufacturing to delivery—to make them as efficient and seamless as possible."[35]

MOTOTRON: A VITAL COMPONENT

THROUGH THE YEARS, MERCURY'S MOTOTRON department—a small workshop of engineers who specialized in developing low-emission engine control systems and applications—had become an invaluable asset to Mercury Marine. Pat Mackey described MotoTron as "an entrepreneur incubator that supplied control technology to engines inside the Brunswick Corporation. ... The people within MotoTron have a burning desire to push the envelope."[1]

Among its numerous other achievements, MotoTron was responsible for developing the direct fuel-injection system of OptiMax and the "customer-helm-interface" known as SmartCraft, introduced in 1999, which linked the engine's gauge and electronic controls.

Gradually, what had started as an "embryonic" business, in the words of Mackey, turned into something much bigger. "MotoTron became more than just a nice thing to have," Mackey said. "It became a piece of enabling technology that we could actually merchandise."[2] That's why, in October 2001, Mercury Marine decided to spin off MotoTron as a sister company under the Brunswick umbrella. As its own company, MotoTron developed, integrated, and sold sophisticated engine control units for both marine and non-marine applications.

In the coming years, MotoTron's engineers, led by Jeff Ehlers, would play a crucial role in developing some of Mercury's most ingenious control systems.

When Mackey began at Mercury, he described the company's product development as somewhat of a trial-and-error process:

We were making products and then breaking them to see how they worked, and that just didn't sit well with me. You need to bring science to the development and predict what's going to happen. You don't make it and break it and keep doing that until you get something that's right. I don't ever want to put product out in the marketplace until I'm sure it's right. I don't care how long it takes.[36]

In essence, Mackey said, Mercury needed "a technological makeover." Within months of his arrival, he implemented a more disciplined, scientific approach to product development, and he aligned everyone around consistent, continuous improvement.

In less than two years, Mackey's drive for improvement would become evident to the entire world, when Mercury became the only marine manufacturer to earn certification from the International Organization for Standardization (ISO), which sets internationally recognized standards for quality. Mercury would also roll out a series of innovative products in the coming years that set new standards for marine engine technology.

Better Communication

Enhancing Mercury's relationship with dealers was another key part to Mackey's drive for continuous improvement. As Mackey explained, dealers "are the interface between us and our boating customers."[37] Thus, the company made a point of improving daily communication with dealers— whether via face-to-face visits or by fax, phone, or e-mail—and it continued to improve training for service technicians. Through its 17 Mercury University schools across North America (10 in the United States and seven in Canada), Mercury offered classroom training for technicians, as well as dealer development activities.

"We teach technicians how to diagnose problems with an engine and how to repair the problems properly," explained Mike Gyorog, who came to Mercury Marine in 1982 and later became vice president of the Service & Parts business unit. "We

also teach service managers how to improve their effectiveness, and we train parts managers to understand Mercury's parts systems and how to be a more effective parts merchandiser." In addition, Gyorog said, "We offer a full range of electronic learning, or 'e-skills'—from CDs and DVDs to web-based online training in our LEARN system—so technicians and dealers can learn at their own pace. They don't have to travel away from the dealership to benefit from the training."[38]

Mackey also did away with the "command-and-control type" of relations the company's management sometimes had with rank-and-file employees. Instead, Mackey set out to engage the workforce by celebrating the company's successes and educating employees about the challenges the company faced in the competitive marketplace. Mercury's *Weekly Wave* newsletter and MercTV programming, broadcast on closed-circuit television monitors, kept employees informed of the company's larger issues. To foster good communication, office department staff, as well as hourly employees, met weekly. In addition, senior executives gave quarterly state-of-the-business updates in face-to-face meetings with employees, and Mackey led a quarterly worldwide teleconference.

Mercury Marine also improved its communication with customers when, in May 2001, Mackey led a reorganization of Mercury Marine to make it more flexible and responsive. By realigning the company around customer categories rather than product lines, Mercury reduced its customer service contact points, which streamlined customer relations and made dealing with the company more effective and convenient. Mercury's new Original Equipment Manufacturer (OEM) Division served the company's North American boatbuilder partners and oversaw Mercury's marketing. The Dealer & Retail Channels Division served North American customers and directed technical service, and the Integrated Operations Division took over R&D and manufacturing. Mercury Racing and International remained as independent divisions.[39]

Jockeying for Position

Not long into Mackey's term, in December 2000, the marine industry got a shake-up when

CASTING THE WORLD

IN OCTOBER 2000, AS MORE AUTOMOTIVE MANUFAC-turers and suppliers began using the castings technology known as "lost foam," Mercury invested $10.7 million to expand and upgrade its casting factory in Fond du Lac, Wisconsin.[1]

With the lost-foam process, molten aluminum is poured into polystyrene pieces that have been assembled into a shape. When the foam vaporizes ("gets lost"), the aluminum takes the shape of the lost foam. Mercury's cutting-edge technology used 150 pounds per square inch (psi) of pressure to force the molten aluminum into more intricate molds than regular die casting or permanent molding could.[2] Recent advances in the process also made lost-foam technology more flexible and less expensive than permanent molding.[3]

When Mercury's 20,000-square-foot expansion of Plant 4 was completed in May 2001, the Fond du Lac facility became the only high-pressure, lost-foam casting foundry in North America and one of only two in the entire world.[4] Mercury's

achievements in designing and employing new casting technology led to two awards for the Mercury Casting Division: *Modern Casting* magazine's 2002 Foundry of the Year award, and the American Foundry Society's 2002 Plant Engineering Award.[5]

Before the expansion began, the Fond du Lac factory already manufactured die castings for customers such as Polaris Industries and Harley-Davidson, so the idea of selling another of its core capabilities—in this case, foam casting—to another company was not new. Mercury planned to sell almost one-third of the new production capabilities to outside companies that made engine blocks and cylinder heads used in small engines, but as of 2007, all of the factory's lost-foam capacity was still being used for Mercury's products.[6] Even so, the expansion freed up some of the plant's other casting capacities—salt core technology, for example—so that those capabilities could be sold to other companies.[7]

A technician (above) installs a foam cast into the lost-foam casting vessel at Mercury Marine's high-pressure casting foundry in Fond du Lac, Wisconsin. With the lost-foam process, molten aluminum is poured (right) into a polystyrene mold. When the foam vaporizes (gets "lost"), the aluminum takes the shape of the lost foam.

Mercury's longtime rival, Outboard Marine Corporation (OMC), filed for bankruptcy. Rising costs and dwindling sales had finally taken their toll on the owner of Evinrude and Johnson engines and Chris-Craft boats.

At that time, OMC held almost a third of the US marine outboard market, so its Chapter 11 filing left a huge gap in the industry. Dealers across the world wondered how the flagging company would deal with engine warranties. They also wondered how they would get OMC parts and accessories.[40] Mercury Marine, now the last of 34 US-owned and -operated outboard engine companies (all others went out of business), stepped in to help fill the gap.[41] The company set up two special dealer phone lines to answer dealers' questions, and Mercury representatives contacted all their dealers to discuss how Mercury could help fill the void. In addition, dealers were able to order many OMC parts from Mercury's Quicksilver Competitors' Parts Guide.[42]

In March 2001, less than two months after the bankruptcy filing, many dealers' concerns were resolved when Genmar Holdings, a maker of pleasure boats, bought OMC's US-based boat divisions (including Chris-Craft, which it sold shortly thereafter). More relevant to Mercury Marine, longtime competitive outboard brands Johnson and Evinrude were sold to Bombardier Recreational Products (BRP), which soon after opened an outboard manufacturing plant in Sturtevant, Wisconsin, right in Mercury's own backyard. Brunswick, in the meantime, made two marine acquisitions of its own in 2001. Purchased in June, privately owned Sealine International Limited, of Kidderminster, England, made luxury sports cruisers and motor yachts. For the time being, Sealine did not have any significant

---

In addition to its low-emission, two-stroke OptiMax series, Mercury manufactured clean four-stroke engines such as this 225-horsepower saltwater outboard motor, which used electronic fuel injection. In the late 1990s, Mercury used blue decals to indicate saltwater engines and red decals for freshwater engines.

impact on Mercury Marine's operations. Then, in October, Brunswick added Hatteras Yachts to its portfolio, which it bought from Genmar. Buckley described Hatteras, a manufacturer of luxury convertibles and motor yachts,[43] as "the Bentley or the Rolls Royce of American boating … [with] very strong brand presence."[44]

That spring, Brunswick also sold its MerCabo saltwater testing facility, in Placida, Florida, where Mercury Marine had been testing the durability and reliability of its engine prototypes since 1947. (Later, the X-site, Mercury's proving grounds near Panama City, Florida, would replace both the MerCabo facility and the legendary Lake X test station located near Clearwater, Florida.)

Staying Competitive

Mercury Marine stayed competitive in 2001 with the introduction of a number of new products. The company's lightweight V6 cowlings (engine coverings) for 2002 Mercury and Mariner V6 (135- to 250-horsepower) outboards were a welcome improvement from the old ones. Because they were not made from fiberglass, they weighed half as much as the older cowls. Also, the pigment on the new cowls was embedded in the cowl material, so painting them was no longer necessary, and most minor scratches and scuffs could be removed by buffing rather than repainting.[45]

More significant than the introduction of new cowls were the strides Mercury made in developing higher-horsepower four-stroke engines. In 2001, Mercury introduced its first 115-horsepower, four-stroke outboard. This was quite an achievement, considering that just a few years before, common belief held that four-strokes, because of their heavier weight, couldn't be power-driven beyond 100 horsepower.[46] Although Mercury had been implementing direct-fuel injection (DFI) in its two-strokes since the 1990s, this was Mercury's first four-stroke engine to feature the technology.[47]

Beginning in 1999, Mercury Marine stopped selling the Mariner brand in the United States but continued to sell it internationally, where it had a larger brand presence.

The company's latest OptiMax models also reached new heights, with Mercury once again proving its merit on the race course. During the 1,100-mile endurance run from Miami to New York City (the second leg of the Bermuda Triangle Challenge), two "out-of-the-box" 2002 model-year Mercury 225-horsepower OptiMax outboards successfully powered a 26-foot World Cat 266 SC cuddy cabin catamaran. According to Louisa Rudeen, editor of *Motor Boating*, "[the OptiMax engines] were bulletproof, as was the boat. Even though the only other vessels out on the ocean with us at night were supertankers and freighters, I never felt like I was in a boat too small to handle the sea."[48]

Despite the positive steps Mackey had taken, and the release of new products, Mercury's 2001 sales fell 11 percent from the previous year, due mainly to the economic recession that was accelerated by the September 11 terrorist attacks.[49] Mercury Marine was not alone; the entire marine industry weathered a slow year as fewer consumers were willing to spend what disposable income they had on big-ticket items such as boats. Although Mercury's domestic sales of outboards, sterndrives, and parts and accessories were down in 2001, international sales rose an impressive 13 percent.[50] International sales would continue to rise in the coming years.

Despite the overall dip in sales, Mercury Marine was able to significantly increase its share of the outboard engine market during 2001, due in part to the outstanding performance and fuel efficiency of its OptiMax line.[51] Pat Mackey's continued focus on technology and dedication to operational excellence would see the company through the economic downturn, and by the end of 2002, Mercury Marine was once again posting record sales.

Mercury Marine and Cummins Marine had an impressive display at the 2002 Miami International Boat Show. Since the engines of Cummins Marine are typically white, Mercury's black diesel engines were painted with white stripes to demonstrate the joint venture between the two companies.

CHAPTER FIFTEEN

EXPANDING BRAND MERCURY

The ethos of our company is to build and integrate the best possible products.

—Patrick Mackey, 2004[1]

DESPITE THE RECESSIONARY ECONOMY, Pat Mackey's drive for continuous improvement brought Mercury Marine to new heights during the first years of the new millennium. Even while boat sales remained depressed, until 2004, Mercury was able to move inventory and gain market share. Sales of outboards, sterndrives, and parts and accessories—all of Mercury's product categories—were on the rise, as were international sales, for an overall sales increase of 9 percent in 2002.[2] Mercury's total 2003 sales jumped another 12 percent,[3] and international sales climbed an astonishing 26 percent that year, thanks to a focused effort to expand Mercury's presence in Latin America, Europe, Africa, and the Middle East.[4]

Mackey's efforts to improve overall quality were clearly paying off as well. "I wanted our products and processes to be utterly world class," Mackey explained. "Not the run-of-the-mill quality, but top-end quality."[5]

To help achieve that "top-end quality," in late 2001, Mercury Marine had begun the certification process of the International Organization for Standardization (ISO), which sets internationally recognized standards for quality. The ISO approach to manufacturing boosts quality by promoting consistency between every facet and individual involved in the manufacturing process.

In July 2002, just 18 months after Mercury began the certification process, all of its facilities had met ISO quality management standards and thus became "ISO 9001-2000 certified." By exceeding its own internal timetable in reaching its ISO goals, Mercury demonstrated its commitment to continuous improvement. As Mercury explained, ISO certification meant that processes "were in place to ensure quality is 'built in' to every product and service ... ISO certification communicates to customers that Mercury's processes [were] solid and consistent and [ensured] quality."[6]

In the past, Mercury Marine had implemented other systems for quality, but this was the company's first-ever quality management system to be put in place across the entire corporation. Mackey was especially proud that Mercury was the first and only marine engine manufacturer to have all of its facilities ISO-certified.[7]

Mercury Marine further improved the company's operations in 2003 by adopting the doctrines of Lean Six Sigma (a combination of Lean

---

MotorGuide pioneered the use of foot-pedal technology for electric trolling motors. Trolling motors are used for fishing because they are quiet enough to propel the boat without scaring away fish.

Manufacturing and Six Sigma methodologies, which focus, respectively, on elimination of waste and improved quality). This reputable corporate methodology helped improve quality while reducing waste and increasing production speed by eliminating defects (nonconformity with product specifications). Soon Mercury workers in all divisions produced measurable results in improved quality and productivity that stemmed from adopting Lean Six Sigma.

In addition, in the spring of 2004, Mackey realigned Mercury's corporate structure into six strategic business units to better suit Mercury's future growth and the current worldwide market. Along with Mackey, Mercury Marine top management now included four unit presidents: Mark Schwabero, who joined Mercury in 2004 with 28 years' experience as a senior executive in automotive and commercial vehicles companies, led Outboard Products; John Ward, formerly president of Mercury's Dealer and Retail Division, became president of Sterndrives and Inboards; Fred Kiekhaefer continued as president of Racing Products; and Theo Wiggill retained his responsibilities as president of International. The remaining two business units were led by company vice presidents Mike Gyorog, who took over the Service and Parts unit,

and Jeff Kinsey, who was in charge of Focused Businesses (propellers, remanufactured engines, inflatable boats, the casting business, and Rigging Products and SmartCraft).

Joining Assets

Meanwhile, parent company Brunswick had been improving its overall profitability. During George Buckley's five-year reign as chief of Brunswick, the company sold off unprofitable businesses and expanded its reach in the marine industry, spending an estimated $600 million to add important brands to Brunswick's lineup. This had a direct, positive impact on Mercury's sales, as Buckley encouraged dealers who sold these Brunswick-owned boats to equip them with Mercury engines.[8]

Mercury did its share of buying, too. One joint venture in particular served as its springboard for success in the diesel marine engine market, where it had been trying to gain a foothold for some time. In February 2002, Mercury formed a 50/50 joint venture with Cummins Marine, a leader in diesel marine engines that had strong sales in North America and Australia. Headquar-

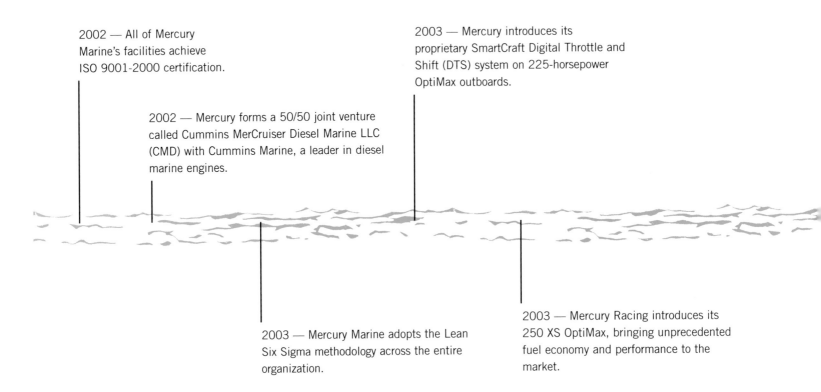

2002 — All of Mercury Marine's facilities achieve ISO 9001-2000 certification.

2003 — Mercury introduces its proprietary SmartCraft Digital Throttle and Shift (DTS) system on 225-horsepower OptiMax outboards.

2002 — Mercury forms a 50/50 joint venture called Cummins MerCruiser Diesel Marine LLC (CMD) with Cummins Marine, a leader in diesel marine engines.

2003 — Mercury Marine adopts the Lean Six Sigma methodology across the entire organization.

2003 — Mercury Racing introduces its 250 XS OptiMax, bringing unprecedented fuel economy and performance to the market.

Mercury Marine and Cummins Marine brought a zebra to the 2002 Miami International Boat Show to help celebrate their new joint venture. The zebra represented the figurative joining of Cummins' white diesel engines with Mercury's black outdrives. From left: Pat Mackey, president of Mercury Marine; Martha Brooks, vice president of Cummins Marine's Automotive Engine division; and Scott Patrohay, president of Cummins MerCruiser Diesel.

tered in Charleston, South Carolina, the joint-venture company, called Cummins MerCruiser Diesel Marine LLC (CMD), designed, manufactured, and supplied integrated diesel propulsion systems to recreational and commercial marine markets worldwide. CMD also provided after-sales support and offered a broad range of power (from 115 to 715 horsepower for recreational applications and from 76 to 715 horsepower for commercial use). Both Mercury and Cummins contributed their own diesel engines to the new venture. In addition, Cummins contributed some of its innovative electronic displays and hardware, and Mercury provided sterndrive units and its trademarked SmartCraft hardware. As an added benefit, the joint-venture company opened up new markets for SmartCraft.[9]

Before the joint venture with Cummins, Mercury had floundered in the diesel marine market, buying diesel engines from other companies

2004 — Mercury's corporate structure is realigned into six strategic business units.

2004 — Mercury introduces Verado, the world's first supercharged four-stroke outboard. The Verado family of engines wins a number of awards that year.

2004 — Mercury's Turn Key Start (TKS) system becomes standard equipment on all of Mercury's carbureted sterndrive and inboard engines.

2004 — Mercury files a complaint with the US Department of Commerce (DOC) and the International Trade Commission (ITC) against Japanese outboard manufacturers' "dumping" practice.

2004 — The DOC determines that Japanese outboard engine manufacturers have been "dumping" and orders a duty tax, but early the following year, the duty tax is overturned after the ITC determines that the dumping had no ill effect on domestic manufacturers.

2004 — Mercury replaces its Lake X testing site with the larger, more flexible X-site, in Panama City, Florida.

MotorGuide, which specialized in trolling motors, joined the Mercury Marine family in December 2002. It was founded in Starkville, Mississippi, in 1961, and purchased by Brunswick Corporation in 1984.

Teignbridge had a reputation for excellent customer service, high-quality products, and precision engineering, and was a major supplier for many Brunswick boat companies. It manufactured propellers made from bronze and Nibral (a blend of nickel, bronze, and aluminum) for yachts, patrol boats, and commercial vessels. Teignbridge also produced stern gear for inboard-powered vessels, including rudders, shafts, struts, seals, logs, and bearings.[11]

Before the end of the year, Brunswick had completed two more acquisitions, buying Integrated Dealer System (IDS) in September 2002 and Northstar Technologies in December. From offices in Raleigh, North Carolina; St. Petersburg, Florida; and Toronto, Ontario, Canada, IDS developed management systems for marine and recreational vehicle dealers.

In December 2002, MotorGuide, which Brunswick had acquired in 1984, became part of Mercury Marine. The Tulsa, Oklahoma–based business manufactured electric trolling motors and thus served as a complementary business for Mercury's fishing segment. Since its founding in 1961, MotorGuide had maintained a reputation for innovation and product quality. It was MotorGuide that developed foot-pedal technology for trolling motors, which quickly became an industry standard.[12]

Mercury Marine further increased its market reach in January 2003, when it entered into an alliance with Polaris Industries to provide the jet-drive technology for a new Polaris-designed sport boat line. Polaris was the largest snowmobile manufacturer in the world and one of the largest US manufacturers of all-terrain vehicles (ATVs) and personal watercraft. Another agreement with Polaris a month later allowed consumers to buy Polaris personal watercraft at select Mercury dealerships in Asia and Latin America. The alliance helped increase sales and exposure for the Polaris watercraft brand and allowed Mercury to offer some of its international customers a line of personal watercraft.[13]

Under Buckley's leadership, Brunswick embarked on a buying spree in 2003, starting with Land 'N' Sea Distributing, Inc., in June. Based in Pompano Beach, Florida, Land 'N' Sea was North America's largest distributor of marine parts and accessories, handling more than

and matching them up with Mercury sterndrives. "We never had the right cost position because we were paying an extra margin on the engine," explained Steve Cramer, who became Mercury's chief financial officer in 2004. Cramer said that Mercury's diesel engine business had quadrupled in the five years since the joint venture, and that the alliance had allowed Mercury to pull ahead of the pack in the diesel marine engine market.[10]

In addition, in February 2002, Mercury acquired Teignbridge Propellers Limited, headquartered in Newton Abbot, United Kingdom.

30,000 different stock-keeping units (SKUs). Also in June, Brunswick acquired a 70 percent stake in Navman New Zealand Limited, a maker of global positioning system (GPS) products. In July, Mercury acquired a minority interest in Rayglass Sales and Marketing Limited, of Auckland, New Zealand, which manufactured fiberglass fishing and cruising boats as well as large, rigid inflatable boats. Then, in September, Brunswick acquired the marine product business of Attwood Corporation, based in Lowell, Michigan, which manufactured marine hardware accessories.

The company's acquisition streak continued in 2004. In March of that year, Brunswick purchased three companies from Genmar Industries that produced a wide array of aluminum fishing, pontoon, deck, and utility boats. Crestliner (based in Little Falls, Minnesota), Lowe Boats (based in Lebanon, Missouri), and Lund Boat Company (based in New York Mills, Minnesota) all had well-established aluminum boat brands, and the acquisitions helped fill a gap in Brunswick's product lineup.[14]

The Mercury brand gained further exposure in June 2004 when Mercury Marine became the official and exclusive engine sponsor of B.A.S.S., the bass fishing federation. (At the same time, Triton Boats, which Brunswick purchased in May 2005, became the official boat brand of B.A.S.S.) The sponsorship was important to Mercury because B.A.S.S., with more than half a million members, is considered the world authority on bass fishing, sanctioning more than 20,000 tournaments worldwide. As Mackey explained, "We are convinced that B.A.S.S. ... [is] focused on growing and strengthening tournament fishing—which is vitally important to our whole industry—and we are very pleased to consolidate our sponsorship with B.A.S.S."[15]

"Hope Is Not a Strategy"

While Mercury expanded its scope through acquisitions and partnerships, Mackey continued to emphasize technology, innovation, and fact-based decision-making. "It used to be that when Mercury people made presentations to senior staff, they'd say, 'We hope you like this' or 'We hope this will work out,' " said Jim Hubbard. "Well, Pat [Mackey] got tired of these types of proposals

and started telling them, 'Hope is not a strategy! Give me details! Give me plans! Give me facts on which to base decision-making!' "[16]

Mackey's "Hope Is Not a Strategy" adage became a sort of slogan around the company, driving engineers to set their sights on developing the next industry-changing product. The slogan served as a reminder that Mercury needed concrete plans to achieve the technological makeover Mackey had envisioned.

Those concrete plans included hiring engineers to strengthen the company's research and development team. One of these new hires was Claus Bruestlé, who joined Mercury in June 2002 as vice president of research and development. Bruestlé had more than 20 years of engineering experience, including 16 years spent at Porsche, in Germany, where he developed high-performance, four-stroke engines for automobiles.[17] Until he retired in 2007, Bruestlé proved instrumental in developing many of the new technologies that Mercury introduced to the marine industry.

Around the same time that Bruestlé began leading Mercury's R&D team, the company released

---

In 2002, Chief Technology Officer Rick Davis (left) and Mercury President Pat Mackey test drive an early version of the 225-horsepower, 3.0-liter OptiMax.

one of its more significant technological advances: the SmartCraft Digital Throttle & Shift (DTS) system. First introduced as a boatbuilder option on MerCruiser's 496 and 8.1 engine models, Mercury began offering SmartCraft DTS on its 225-horsepower OptiMax outboards in September 2003.[18]

Mercury's DTS system used digital signals rather than cables between the helm and engine to provide smoother, more responsive throttle control. The bulky mechanical cables commonly found in traditional systems need to be adjusted on occasion. They also wear out over time after getting kinks and bends in them, which causes abrupt shifting and inconsistencies in the engine's throttle. But with DTS, the engine console or panel lever is connected to the engine's computer control module via an electronic wiring harness. The DTS system constantly tunes the fuel/air mixture and the timing of the engine spark so that boaters enjoy an extremely precise throttle response. As a bonus, DTS is designed to last for the entire life of the boat.[19]

The US military also benefited from Mercury's technological advances. In the summer of 2003, after the Department of Defense declared it would ban the transport of gasoline by US ships and aircraft (to avoid the risk of explosions) as of 2010, Mercury developed an alternative-fuel marine engine and began supplying it to the US military. As with many of Mercury's innovations, the 3.0-liter V6 two-stroke OptiMax outboard, which ran on JP5-class jet fuel (an alternative fuel less volatile than gasoline),

was the brainchild of Mercury's Racing Division.[20]

Mercury worked closely with the Pentagon to develop the 3.0-liter OptiMax JP outboard, continuing its history of supporting the needs of the military. During World War II, for example, Mercury had developed chainsaw and target drone engines for the US military. Through the years, the US military and Special Operations Forces have employed Mercury engines for environmental protection service, port security, and US border protection.[21]

Above: Mercury's SmartCraft Digital Throttle & Shift (DTS) system brings digital precision to engine throttle and shift. Its ergonomic design includes custom-molded handles.

Right: Mercury's Turn Key Start (TKS) system uses a carburetor with an automatic fuel enrichment system to make it easier to start the engine in cold water. Here, a Mercury technician starts the TKS 3.0-liter sterndrive in a cold-room environment to demonstrate the engine's cold-water capabilities.

AN X-TRAORDINARY SITE

FOR 47 YEARS, LAKE X, LOCATED IN CENTRAL Florida, had served as a confidential testing site for Mercury's industry-changing technologies. Lake X held legendary status as the site where Mercury engineers ran motors through punishing endurance trials. Though the water was infested with alligators, Mercury founder Carl Kiekhaefer chose Lake X because it was secluded from the public eye. At Lake X, Mercury could test its latest innovations without fear that its secrets would be revealed to its fiercest rival, Outboard Marine Corporation.

But through the years, as boats became speedier, Lake X's relatively small size turned into a liability. "As a kid, when I was driving endurance there, it seemed like hours to get around the lake," explained Fred Kiekhaefer, son of Carl Kiekhaefer and president of Mercury Racing. "At today's speeds, it's seconds! This has become a limitation in the services we can provide."[1]

Above right: At Mercury's X-site, test drivers download data from the test boats they drove that day.

Below: Mercury Marine's "X-Site" at Watson Bayou in Panama City, Florida, provides everything the company needs to test its engines, including access to both freshwater and saltwater, boat-rigging buildings, an R&D facility, and an office.

Thus, in March 2004, Mercury decided to leave Lake X to legend (and the alligators) and move to a larger testing site at Watson Bayou in Panama City, Florida. As Kiekhaefer explained, "Since we could not stretch [Lake X], we needed a new X-Site."[2]

The new X-Site at Watson Bayou was larger and more flexible than the proving grounds at Lake X. It sprawled over 8.4 acres and included an integrated research and development facility, multiple in-water slips, an office, and a boat-rigging building. X-Site provided access to freshwater and saltwater (the bayou opens into the Gulf of Mexico) and offered both rough and calm testing conditions.[3] All of the former Lake X operations, including offshore race support, would now be based at X-Site.[4]

Mercury experts had done a thorough analysis of Watson Bayou before choosing it over 52 other potential sites. They examined criteria such as boating conditions, the availability of marine technical experts, and the level of seclusion. The new X-Site wasn't quite as secluded as Lake X, but Mercury wasn't worried. "We will have to be more cautious about how we handle new products at Watson Bayou, perhaps covering them up better," Kiekhaefer said. "But any problems will be outweighed by the benefits of having more room and more varied conditions. It's time to move on, even though it's bittersweet."[5]

Mercury launched another ground-breaking technology in September 2004, when its patented Turn Key Start (TKS) system became standard equipment on all of Mercury's carbureted stern-drive and inboard engines. MerCruiser's TKS system eliminated the hassles of starting a cold engine because it used a carburetor with an automatic fuel enrichment system rather than a choke.[22]

Verado: The Best of the Best

Throughout Mackey's term as president, the company continued to embrace the "Hope Is Not a Strategy" mantra by creating products like DTS and TKS that enhanced the overall boating experience. Mercury's drive to produce faster, more

Mercury's TKS system uses a carburetor with an automatic fuel enrichment system rather than a choke to make the engine easier to start when the engine is cold.

powerful, more environmentally friendly engines continued as well.

The development of one of Mercury's most pioneering outboards began during Buckley's term, when he challenged Mercury's engineers to create an engine that would "leapfrog" ahead of the competition and provide a platform for further innovations. Progress on the engine continued under Mackey's leadership, and—as in the days of Carl Kiekhaefer—its evolution stayed a closely guarded secret. Known in its early days as "Family 3" (named after one of Mercury's engineering groups), it later became "Project X"—until its official release in February 2004 as "Verado"—a name that soon became a commonplace word among boaters.

Since 1999, Mercury's engineers had been toiling over Project X, a four-stroke engine that promised to set new standards in marine engine development. Mercury was so determined to make its new engine a truly pioneering product that designers spent two years conducting research

At a 2002 VIP dealers meeting in Nashville, boat dealers and members of Mercury's management team prepare to take an outing on a Whaler equipped with Mercury's highly anticipated "Project X" engine. Mercury gave the media and dealers several sneak peeks of Project X before its official release in February 2004.

before they assembled the first prototype—and thousands of hours testing, discarding, and refining various models. The company's leaders originally wanted to introduce Project X in late 2002, but when Bruestlé, Mercury's new vice president of research and development, recommended additional refinements, Mackey and Buckley (CEO of Brunswick at the time) reluctantly agreed to postpone the release date and authorized even more spending, research, and testing. "That was a big frog for them to swallow," Bruestlé said. "But by that time, Mercury's management style had changed to a 'management-by-data-only' mentality. We were [just dealing] with the facts."[23]

As Bruestlé explained, "dealing with the facts" required his R&D team to master all the complexities of the new product. For example, the Verado engine contained more than 500 subsystem components, all of which were new to Mercury "except for the propeller nut." In addition, the DTS (Digital Throttle & Shift system) had to meet stringent safety and reliability requirements, and thus required more than 50,000 hours of testing.[24]

Tim Reid, who joined the company in 1995 and later became director of engine design and devel-

opment, remembered the long days and sleepless nights that so many of Mercury's engineers spent while working on Verado. "Innovation isn't easy; it comes with a lot of pain. But when we got discouraged because we were having test failures or needed to get issues resolved, we'd go out and just ride the product. After that, we'd come back smiling and refocused. Even in the development stage, Verado was a beautiful product, and we knew we were doing something extraordinary."[25]

Finally, after five years in development and a $100 million investment, Verado was ready for its unveiling. Accompanied by shark videos and booming sound effects, the industry's first supercharged four-stroke engine was presented by Mackey and Buckley before a huge crowd at the

Members of Mercury's senior management team show off "Project X" at a 2002 VIP boat dealers meeting in Nashville. The meeting provided dealers with a sneak peek at what would later become Verado. Seated, from left: Rick Davis, vice president of engine development and chief technology officer; Fred Kiekhaefer, president of Mercury Racing; Pat Mackey, president of Mercury Marine; and Claus Bruestlé, vice president of research and development. Standing, from left: John Schroeder, chief financial officer; Dale Tompkins, vice president of strategy and business development; and Fred Brightbill, president of the Outboard business unit.

opening of the 2004 Miami International Boat Show. "The introduction of Verado [was] a landmark for Mercury Marine, and the dawning of a new era for the outboard industry," Mackey said. "It's impossible to fully convey the passion, dedication, and effort—not to mention the thousands upon thousands of hours—that [were] poured into researching, designing, testing, and producing this amazing integrated outboard system ... the very essence of Mercury Marine: power, reliability, and state-of-the-art technology ... [that] will forever change the way boating owners regard outboard engines."[26]

The Verado family of engines combined all of the ecological benefits of four-strokes with the speed and torque traditionally found only in two-stroke engines. Debuting with a choice of 200, 225, 250, or 275 horsepower, the Verado six-cylinder was Mercury's most powerful engine yet. Its newly developed supercharged induction system, which forced more air into the combustion chamber than naturally aspirated systems, gave the 2.6-liter engine better torque and acceleration than many 3.0- and 3.6-liter four-strokes.[27] (Mercury would introduce a 1.7-liter, four-cylinder, 135- to 175-horsepower variation in 2005.)

Mercury worked with IHI Turbo America to develop Verado's supercharger, which, unlike

superchargers for automobiles, had to withstand the harsh environment of saltwater. Bruestlé said Mercury could have skipped the supercharger and designed a line of eight-cylinder engines with more horsepower and more torque, but the engines would have been too heavy and bulky, and they would have produced too much vibration. Verado was the quietest engine in its class, thanks in part to its unique cowl design with an acoustic foam lining. The Verado line easily met US Environmental Protection Agency (EPA) 2006 emission standards, and earned a three-star emission compliance rating from the California Air Resources Board (CARB).[28]

Furthermore, Verado came standard-equipped with Mercury's proprietary DTS system, which provided super-smooth shifting and throttle response, freeing boaters of the hassles involved with bulky, malfunctioning cables. Also, Verado's standard-equipped electro-hydraulic power-steering system offered superior torque to diminish hard-to-control steering. Moreover, Mercury's SmartCraft digital engine-management system monitored the engine's vital functions, warning the driver of potential problems and initiating corrective actions automatically to avoid damage to the engine.[29]

Even Verado's cowl design was unique. Mercury's design team wanted the cowling to be as technologically advanced as the engine itself. An engine's cowling (the assembly of parts that covers the engine) serves several functions. Not only does it protect the engine's components from the environment, but it also lets air into the engine while preventing water from entering. Moreover, the cowl reduces the engine's NVH (noise, vibration, and harshness) characteristics and enhances the engine's overall aesthetics.[30]

Instead of making Verado's cowl from sheet molding compound (SMC) materials or thermoplastic sheet material, as traditional cowlings were, Mercury's designers worked with DuPont to design Verado's cowl from injection-molded plastics. The result was a more durable cowling that improved the engine's NVH characteristics and weighed 30 percent less than those that incorporated SMC materials. As an added bonus, the injection-molded cowling cost 46 percent less to produce than those assembled with SMC materials.[31]

While conventional outboard engines consist of a top cowl, which covers the engine portion, and a lower cowl, which covers the driveshaft structure below the engine, Verado required something different. To better accommodate the narrow, tall, compact shape of the engine, Mercury designers created a rear cowl in addition to the lower cowl, and reduced the size of the top cowl. The top cowl design achieved notoriety by becoming the world's largest injection-molded, glass-filled nylon part ever manufactured. Verado's cowling included other plastics parts, such as a highly durable latching system, an air dam cap to channel air into the engine, and a structural rib to give the rear cowl added strength.[32] The multi-component assembly gave service technicians easier access to the engine components, and the use of injection-molding resulted in components with a natural gloss that required less paint and had fewer defects than SMC-based parts.[33]

Based on the engine's uniquely tall design, Mercury's Styling Studio created a sleek, rounded covering that one reviewer compared to a "sea horse on

steroids." John Zebley, who led the cowling design team, said his goal was to give the cowling "a real aggressive, powerful look ... [like] something that ... was in motion."[34]

Verado's release created quite a stir in the industry. Boating enthusiasts could hardly believe how quiet it was. One industry insider described it as "so quiet a seagull 'squawk' overhead was louder."[35] Another noted that it was "nice to be able to have a conversation in a boat."[36]

One story in particular demonstrates why Verado set new standards for sound and vibration quality. At the Miami International Boat Show, two Japanese engineers were admiring the pair of Verados on the back of Mercury's demo boat. "Do you want me to turn them on?" asked the Mercury representative. When the engineers nodded, the Mercury rep slapped his forehead, only then realizing that the engines were already idling. "Those engineers were so astonished that you could see their faces drop," said Fred Kiekhaefer. "The only way you could tell the engines were on was by the cooling water running out."[37]

Verado received high praise for its other attributes as well. One industry pundit described it as "awesome," saying it displayed "torque all the way through ... just raw power all the way to the end." Another reviewer praised the DTS system as giving "unbelievable response and shifting ability," while still another said it had the braking effect of a Ferrari. Barry Tyler, editor of *Propeller Magazine Australia*, wrote that Verado was "most certainly the greatest advancement I have witnessed in my 23 years writing on the marine industry."[38]

Verado was so remarkable that it threatened to make other

When it debuted in February 2004, the Verado six-cylinder, 2.6-liter outboard became the world's first supercharged four-stroke engine. Verado delivers far better torque and acceleration than any other comparably sized four-stroke and most two-strokes.

A DIFFERENCE OF OPINION

MERCURY MARINE'S HIGH-PROFILE "DUMPING" case against Japanese engine makers caused major disagreements among US boatbuilders, engine makers, and dealers. The US Department of Commerce (DOC) had agreed with Mercury that Japanese engine makers were charging much less for outboards in the United States than they were in Japan, a practice known as "dumping." Mercury believed that the dumping harmed not only Mercury Marine but the entire domestic outboard engine industry.

Unfortunately, Mercury's petition to the DOC sent the marine industry into an uproar. Some dealers, boat makers, and engine makers didn't want Japanese companies to raise the price of their engines because then the engines would be harder to sell. Perhaps the most vocal criticism came from Irwin Jacobs, chairman of Genmar

Holdings, who called Mercury's claim "ridiculous."[1] In August 2004, after the DOC imposed a 22.52 percent duty tax on all imported Japanese outboards, Jacobs' accusations became even more critical—toward both Mercury Marine and the DOC. Because Mercury would have to pay a bond on each motor and powerhead it imported from Japan, Jacobs felt that Mercury had "caused a bigger problem potentially for themselves than for anyone else."[2]

Mercury defended its position, arguing that it only sought "for everyone to play by the same rules."[3] President Pat Mackey expressed sympathy for people's concerns and explained that Mercury was taking a long-term view of the situation:

Our first commitment is always to the consumer, but we must also weigh the effects of

outboards obsolete. Indeed, when the Verado 275 was tested against Yamaha's 300 HPDI (high-pressure direct injection) outboard, Verado beat the higher-horsepower Yamaha engine in top speed, acceleration, and fuel economy.[39]

Just a few months after Verado engines started rolling off the production line, the new family of engines began racking up awards. A Boating Writers International panel awarded Verado the 2004 IBEX (International Boatbuilders' Exhibition and Conference) Innovation Award for its groundbreaking design. *MotorBoating* magazine gave Verado its "Best of the Year" Award, noting that it offered "a level of sophistication more akin to a Porsche or Ferrari than a boat motor," and *Boating Life* called Verado the most significant advance in outboards in 30 years.[40] Also, *Field & Stream* magazine bestowed Verado with its ultimate honor, naming it a "Best of the Best" product for 2004. Anthony Licata, editor of *Field & Stream* at the time, described how Verado beat out the competition:

For the Best of the Best Awards, we're always looking for innovation. We're looking for something

a company does that is a little different from other companies, really pushing its product to the limit. ... We felt Verado was very typical of what we are looking for in a Best of the Best winner. It's a bold design that uses new technology to do something that other outboard engines haven't been able to do in the past.[41]

Even Verado's cowling design was considered revolutionary, sweeping the awards at the 2004 New Product Design Competition sponsored by The Society of the Plastics Industry's Structural Plastics Division. The cowl also won the 2004 Industrial Designers Society of America/Plastics News Design Award.[42]

A Corporate Responsibility

Thanks in part to Verado, as well as Mercury's other innovative products, the company was able to post record sales during the post–September 11, 2001, recessionary economy—despite a disturbing fact: For several years, certain Japanese manufacturers, such as Yamaha, Honda, and Suzuki, had *unfair trade practices on other elements, such as Mercury suppliers, employees, and the boating industry in general. US trade laws are in place to specifically guard against predatory and unfair trade practices that may cause injury to US industries.[4]*

Mercury had its share of support, too. Many dealers and boat manufacturers chose to side with Mercury—as did several politicians. US Congressman Tom Petri (Wisconsin) testified to the US International Trade Commission (ITC), praising Mercury for its innovation in producing lower-emission engines and noting that "markets work best with clearly defined rules and [that] governments must respond appropriately when domestic industries are harmed by

competitors who break those rules."[5] Wisconsin Governor Jim Doyle also testified at the ITC hearing, saying, "It would be unfair to allow our American outboard engine manufacturers and their workers ... to fall prey to unfair pricing strategies being used by Japanese manufacturers in a blatant effort to grab market share. ... A permanent import tax should be issued against Japanese makers of outboard motors to keep companies from dumping their products at below-market prices in the United States."[6]

Eventually, the ITC overturned the duty tax that the DOC had imposed on Japanese engine makers, determining that the dumping had no ill effect on Mercury's profits.

been selling outboards in the United States for much less than their selling price in Japan. Mercury believed that the Japanese companies' unfair pricing—a practice called "dumping"—had eaten away at American companies' market share and suppressed domestic prices. In the short term, American consumers might have saved money because of the lower prices on Japanese outboards, but in the long term, dumping could have caused Americans to lose jobs if US engine manufacturing plants were forced to close down.[43]

After careful deliberation, Mercury's leaders decided they had a responsibility to their employees, shareholders, and the marine industry as a whole to report the dumping, and on January 4, 2004, Mercury filed a complaint with the US Department of Commerce (DOC) and the International Trade Commission (ITC). Mackey explained Mercury's goals in making the complaint:

What we seek is a level playing field upon which all outboard engine manufacturers sell at "fair value," competing solely on the basis of their products' features, appeal, price, and value. As

other industries have seen, by deliberately undercutting pricing to create an artificial advantage in the marketplace, these Japanese companies did not follow US law. Our hope is that these findings will ensure that everyone competes on an equal footing in the marketplace going forward.[44]

In January 2004, both parties presented their case at an ITC staff hearing in Washington, DC. The DOC investigated, and in August 2004, it issued a preliminary determination that Japanese outboard engine manufacturers had, indeed, been "dumping." To help offset the harm caused by the dumping, the DOC issued a 22.52 percent duty tax on every Japanese outboard brought into the United States.

Mercury Marine and others in the industry were gratified by the DOC's preliminary judgment, but their satisfaction was short-lived. In December 2004, after further investigating how much the US outboard industry had been injured by the dumping, the DOC reduced the duty tax from 22.52 to 18.98 percent. This ruling was satisfactory for Mercury, but was contingent on the ITC's

With its swept-forward cowl design, Mercury's Verado supercharged engine is said to resemble a giant black shrimp. Available in 200, 225, 250, and 275 (pictured) horsepower, the engine has won multiple industry awards for its performance and design.

determination. In February 2005, after hearing testimony in support of Mercury's position from industry leaders, boat manufacturers, dealers—as well as Wisconsin Governor Jim Doyle and Congressman Tom Petri—the ITC determined by a vote of 4 to 2 that the dumping by Japanese outboard makers had caused no injury to domestic manufacturers. Consequently, the ITC removed the duty tax altogether.[45]

Publicly, Mercury expressed its disappointment in the government's ruling and made the assurance that it would continue to compete as it previously had.[46] "We accept the [ITC's] decision ... and understand that the challenge ahead of us is to develop profitability and success in our outboard unit through innovation, quality, and industry leadership," Mackey said.[47]

Privately, however, many of Mercury's executives were aggravated by the ITC's ruling, including Joe Pomeroy, Mercury's chief counsel and vice president of its law department. Pomeroy said that given the evidence presented, the ITC's vote "was something of a surprise," and he found the decision "deeply disappointing."[48]

Ultimately, Mercury found that it couldn't compete with the Japanese manufacturers' prices on low-horsepower outboards and stopped manufacturing them in the United States.[49] Just as Mercury had feared, the domestic market had suffered, and American jobs were lost.

Strained Relations

Meanwhile, the relationship between Mercury and Yamaha was becoming more strained. Executives at Yamaha thought Mercury's claim against the Japanese manufacturers was somewhat like biting the hand that feeds them, as Mercury imported four-stroke engine parts through a supply agreement with Yamaha.[50] Indeed, Mercury pursued the anti-dumping case knowing that the Yamaha powerheads it was using in its 75-, 90-, and 115-horsepower outboards might also be subject to a higher duty tax. Mercury acknowledged that its actions would raise the price of the engines it imported but believed that pursuing justice according to US law was the company's corporate responsibility.[51]

Not long after the DOC's decision to impose a duty tax on imports of Japanese outboards, Yamaha fired back by raising the price of the powerheads it was selling to Mercury by a whopping 91.6 percent, effective November 1, 2004. Yet according to a 1998 contract between the two companies, Yamaha was to supply powerheads to Mercury until March 31, 2006—while following specific pricing terms that put clear limits on price increases. In September 2004, Brunswick, on behalf of Mercury Marine, sued Yamaha for anticipatory breach of contract. The issue was resolved in October 2004, when a federal district court in Wisconsin ordered Yamaha to continue supplying power heads to Mercury in accordance with the initial agreement.[52]

Mercury's leaders were satisfied with the judge's ruling, but the dispute prompted Mercury to become self-reliant. Once the contract between the two companies ended, Mercury planned to manufacture its four-stroke engines without buying parts from Yamaha.[53]

Just the Beginning

After 10 years of flat boat sales, the market began looking up in 2004. Wholesale boat sales rose 17 percent during the first nine months of the year, compared to the same period the year before.[54] That fact, plus Mercury's drive toward improved quality and innovation, led the company to new pinnacles of success. Mercury's sales crossed the $2 billion mark in 2004, and the company retained its position as the undisputed leader in recreational marine propulsion, thanks to its new and innovative technologies.

In a letter to dealers, Mackey expressed his satisfaction with Mercury's recent achievements. "We've improved the way we do business, and the ethos of our company is to build and integrate the best possible products. Additionally, truly innovative research and development are resulting in better products and services. ... Mercury has enjoyed creating these advancements, but we've also enjoyed the satisfaction on the faces of our customers. And here's a promise. ... We're just getting started."[55]

The Axius sterndrive package gives this Sea Ray boat unprecedented turning capabilities, even at high speeds. Mercury software then limits steering range for safety at all speeds. (Pictured are two professional test drivers on a closed course.)

CHAPTER SIXTEEN

BIGGER AND BETTER

While we'll never be able to remove the cyclical nature of our business, we can separate our company by managing better, and we're managing much better than other cyclical companies. Our peaks are higher than our previous peaks, and our troughs are higher than our previous troughs.

—Pat Mackey, 2006[1]

YEARS AGO, BOAT OWNERS HAD A SAYING that spoke volumes about the boat industry's track record for customer satisfaction. As the saying went, the two happiest days in boat owners' lives are the day they buy the boat of their dreams and the day they sell it.

For years, Mercury Marine had sought to do away with the hassles of boat ownership—hassles related to driving, maintenance, and repair. In short, Mercury wanted to make owning a boat as convenient and as satisfying as owning an automobile.

Mercury had made great strides in reaching that goal by the end of 2004, thanks to the company's renewed focus on innovative technology, improved customer service, fact-based decision-making, and overall quality.

Yet despite the company's successes, Mercury's sales in the United States remained sluggish. Any hopes that the pendulum of the cyclical boat industry would take an upward swing were dashed by the end of 2005, as rising fuel costs and poor weather conditions dampened enthusiasm for boating. Although the weather improved, higher interest rates and soaring prices for oil and other raw materials continued to weigh heavily on the US economy. Mercury's domestic outboard business, which faced more competition than the company's other segments, increased by only 1 percent, to $480 million, in 2005. Domestic sterndrive

sales didn't fare much better, rising a mere 4 percent to $561 million.[2]

Despite slow domestic sales, Pat Mackey assured employees and shareholders the company was "still on track. While we'll never be able to remove the cyclical nature of our business, we can separate our company by managing better," he said. "And we're managing much better than other cyclical companies."[3]

Indeed, Mercury's management had anticipated that US sales—especially of outboards—would continue their lackluster pace, so they poured more resources into the international business segment. As a result, Mercury's international sales increased by 10 percent, to $791 million, in 2005. The spike in international sales helped offset the company's slower domestic sales that year, a trend that would continue in the years to come.[4]

Expanding the Global Footprint

Since starting his term as Mercury Marine president in 2000, Mackey had been gradually

---

Pat Mackey's background in mechanical engineering helped him lead Mercury Marine through a technological makeover. He also helped the company strengthen its international presence by forming several partnerships in Europe and Asia.

expanding the company's global footprint. As he pointed out, tongue-in-cheek, "Our idea of buying global when I first joined Mercury meant buying in Michigan as opposed to Wisconsin."[5]

In Europe, the company secured distribution by forming partnerships with independent boat companies, who agreed to sell boats with Mercury engines. Mercury also had boats made to its specifications by regional contract boatbuilders and then sold them through their established dealer networks. In Latin America, it diversified into new product lines—including items such as personal watercraft and ATVs—and enhanced its relations with dealers. But it was in the Asia Pacific region where Mackey's dedicated focus on becoming more global had the most immediate impact.

In Asia and elsewhere, Mackey set out to sell globally but act locally. As Mackey described it, he wanted to do more than simply sell Mercury's product in another country. He wanted to create "mental diversity." He said: "I tried to make our Asian business model suit the Asian business environment, as opposed to selling American ideas into Asia. For example, Asia is a commercial saltwater market, so trying to push a recreational freshwater approach on people is not very smart. They're different business models."[6]

Mercury's ability to customize its approach to fit the specific needs of the Asian market eventually led to the building of a factory in Suzhou, China, in 2005. After Mercury built the Mercury Marina in China's Suzhou Industrial Park back in 1998, Mackey asked Scott Hoffman, who joined Mercury in 1999 and later became vice president of the Focused Business Unit, to set up a sourcing office there. The employees didn't necessarily need a background in engines, but it was important to Mackey that they be Chinese and have a background in Lean Six Sigma or some other quality methodology. Once Hoffman hired and trained two employees, Mercury's tiny sourcing office began looking for high-quality, Chinese-manufactured components that could be shipped back to the United States.[7]

"These two Chinese employees were finding really good opportunities for us," Hoffman said. "Then that led Pat [Mackey] to say, 'If you can do that well with two employees, what can you do with 12?' So we set up a nice department at our marina, and once we had that set up, we realized we had a supply base that could support a factory. At first, we thought we might begin assembling two-strokes there, but then we saw one engine

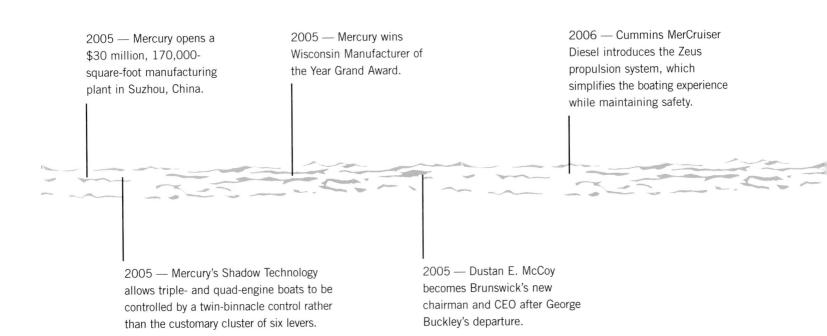

2005 — Mercury opens a $30 million, 170,000-square-foot manufacturing plant in Suzhou, China.

2005 — Mercury wins Wisconsin Manufacturer of the Year Grand Award.

2006 — Cummins MerCruiser Diesel introduces the Zeus propulsion system, which simplifies the boating experience while maintaining safety.

2005 — Mercury's Shadow Technology allows triple- and quad-engine boats to be controlled by a twin-binnacle control rather than the customary cluster of six levers.

2005 — Dustan E. McCoy becomes Brunswick's new chairman and CEO after George Buckley's departure.

category that needed some competitive help, and that was the smaller-horsepower four-strokes."[8]

When it opened in March 2005, Mercury's $30 million, 170,000-square-foot plant in Suzhou manufactured four-stroke outboards (40 to 60 horsepower). Mercury had already been manufacturing some of its engine components in China, but now the company was able to reduce production costs for an engine category that was becoming less and less economical to produce.

Mackey pointed out that Mercury was not merely "outsourcing low-cost work to low-cost labor." Rather, he saw the China plant as "a strategic part" of Mercury. "It's a high-quality, modern operation," Mackey said. "Having facilities in different parts of the world and making sure that different cultures are at the table" was part of Mercury's strategy in developing a global company—"not just having a low-cost [facility]."[9]

Though Mercury did save money by manufacturing its smaller engines overseas, the plant opening in China caused no job losses in the United States. Most of the domestic plant work that was transferred to China was replaced with production of Mercury's new Verado engines, and many employees who retired were not replaced.[10]

Mackey took pride in the fact that the plant in China was built in just 18 months. "You just can't conceive of doing that on a greenfield site — hiring brand-new people off the street and training them in a different culture," Mackey said. "But we got it up and running."[11]

That was due, in part, to Mercury's scrupulous training. John Pfeifer, president of Brunswick's Asia Pacific Group, noted that to keep pace in China, Mercury needed to employ "the best people in the industry." But that could be challenging, he said, because of the "big demand" for talent in China.[12]

Indeed, China presented a vast potential market for marine companies. The US Department of Commerce Commercial Service in Shanghai predicted China's recreational boating industry would reach $10 billion in sales by 2015. And the Chinese government had already spent hundreds of millions of dollars to build marinas and yacht clubs since Mercury built China's first-ever recreational boating marina in 1998.[13]

With the Mercury's Suzhou plant up and running, the company wasted no time establishing itself as a quality manufacturer in Asia's growing market. Just six months after the plant opened, it

2006 — Both OptiMax and MerCruiser win "Highest in Customer Satisfaction" awards from J. D. Power and Associates. The awards are repeated in 2007, and OptiMax wins again in 2008.

2007 — Mercury's SeaCore sterndrive package offers unprecedented corrosion protection for the engine, transom, and drive.

2008 — Mercury Racing announces the 350-horsepower Verado.

2006 — Mercury Racing introduces the 300XS OptiMax, the world's first 300-horsepower, direct-injected, two-stroke outboard. Racing's NXT drive fills the gap between Bravo and #6 drives.

2007 — The company's Axius sterndrive package makes close-quarter maneuvers, including docking, a breeze.

2007 — Mercury launches its Dealer Advantage program.

2008 — Patrick Mackey retires as president of Mercury Marine.

obtained certification from the International Organization for Standardization (ISO).[14]

"The plant in China is a wholly owned Mercury facility, so its quality standards are Mercury's quality standards," said Mark Schwabero, who joined Mercury in 2004 as president of Mercury's Outboard Products and was charged with getting the China plant up and running. "We also apply Lean Six Sigma methodologies, and we have the same safety standards as well. If you walked into that facility in China, you wouldn't know you weren't in a US assembly facility. We've maintained the same or [higher] standards [there versus any] plant that we have anywhere in the world."[15]

Mercury simultaneously increased its presence in other parts of Asia. Earlier in 2005, Tohatsu Marine Corporation, or TMC (Mercury's joint venture with Tohatsu Corporation), built a 250,000-square-foot factory in Komagane, Japan, to manufacture four-stroke outboards ranging from 2.5 to 30 horsepower. The new building replaced an older TMC factory, and it, too, quickly became ISO-certified.[16]

In the Technological Lead

While Mackey took a greater interest in growing Mercury's international business, he also continued his mission to put Mercury "in the technological lead," he said, so that dealers, boatbuilders, and consumers would look first to Mercury for ways to make the boating experience more convenient and pleasurable. "We decided that we were going to get new products in the market," he told *Boating Industry* magazine, "and they were not going to be experimental products; they were going to be high-quality, durable, modern, contemporary products."[17]

To accomplish that goal, Mercury continued turning out a constant flow of technologically advanced engines. Just 19 months after the revolutionary Verado's 2004 release—perhaps the shortest amount of development time in the business, said retired Mercury R&D execu-

Above: Two test drivers at Mercury's X-Site proving grounds in Panama City, Florida, prepare to test twin Verado engines on board one of Mercury's canary-yellow test boats. The X-Site employs about a dozen test drivers at any one time.

Below: In 2005, Mercury introduced three four-cylinder members to the Verado family, available in 135, 150, and 175 (pictured) horsepower.

tive Claus Bruestlé—Mercury's Outboard division introduced the four-cylinder versions, available in 135, 150, and 175 horsepower.[18] Like the six-cylinder models, these new four-cylinder Verados boasted a supercharged and inter-cooled design, SmartCraft Digital Throttle & Shift (DTS), and Mercury's patented sound-dampening technology. As Mackey pointed out, the newer models allowed a wider range of boaters to benefit from Verado's technological advancements.[19] Mercury added another two Verado models in 2007: a 200-horsepower, in-line four-cylinder (the industry's lightest four-stroke outboard), and a 300-horsepower, six-cylinder designed for larger boats. A year later, Mercury Racing came out with the Verado 350 SCi, an in-line six-cylinder engine that combined "the brains of Verado with the brawn of Mercury Racing."[20]

Mercury introduced several "Pro XS" models of its two-stroke OptiMax as well. Designed and developed by Mercury Racing, the OptiMax 225 Pro XS outboard, which debuted in 2005, was ideal for bass fishing boats. Its Mercury Racing Torque Master gear case had no problems with-standing the demands put on high-performance bass boats, and its direct-fuel-injection system and superior fuel economy helped it earn a three-star rating from the California Air Resources Board (CARB). Its superior speed and power when compared to other 225-horsepower outboards made it the gold standard for tournament and higher-end recreational bass anglers.[21] The next year, Mercury Racing introduced the OptiMax 250 Pro XS, which was ideal for salt-water and aluminum boats.[22] The OptiMax 175

A RACING TRADITION

SINCE THE DAYS OF FOUNDER CARL KIEKHAEFER, racing has been a part of Mercury Marine's culture. The company participates in a variety of marine races, including the 24 Hours of Rouen powerboat race. As testament to the power and durability of Mercury's engines and the ingenuity behind Mercury Racing's engineering, Mercury has powered more first-place winners than any other engine builder in the 24 Hours of Rouen. From 1994 to 2008, Mercury engines have had a near-perfect record in terms of speed, powering every first-place boat with the exception of the 2006 winner. In 2007, Mercury made up for its loss in 2006, when Mercury-powered boats secured the top 12 spots at Rouen.[1] Mercury engines again finished first through eighth in 2008.

Mercury got involved in less traditional areas of racing as well, including the *Earthrace* project, a speed event founded by Pete Bethune, a former oil industry engineer from New Zealand, to help promote the use of renewable fuels. In February 2006, Cummins Mercury Diesel (CMD), the joint venture between Mercury Marine and Cummins Diesel, became a major sponsor of the *Earthrace* boat, a 78-foot trimaran that used only 100 per-cent–renewable biodiesel fuel in its April 2008 attempt to circumnavigate the globe (more than 24,000 nautical miles). *Earthrace* beat the world record by a powerboat in only 61 days. The previous record was 75 days, set in 1998 by the British powerboat *Cable & Wireless*. As part of its sponsorship, CMD provided the engines to power the boat.

Mercury Racing gained exposure in the mainstream market in the summer of 2006, when its engines starred alongside Colin Farrell and Jamie Foxx in the movie *Miami Vice*. Twin Mercury Racing 575 SCi engines and Mercury Racing dry-sump six drives powered the 39-foot catamaran perfor-mance boat used in most of the film's water action scenes, and Mercury's engines were hook-ed up to many of the movie's other boats as well. The Mercury Racing logo was prominently dis-played on the hull of the star boat and all of the race boats with Mercury engines.

"When it came time to select power and drives, reliability was of the utmost impor-tance," said *Miami Vice* director Michael Mann. "[The boats] were a major dynamic of the movie. The fact that [they're] racing equipment [adds] an authenticity that I like. If [the boats were] just decoration, I don't think I would have been interested."[2]

HELPING VICTIMS OF HURRICANE KATRINA

AFTER HURRICANE KATRINA DEVASTATED THE US Gulf Coast on August 29, 2005, Mercury Marine, along with two other Brunswick-owned companies, Triton Boat and Sea Pro, worked quickly to aid rescue efforts. Mercury was one of the first Wisconsin companies to leap into action after the hurricane struck.[1]

The plan started with Mercury overnight-shipping its 40-horsepower four-stroke EFI engines to Triton's boat plant in Prairie, Mississippi. Once the shipment arrived, technicians worked round the clock to hang the Mercury engines on Triton 1648 SFB aluminum boats, which were ideal for maneuvering in flooded areas. Workers then fully rigged the boats, fueled them, and equipped them with safety gear before putting them on trailers and towing them to the New Orleans area. On September 2, just a few days after the hurricane struck, 10 Mercury-equipped Triton boats were in New Orleans helping those still stranded by the floodwaters.[2]

Mercury also donated engines for the five shallow-draft skiffs provided by Sea Pro and brought in 10 of its own inflatable boats to help

Pro XS, the third member of the "Pro XS" family, came out in 2007 and was tailored for owners of smaller boats. All three Pro XS engines boasted reductions in noise, vibration, and harshness.[23]

Mercury introduced yet another new OptiMax in 2006. Based on the technologies of Mercury Racing, the 3.2-liter V6 300XS OptiMax surpassed the 250XS as the world's most powerful low-emission outboard. Called the "Stroker" because of its stroked and balanced crankshaft, the 300XS outperformed competitors' engines with the same horsepower rating. According to Fred Kiekhaefer, president of Mercury Racing, the 300XS contained several innovations—including its exhaust port, combustion chamber, and fuel-induction designs—that were lifted directly from Mercury's Formula 1 racing engines. In addition, the Stroker's air box design, thinner reed material, and unique reed shape were based on modified racing engine specifications. Kiekhaefer noted that the technology for developing racing engines often trickled its way into the company's consumer engines. He expressed his pride that the constant innovations made by the men and women of Mercury Racing helped keep people interested in Mercury Marine products.[24]

OptiMax celebrated its 10th anniversary in 2006, the same year it received worldwide calibra-tion, a designation meaning OptiMax outboards met environmental standards for most of the world. Jacques Bronchart, president of Brunswick Marine EMEA (Europe, Middle East, Africa), noted that OptiMax models were "a big winner" in his territory overseas. "I consider them bulletproof," he said. "They allow us to compete against the four-stroke prices of our competition."[25]

In 2005, Mercury ended sales of conventional US Environmental Protection Agency (EPA)–noncompliant two-stroke engines in the United States, becoming the first major engine maker to do so.[26] Also that year, Mercury and Mariner (an additional brand sold outside the United States) began offering the benefits of electronic fuel injection (EFI) in smaller engines (25, 30, 80, and 100 horsepower). Customers liked EFI four-strokes because they were easier to start, offered smoother throttle response, and were more fuel-efficient than carbureted ones. These small engines were the first battery-free, manual-start EFI four-strokes in the industry, and the 25-horsepower EFI outboard was the first of its kind.

By 2006, Mercury boasted the widest range of low-emission outboards in the industry, with 35 models.[27] Some of these were OptiMax models, but Mercury offered a wide range of low-emissions four-strokes as well. In 2005 and 2006, the com-in the rescue efforts. (When the inflatable boats were found to be ineffective amid the debris and underwater obstacles, Triton donated another 10 aluminum boats. A few weeks later, Mercury's inflatable boats proved useful in search and rescue efforts following Hurricane Rita.)[3]

In addition, Mercury loaded two semitrucks with relief supplies from the Fond du Lac area, and Mercury drivers delivered the supplies to New Orleans.

"We wanted to do all we could to help, and we wanted to do it immediately," said Pat Mackey. "This is truly a time of crisis that is difficult for most of us to comprehend. People down there need help, and this is an area in which we're qualified and capable of making a difference."[4]

Employees at Mercury Marine also showed their generous spirit by aiding in the rescue and recovery of Katrina victims. Mercury,

along with the International Association of Machinists and Aerospace Workers Local 1947 (which represented Mercury's Fond du Lac hourly paid production employees) hosted a fund-raising drive and donated the proceeds to the American Red Cross. Employees could also spread their monetary gift over several paychecks via automatic payroll deductions. By mid-September, Fond du Lac employees had given more than $20,000 to the American Red Cross, and Brunswick matched that amount dollar for dollar.[5]

Mercury also partnered with the Salvation Army of Fond du Lac to provide victims with non-perishable items such as toiletries, bottled water, baby formula, and diapers, and the company granted one week of paid leave to volunteers who were certified in disaster relief or who had other skills sought by relief agencies.[6]

pany met a growing consumer demand by releasing a family of mid-range EFI four-strokes (in 75, 90, and 115 horsepower).[28] Although they weren't supercharged, they shared the same engine block as the award-winning Verado, as well as many of the same components, such as the rods, crank, bearings, and pistons. The mid-range EFI four-strokes were praised for being "exceedingly quiet" and "among the toughest available."[29]

Mercury added to its sterndrive lineup as well, introducing several high-performance models from Mercury Racing, including the HP850 SCi, the HP600 SCi, the HP700 SCi, and the HP1075 SCi. Then in 2007, Mercury Racing launched the HP1200 SCi, its most powerful consumer sterndrive yet. "Think of it as a street-legal race engine," the company announced.[30] It shared "all of the mild-mannered running qualities [of] its HP850 SCi and HP1075 SCi counterparts," as well as the propulsion control module (PCM) 07

microprocessor, developed exclusively for Mercury engines. "It is docile around docks and ferocious once unleashed," the company said. And although it was based on a 557-cubic-inch, V8 cylinder block, its 800 revolutions per minute (RPM) idle speed meant it didn't have the drawbacks normally associated with large-scale horsepower. In addition, it shifted in and out of gear smoothly, so there was less chance of stalling while docking.[31]

Mercury's Focused Business Unit also added to its product lineup, when, in 2005, the company officially began engineering, manufacturing, and selling commercial wire harnesses. A wire harness is a bundle of wires or cables with electrical connectors on each end. Wire harnesses simplify the assembly of electronic equip-

In 2005, Mercury introduced electronic fuel injection (EFI) in smaller-horsepower four-stroke engines, including the 30-horsepower EFI outboard, shown here.

ment because they bundle wires together, thus eliminating confusion as to which individual wire attaches to which plug. For the past 27 years, Mercury had been manufacturing wire harnesses for its own products at Plant 22 in Juárez, Mexico, but now it would begin making them for Brunswick-owned boat brands and for Mercury's other strategic partners. By that time, Plant 22 had become a world-class production facility; it was ISO-certified and had adopted the Lean Six Sigma manufacturing processes and procedures.[32]

Mercury's trolling motor segment, MotorGuide, also part of the Focused Business Unit, came out with a digital wireless freshwater trolling motor in the fall of 2005 that could be controlled via a wireless foot pedal. Because it was wireless, the pedal could be placed anywhere on the boat. An optional key fob remote could also be worn on the boater's belt or shirt. *Field & Stream* magazine was impressed with the new technology, naming it the industry's finest trolling motor of 2006 and honoring it with a "Best of the Best" award for its innovation, quality, and value to fishermen.[33] *MotorGuide* released a saltwater version of the wireless trolling motor in 2006.[34]

Shadow Technology

Mercury Marine proved many times over that it was more than just a marine engine company, for some of its most significant technological breakthroughs during this time had more to do with advanced electronics than with engine mechanics.

Mercury's Shadow Technology was one such technological breakthrough. Introduced in September 2005 for SmartCraft DTS control systems, Shadow Technology allowed the driver of a triple- or quad-engine boat to throttle and shift from two levers (designed like a dual-binnacle control) rather than the cumbersome and rather intimidating arrangement of six levers.

As with conventional systems, the port lever controlled the port engine, and the starboard lever

---

Mercury-owned MotorGuide designs and manufactures trolling motors. Trolling motors are used to move around the water while fishing because they're quieter than main engines, which tend to scare off fish.

controlled the starboard engine. But with Shadow Technology, the center engine did not need its own lever. Rather, it was controlled by SmartCraft software that made it "shadow," or follow, the operator's movement of the port and starboard levers. For example, if the port and starboard levers were within five degrees of each other, the computer knew the engines should all be running at the same speed without the driver having to read the tachometers and adjust the engines manually. Docking maneuvers were much easier with Shadow Technology, too, for the computer recognized when the port and starboard engines were in opposite gears and automatically shifted the center engine into neutral. In short, Shadow Technology made operating a triple- or quad-engine boat much more intuitive.[35]

As with Mercury's other DTS systems, Shadow Technology was an electronic system, so it didn't encounter the hassles involved with bulky cables. Also, the digital system protected against damage caused by improper shifting. As testimony to Shadow Technology's groundbreaking influence, it won the 2005 International Boatbuilders' Exhibition and Conference (IBEX) Innovation Award in the OEM Electronics Division from Boating Writers International.[36]

Above: The Zeus propulsion system allows for incredible control, even at high speeds, as demonstrated by this Zeus-powered Sea Ray.

Inset: Thanks to its intuitive joystick, the Zeus propulsion system makes large yachts easy to dock, even against strong currents and crosswinds.

The Mighty Zeus

In February 2006, a few months after Mercury's Shadow Technology debuted, Cummins MerCruiser Diesel (CMD), the joint venture Mercury formed in 2002 with renowned diesel-engine builder Cummins, unveiled a revolutionary propulsion system called Zeus, named after the powerful Greek god.

The Zeus propulsion system lived up to its mighty name, introducing to yachts the maneuvering abilities that were common to aircraft and automobiles. Zeus included a steering wheel and a joystick to make the boat easier to control, and each engine operated independently, allowing the boat to turn at sharper angles. Moreover, thanks to its "station keeping" technology, later named

"Sky Hook," the operator could simply press a button to keep the boat in the same spot if it encountered wind or a current. Zeus, in fact, made traditionally stressful tasks, such as docking in choppy waters, far more intuitive and helped resolve one of the main disincentives to purchasing larger boats: fear of docking. Using the Zeus joystick, boaters could parallel park even the largest cruisers with ease, even in strong currents and windy conditions.[37]

"If you can maneuver your boat easily, that removes a huge hurdle for many people who otherwise might be afraid of crashing into a seawall or something [else]," said Jeff Ehlers, president of

MotoTron, the Brunswick-owned technology think tank that worked in cooperation with Mercury and CMD to develop Zeus. "It really does revolutionize the experience."[38]

Zeus' debut at the 2006 Miami International Boat Show was nothing short of astounding, according to Rick Davis, vice president of advanced engineering. "We did a bit of grandstanding," he admitted. "But that just got our point across." He continued:

With everybody looking on, we came down the slip sideways in our 44-foot boat. There were only two of us on board, and when we approached the dock, we hit "station keeping." With station keeping, the GPS locks you on a location, and your drives are dynamically hovering so you can walk around the boat and get your lines ready. I went up on the bow, and the captain went back on the swim platform to get the lines ready, so nobody was at the helm. The boat was just sitting in the water as the tide washed by, and everybody on the dock was asking us what was going

Pat Mackey emcees Mercury's product unveilings from the Mercury booth at the 2006 Miami International Boat Show. Mercury's new products that year included the revolutionary Zeus propulsion system (produced by Mercury's joint venture company with Cummins Diesel); the 300 XS OptiMax from Mercury Racing; and new 75-, 90-, and 115-horsepower EFI four-strokes. *(Photo by Joshua Prezant © 2006.)*

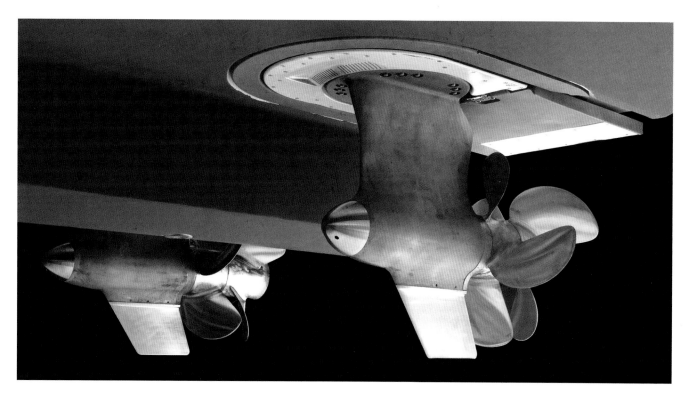

on and if we needed a hand. "No," we told them. "It's on hover mode." Then after the lines were prepared, we touched the joystick and quietly backed into the slip, no fuss, no muss. Everybody's mouth was agape.[39]

Two Zeus drives show their unique positioning at the bottom of a 44-foot Sea Ray. Zeus' rear-facing propellers provide better safety than forward-facing ones in case the boat should hit debris or other underwater obstacles.

The Zeus propulsion system brought other benefits in addition to greater maneuverability. Compared to traditional inboards, Zeus increased the boat's top speed by up to 15 percent and provided up to 30 percent better fuel economy. Moreover, Zeus' rear-facing propellers provided better safety than forward-facing propellers.[40]

Zeus was so revolutionary that in the spring of 2007, *MotorBoating* magazine honored Zeus with its "Best of the Year" appellation in the Advanced Propulsion category, calling it "a significant technological achievement."[41]

Achieving Excellence

Mercury's reputation for innovation and quality was underscored by the variety of awards it won during this time, some for specific products and some for overall performance. In addition to *Field & Stream*'s "Best of the Best" award, won by MotorGuide's digital wireless trolling motor;

the IBEX Innovation Award, won by Mercury's Shadow Technology; and *MotorBoating* magazine's "Best of the Year" award for Zeus, Mercury Marine won the 2005 Wisconsin Manufacturer of the Year Grand Award. According to the judges, Mercury earned the award because of its commitment to excellence, to its employees, and to the state of Wisconsin.[42]

In naming Mercury "Manufacturer of the Year," the award sponsors—law firm Michael Best and Friedrich, accounting and consulting firm Virchow, Krause & Company, and the Wisconsin Manufacturers and Commerce business association—commended the company as the world leader in recreational marine propulsion. Judges for the award liked the fact that Mercury spent $30 million each year to maintain and upgrade its Wisconsin facilities and processes and that all of its facilities were certified as meeting ISO 9001:2000 quality management standards. Furthermore, the company's adoption of

In 2007, for the second consecutive year, J. D. Power and Associates recognized Mercury Marine for delivering the highest customer satisfaction in both direct-injected outboard engines (OptiMax) and in sterndrive engines (MerCruiser). Pictured from left: Mark Schwabero, then president of Mercury Outboards; Kevin Grodzki, president of Mercury MerCruiser; and Patrick Mackey, president of Mercury Marine.

Lean Six Sigma continuously improved quality and eliminated waste, it had a reputation for being a safe place to work, and it contributed more than $500,000 each year to support local agencies that sought to improve the quality of life in their communities.[43]

Mercury saw the award as an accolade for the cooperation that existed among all aspects of its Wisconsin workforce. As Mackey noted, "Mercury has undergone a complete transformation in the past five years, and the result is awards such as this."[44]

The following year, Wisconsin Governor Jim Doyle recognized Mercury Marine for its extraor-

dinary results in international sales, honoring it with the Governor's Export Achievement Award. Doyle said Mercury "demonstrated leadership and innovation in responding successfully to international market challenges." By 2005, Mercury was exporting $163 million worth of products to 175 countries. Mercury also supported Wisconsin's economy by purchasing more than $200 million worth of materials from about 1,500 Wisconsin companies.[45]

But the ultimate recognition—an honor that clearly demonstrated that Mercury's efforts to improve quality were paying off—came in February 2006. That month, Mercury earned recognition from J. D. Power and Associates, one of the most prestigious consumer and business research and marketing organizations in the world. J. D. Power ranked both OptiMax (Mercury's line of low-emission, direct-fuel-injected two-stroke engines), and MerCruiser (its line of 12 electronic fuel-injected sterndrives) as "Highest in Customer Satisfaction" in their categories. In honoring OptiMax and MerCruiser, J. D. Power considered the engines' starting ease, quietness at cruise, reliability, fuel economy, shifting smoothness, and lack of engine fumes.[46]

"Mercury has worked hard to focus on improving its product quality and customer service, and it shows," said Eric Sorensen, director of the marine practice at J. D. Power and Associates. "Mercury's success this year in these two engine segments shows that positive change happens when companies are serious about both listening and decisively responding to their customers."[47]

"I can't begin to tell you how important these [awards] are to Mercury Marine," Mackey said at the 2006 award ceremony. "It's great to be recognized in the industry for a job well done, but more importantly these awards represent the voice of the consumer telling us we are building high-quality products and standing behind them. … Customer satisfaction is the reason behind everything we do, so this feedback is extremely pleasing."[48]

OptiMax and MerCruiser won the same J. D. Power awards in 2007, demonstrating that Mercury had made lasting improvements in its products, processes, and services. Mercury, in fact, was the only marine propulsion company to receive multiple customer satisfaction awards from J. D. Power in

the same year—and the company had accomplished that feat twice.[49] In 2008, J. D. Power and Associates again ranked OptiMax highest in customer satisfaction, making Mercury the only marine engine manufacturer to receive a J. D. Power and Associates award three years in a row.[50]

Dealer Relations

Even while the company improved its products and turned out groundbreaking technologies, Mackey made a concerted effort to build awareness of its product line among dealers, especially for its lesser-known products. To educate dealers on the vast array of replacement parts the company offered, Mercury Remanufacturing began touring the country with a customized exhibit trailer in June 2005. The trailer, which carried samples of every product that Mercury Remanufacturing offered (everything from power heads and gear cases to electronic control modules and starter motors), was, in essence, its own trade-show exhibit—only this trade show went door-to-door to communicate the value Mercury Remanufacturing could bring.

The trailer made the expected stops at such places as dealer meetings and trade association activities, but it also visited individual dealers. The dealerships welcomed the hands-on exposure to Mercury's wide array of cost-effective

---

Mercury Marine employed its own truck to showcase engines and other parts to dealers across the country in the "Take Charge" tour.

replacement parts, and Mercury reps enjoyed meeting the dealer owners, service managers, and technicians who were involved in selling Mercury products every day.[51]

Also that June, Jack Malone—vice president of dealer sales for Mercury—and his team took a large tractor-trailer known as the "Take Charge" truck to dealer meetings, where dealers received information about various Mercury departments and participated in question-answer sessions. That month, Mercury also hosted a series of dealer meetings in Fond du Lac and Oshkosh, Wisconsin, where dealers toured Mercury plants to get an insider look at product design and manufacturing.

Beginning in 2005, Mercury took its "Take Charge" tractor-trailer to dealer meetings around the country. The trailer was so large that Mercury designed its own tent to hold it—an inflatable shelter known affectionately as the "roach motel." The black awning in the center of the giant tent covered the trailer.

The dealers were also invited to experience Mercury products by riding on one of 25 boats powered by Mercury engines. To cap off the dealer meetings, more than 700 Mercury employees and their families gathered for the company's Employee Demo Days, where they became more knowledgeable about the products they produced by enjoying Mercury-sponsored boat rides.[52]

Mercury further solidified its relationship with dealers in 2007, when it introduced the Dealer Advantage program. Brunswick offered a similar program to its boat dealer partners and directed the program for Mercury. The Dealer Advantage program was designed to reward dealers who were committed to selling Mercury engines. The stronger the partnership, the more benefits the dealer received. Any US dealership that carried Mercury engines automatically achieved "Silver Level" status and received such amenities as real estate advisory services and discounted rates on office supplies, credit-card processing, wireless phone service, and small package freight. In addition, through their relationship with Mercury, dealers could offer customers competitive retail financing, extended warranties, and insurance.

Dealers achieved "Gold Level" status if at least 50 percent of their outboard engine sales came from Mercury engines and if at least 75 percent of their sterndrive and inboard engine sales were MerCruiser. At the Gold Level, dealers had access to workers' compensation insurance programs, payroll processing, property insurance, retirement plans, and college scholarships for children of the dealership's employees.

To earn "Platinum Level" status, at least 75 percent of the dealers' outboard sales had to come from Mercury and at least 90 percent of its sterndrive and inboard business had to be MerCruiser. In addition to all of the benefits of Silver and Gold status, Platinum membership meant dealers could explore multiple-year agreements with Mercury, which was important for strategic planning and the dealership's overall success.

Dealers liked the Dealer Advantage program because it helped reduce their operational expenses, improved employee retention, and enhanced the retail customer experience. And Mercury benefited because the program helped build lasting business relationships.[53]

Listening to the Customer

In addition to improving its relations with dealers, Mercury sought to more firmly address consumers' specific needs—an effort that helped Mercury earn its awards for customer satisfaction from J. D. Power and Associates.

To help ensure that customers were getting reliable, durable products through a pleasant and professional buying process, in June 2005, MerCruiser President Kevin Grodzki assembled a cross-functional team to implement a new program called Customer Relationship Management (CRM). As part of the initiative, Mercury representatives contacted more than 14,000 customers who had purchased a Mercury MerCruiser MPI or a Mercury OptiMax engine during the past year to ask them about their experience with their purchase. The main goal was to make sure customers were satisfied—to improve customer service one call at a time.[54]

Most customers rated their overall experience with Mercury at the top of the scale, but for those who were not totally happy with their purchase, Mercury experts worked quickly to resolve their problems. If a service expert was not immediately available, the call rep would have the service expert call the customer back, often within 30 minutes. Even Mackey placed calls. One customer's wife did not believe that her husband had just talked to the president of Mercury, so the customer asked Mackey to call back and talk to his wife, too.[55]

Mercury expanded the CRM program the following year to include different engines and reach out to more than 75,000 customers, almost half of whom offered feedback. Most of the people surveyed rated their experience with Mercury as a 9 on a 0-to-10 scale.[56] All in all, the CRM program provided an excellent means for Mercury to learn how customers used its products and how they felt about their relationship to Mercury—information the company then used to improve products and services.

On the Same Page

Mercury furthered its success by fostering good communication among employees. No one worked in a vacuum at Mercury. Every new prod-

Kevin Grodzki became president of Mercury MerCruiser in 2004. He joined Brunswick in 2000, where he was president and CEO of Brunswick's Life Fitness Division.

uct program was run by a project manager, who had cross-functional team meetings once a week to deal with the top issues of the week. Multiple facets of the company were represented at these meetings—including R&D, manufacturing, marketing, service, purchasing, and supply chain—to ensure that everyone was "on the same page" and that the product stayed on track.[57] Such communication helped avert potential problems. If, for example, manufacturing representatives believed that R&D's engineering ideas would be impossible to manufacture, or service technicians on the project team recognized that an entire engine would have to be disassembled to change the oil filter, they could voice their concerns at the weekly meeting.[58]

Mercury also implemented a 90-day review system in which all project team members reported to

In 2006, Dusty McCoy, Brunswick's new chairman and CEO, prepares to board a plane in Fond du Lac, Wisconsin, on his way to MerCruiser's facilities in Stillwater, Oklahoma. From left: Patrick Mackey, Mercury Marine president; Pete Leemputte, Brunswick CFO; Russ Lockridge, a Brunswick vice president and chief human resources officer; and McCoy.

their business leader 90 days after the startup of a project to ensure that they understood their responsibilities and the future actions that would be required. In addition, Mercury continued to hold quarterly managers' meetings as well as an annual Leadership Meeting in which the top 200 Mercury managers worldwide gathered in Fond du Lac to plan future strategies.[59]

Changes at the Top

Although Brunswick's acquisition streak had slowed considerably by the middle of the decade, the parent company did buy several marine businesses that gave Mercury more access to certain boat brands. In 2005, Brunswick acquired Sea Pro and Sea Boss (both based in Newberry, South Carolina), makers of saltwater fishing boats; Albemarle (based in Edenton, North Carolina), which built sport fishing boats;[60] Triton Boat Company (based in Ashland City, Tennessee), maker of fiberglass bass and saltwater and aluminum fishing boats; Valiant Boats (based in Vila Nova de Cerveira, Portugal), which made rigid inflatable boats;[61] and Harris-Kayot Boats (based in Fort Wayne, Indiana), which manufactured pontoon, sport, and deck boats.[62] In 2006, Brunswick acquired Cabo Yachts (based in Adelanto, California), a maker of offshore sport fishing boats.[63]

In the midst of all those acquisitions, Brunswick underwent some changes at the top. In December 2005, Dustan E. McCoy became Brunswick's new chairman and CEO after George Buckley resigned to become chief of 3M Company. Since 2000, "Dusty" McCoy had been president of Brunswick Boat Group, where he nearly doubled its size, mainly through acquisitions, and significantly built up the group's relationships with dealers. He joined Brunswick in 1999 as vice president, general counsel, and corporate secretary. Before that, he spent six years in senior management positions at Witco Corporation.[64]

McCoy's overarching goal for Brunswick's marine group, which included Mercury Marine, was to positively influence the industry—an industry that had traditionally "underserved" boat dealers and customers. Like Mackey, he stressed innovation and technology to differentiate Mercury's products from the competition.[65] And to grow the business, McCoy said, the company needed to "provide the best product, at the best cost, with the best quality in the market faster than the competition."[66]

Investing in Sterndrives

Around the same time that McCoy became CEO of Brunswick, Mercury began a concerted effort to improve and enlarge the MerCruiser sterndrive business, setting aside about $13.5 million to expand

the plant in Stillwater, Oklahoma, by 21,000 square feet.[67] The company also shifted more of its R&D spending to MerCruiser. "After we released the four-stroke Verado, it would have been so easy to reduce R&D spending by $20 million and take that $20 million to the bank," said Chief Financial Officer Steve Cramer. "But we purposefully locked arms and said, 'No, now is the time to invest in the sterndrive business.'"[68]

In 2005, Mercury introduced the MerCruiser Vazer, a 100-horsepower sterndrive engine built with an exceptionally compact structural design that allowed boatbuilders to create more spacious vessels.[69] The engine, which was capable of going up to 300 hours between many routine services, also eliminated much of the hassle involved with regular maintenance and engine use.[70] Unfortunately, in part due to quickly changing economic conditions, the Vazer was not able to capture the market effectively. However, the technology explored in the design of the revolutionary engine, along with the increased emphasis in sterndrive R&D, would ultimately prove rewarding for Mercury.

SeaCore Protects to the Core

MerCruiser unveiled its next groundbreaking product, an anti-corrosion sterndrive package called SeaCore, at the 2007 Miami International Boat Show. Rather than simply masking saltwater corrosion, SeaCore actually prevented corrosion by protecting the engine, transom, and drive from the harsh saltwater environment.

Preventing corrosion from saltwater would not have been possible without SeaCore's integrated system engineering, which enhanced the engine's saltwater durability at all levels. All components that would be exposed to saltwater were anodized to create a protective shield against corrosion. (Anodizing is a heavy-duty industrial treatment that changes the chemical structure of

Kevin Grodzki, president of Mercury MerCruiser, and Pat Mackey, president of Mercury Marine, examine the Vazer 100-horsepower sterndrive. Vazer's compact design gave boatbuilders more freedom in designing boats, since the engine could fit under seats, platforms, and decks on a variety of boat types.

SAFETY IN NUMBERS

KEEPING EMPLOYEES SAFE WAS ONE OF PAT Mackey's chief goals when he began his term as Mercury's president in 2000. In fact, safety performance became a key metric for success at Mercury Marine, especially after Fond du Lac employee Dwayne Shepro died in an on-the-job accident. Shepro's tragic passing marked Mercury's first on-the-job–related death, and the company took the matter very seriously.

Mercury renewed its emphasis on workforce safety by building awareness and practicing workplace safety programs such as the Safety Management System (SMS), formed in 2005.[1] With clearly defined steps and measurable goals, SMS laid a solid, consistent foundation for safety in all of the company's locations. Mackey also created the Health, Safety and Environmental Council in 2005 to get employees actively engaged in a defined safety process and empower them to work safely.[2]

One of Mercury's main safety goals was to reduce lost-time incidents. (A lost-time incident, or LTI, occurs when a physician releases an employee from work due to occupational injury or illness.) Mackey's safety strategies helped

reduce the company's LTIs from 68 in 2004 to just 42 in 2005.[3]

Since then, Mercury's workforce safety programs have resulted in Mercury earning a world-class reputation for low rates of lost-time incidents. Avoiding injuries is particularly difficult in manufacturing, where employees often work around heavy machinery, forklifts, and chem-

the aluminum surface to harden it.) Then, the anodized surface was specially primed and painted to add even more protection. As Grodzki explained, "Rather than just enclosing the drive components in a plastic shell, we protect them all

the way to the core with industrial hardcoat anodizing, a closed-cooling system, and widespread use of stainless steel components."[71]

In addition, SeaCore included a freshwater cooling system to protect the engine and a "fish-friendly," nonchemical freshwater flushing system. Mercury was so confident in SeaCore's ability to inhibit corrosion that all SeaCore models came with a standard four-year limited corrosion failure warranty. Those packages installed

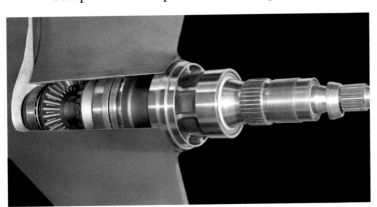

This cutaway of the inner workings of a Bravo Three gearcase shows how SeaCore, which Mercury introduced in 2007, adds stainless steel and corrosion protection properties to the sterndrive.

Right: As part of Plant 15's celebration in reaching 2 million hours without a lost-time incident, Mercury executives and other employees served turkey dinner to all three shifts.

Opposite: Pat Mackey addresses workers at Mercury's Plant 15 outboard manufacturing facility in Fond du Lac after the plant achieved 2 million hours without a lost-time incident in October 2005.

icals, but Mercury managed to reach numerous safety milestones through the years. Plant 95, an engine distribution warehouse in Fond du Lac, reached four and a half years without a lost-time incident. Plant 22 in Juárez, Chihuahua, Mexico, achieved 1 million hours without an LTI, and Plant 3, a distribution center in Fond du Lac, celebrated one year without an LTI.[4]

Mercury reached one of its most significant safety milestones in October 2005, when its main outboard manufacturing facility, Plant 15 in Fond du Lac, surpassed 2 million hours without a lost-time incident. This was an astounding feat considering that the plant employed about 1,200 people. Pat Mackey, then-Outboard Products President Mark Schwabero and other Mercury executives helped the

plant's employees celebrate the achievement with a turkey dinner.[5]

Plant 15 celebrated another 1 million hours without an LTI in June 2007. Also in 2007, Plant 98, Mercury's propeller manufacturing plant in Fond du Lac, reached 2 million hours without a lost-time incident. Considering that the plant's 75 workers pour 3,000-degree metal, reaching the 2-million-hour LTI safety milestone was a tribute to the plant's safety committee and to the workers' dedication to the injury prevention programs.[6]

through Mercury's Installation Quality program received a four-year limited warranty.[72]

Axius: 50 Years of Docking Experience

MerCruiser unveiled another revolutionary sterndrive package in 2007 with Axius, a technology derived from the Zeus propulsion system. Designed for dual-engine boating, Axius employed twin MerCruiser Bravo Three gas-powered sterndrives (which worked together, but were not connected) for unprecedented maneuverability. Using only a joystick, boat operators could easily move the boat laterally, at an angle, forward, backward, or even in a circle. The longer the operator pushed the joystick, the stronger the movement. In addition, the Axius system allowed

the boat to maintain its position, even against wind and current. And it was attractive to boatbuilders because it didn't require modifications to boat hulls.[73]

Like Zeus, Axius' joystick made docking the boat much easier. "We're always looking for something new in sterndrives that will change the boating industry, and we've done that," said Reinhard Burk, MerCruiser's director of R&D. "Many boaters and potential boaters out there are intimidated by docking a boat, especially if the boat is 34 to 40 feet long and there's a crosscurrent and side winds. Well, they're right to be intimidated. It's not easy. However, with our Axius and Zeus joysticks, docking becomes very intuitive. Our joystick gives you about 50 years of docking experience."[74]

LEAN SIX SIGMA: NOT JUST THE FLAVOR OF THE MONTH

SINCE 2003, MERCURY MARINE HAD BEEN EMbracing the principles of Lean Six Sigma (LSS), a business improvement methodology that analyzes processes to reduce variation and wasted effort. The "Lean" part of the methodology focused on eliminating waste, and as Pat Mackey liked to say: "There's nothing more inefficient than doing that which should never be done in the first place." The "Six Sigma" aspect helped remove process variation, "whether it's physical attributes or time or paperwork," Mackey said.[1]

LSS provided an opportunity to engage the minds and skill sets of every employee. At Mercury, both salaried and production employees (including those represented by their union) could become LSS project leaders by earning "belts." Mercury, in fact, was one of only a few companies to turn out black belts from its production workforce, thanks to the strong relations it fostered between management and the union. Those who earned "black belt" status became proven masters of the Lean Six Sigma methodology after undergoing weeks of training, inter-

In 2007, Axius won an IBEX Innovation Award from the National Marine Manufacturers Association and Boating Writers International. This was the third IBEX Innovation Award presented to Mercury in the past four years. Jan Munday, editor of *DIY Boat Owner* and one of the IBEX Award judges, noted that Axius overcame "the greatest challenge for every boater: close-quarter maneuvering.... Until now, we've never seen two sterndrives

that move autonomously. Axius is truly a unique innovation in the industry."[75]

Meeting the Future

Mercury was well on its way to meeting future emissions requirements. In April 2007, the EPA proposed new rules that would take effect in 2009 and cut harmful emissions for all spark-ignition outboard engines, personal watercraft, and sterndrive/inboard engines. More specifically, the rules for sterndrives and inboards proposed reducing hydrocarbon and nitrogen oxide by 70 percent, carbon monoxide by 20 percent, and evaporative emissions by 70 percent. (By then, CARB had already tightened emissions standards for small engines, effective in January 2008.)

Mercury MerCruiser planned to meet the more stringent requirements by developing an exhaust system with a catalytic converter, which would break down pollution from engine exhaust. Though

The Axius sterndrive package, introduced in 2007, gives this Sea Ray boat extraordinary ease of control simply by moving the joystick.

spersed with months of practical experience. Black belts became full-time agents of LSS, which meant leading LSS projects, using the LSS tools on a daily basis, and mentoring those who had earned "green belt" status. Green belts had a shorter period of training and less practical experience, and spent about half their time on LSS projects.[2]

"I don't want employees to 'leave their brains at the gate,' " said Mackey. "I want employees to bring in their creativity and energy and be involved. ... You can't have them doing mundane, routine things day in and day out and [have them] feel motivated. But once you get people involved with each other and building off each other's creativity, great things happen."[3]

Throughout the company—in product design, manufacturing, planning, sales, distribution, and service—the benefits of Lean Six Sigma became evident in the form of improved product quality, better customer service, and lower costs. By August 2006, Mercury had reached its goal for deploying LSS after employees completed their 1,000[th] Lean Six Sigma project. By that time, almost 700 employees had been formally trained in LSS methods, and many others were in training every quarter. Also, Lean Six Sigma had resulted in a savings of more than $74 million.[4]

"I am most proud that Lean Six Sigma has become a way of doing business for Mercury Marine, providing the foundation for the continuous improvement that will drive our customer satisfaction," Mackey told employees after reaching the 1,000-project milestone. "While we spend a lot of time talking about the amount of money we save from completing projects, it's really the cultural transformation of our business that is the most significant part of our journey."[5]

automobiles had long been using catalytic converters to reduce harmful emissions, adapting the technology to inboards and outboards proposed its own set of complex engineering problems, not the least of which was cost.

"We don't want to drive people out of boating because of the cost, but the precious metals required to build a catalytic converter—platinum, palladium, and rhodium—are extremely expensive," said Reinhard Burk, MerCruiser Engineering leader. "Also, we vowed not to lose horsepower with the catalytic converter. If you stuff a catalytic converter into an exhaust system, you're going to increase back pressure and that's going to cost you horsepower. So we've redesigned our exhaust systems so we actually increase and improve horsepower without the catalyst. Then, when we put the catalyst back in, we're able to overcome the horsepower loss."[76]

Despite the potential problems, Mercury was up to the challenge. By 2005 the company had already designed a prototype exhaust system that reduced carbon monoxide emissions,[77] and in the spring of 2007, Mercury was "close to being in agreement with various issues within the [EPA] proposal," according to Mercury's regulatory development manager.[78]

With its vast pool of talent and experience, Mercury was well prepared to meet any technological challenges that would confront it. However, as 2007 drew to a close, challenges of a completely different nature threatened to overwhelm not just Mercury, but the entire industry.

As the US market began to cool down in 2007, sales overseas in markets such as Singapore (above) helped boost Mercury's bottom line.

CHAPTER SEVENTEEN

NAVIGATING TROUBLED WATERS

I never personally felt that this was anything but a real, sincere effort on [Mercury's] part to make the best business decision at the time. And it was our job to make sure that the best business decision was to remain in Fond du Lac.

—Allen Buechel,
Fond du Lac County Executive,
2013[1]

THE OPENING YEARS OF THE NEW MIL-lennium were an exciting time for Mercury Marine. President Patrick Mackey had managed to overhaul almost every facet of Mercury's operations. By achieving ISO certification, the company greatly improved the quality of its products, and the Lean Six Sigma methodology helped the company improve processes and reduce waste. Mercury also gained greater growth in the international market and significantly grew all of its business units with innovative products. However, as the millennium's first decade began drawing to a close, events beyond the company's control created a perfect storm of economic and business woes that would have given pause to even legendarily resolute Mercury founder Carl Kiekhaefer, bringing the company to its darkest hour.

In Clear Skies, Warning Signs

Mercury stayed at the forefront in 2007 by bringing in a constant stream of new talent, including people "from outside the business, many of whom are newly minted MBAs from some of the top MBA schools," said Marty Bass, vice president of global category management. "These men and women are very bright. They have a good education, and they're in this career path transition point. We bring them into our leadership development program, and most of them end up impacting the business in a highly positive way."[2]

David Dwight, director of strategic planning and business development, also helped Mercury's leaders make decisions based on logic and data, which proved helpful in developing a stable of groundbreaking products. Innovations such as Shadow DTS, Zeus, SeaCore, and Axius took many of the hassles out of boating and made the experience more pleasurable. Likewise, Mercury's broad line of fuel-economic outboards helped ease the bite out of boating costs. Its OptiMax line of two-stroke engines combined superior fuel economy with stellar performance, and its four-stroke engines were environmentally friendly without sacrificing power. In 2008, to help reduce the impact from rising fuel costs, engineers modified the 150-horsepower model Verado to burn 22 percent less fuel at

In response to rising fuel costs, Mercury used computer-aided design to develop engines such as the OptiMax, whose fuel-injection system provided both superior performance and fuel economy.

wide-open throttle and 18 percent less fuel at cruising speed.[3]

Mercury's strong international sales continued to offset slower domestic sales. According to Chief Financial Officer Steve Cramer, Mercury's international business accounted for close to 40 percent of its overall sales in 2007. "Mercury's international presence has been a real strong suit for us," he said. "There's no question that the international markets are going to continue to outpace the US market for the foreseeable future."[4]

Mercury's success overseas was even more impressive considering the nature of international competition, which was fiercely driven by competitors who gained market share by reducing price. Mercury overcame that obstacle in part from diversification of its product line and by maintaining good relations with dealers, most of whom were longtime business partners loyal to the Mercury brand. In short, the fact that the company was able to sell so many units outside the United States spoke volumes for the quality of Mercury's products and services.[5]

Thanks to a strong overseas market (and a modest growth in the sales of parts and accessories), in 2007, the company's earnings increased

Mercury's dedication to quality helped assure its success outside the US, such as at this dealership in South America.

in its fourth quarter—up 7 percent compared to the previous year.[6] Despite the profitable finish, that year also provided signs of trouble ahead. Although sales abroad were strong, the domestic market was not. Despite the industry downturn, Cramer noted the importance of Mercury's continued investment in the future, stating "I wait anxiously for the mar-

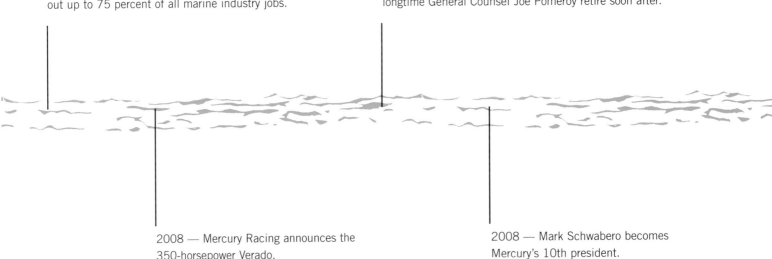

2007 — A stock market crash and resulting credit crunch usher in the Great Recession, which would wipe out up to 75 percent of all marine industry jobs.

2008 — Patrick Mackey retires as president of Mercury Marine in March. Vice President and Chief of Staff Jim Hubbard and longtime General Counsel Joe Pomeroy retire soon after.

2008 — Mercury Racing announces the 350-horsepower Verado.

2008 — Mark Schwabero becomes Mercury's 10th president.

ket to turn," he said. "We all know that 'hope is not a strategy,' but we do know the market will turn, and when it does, we're poised to succeed."[7] In addition to its regular pipeline of new products, Mackey said Mercury needed to make sure the company stayed "cognizant of the environment, whether it's fuel economy or emissions control or noise control. We need to be proactive ... to make this industry attractive."[8]

When the subprime mortgage lending market tanked earlier that year, it triggered a stock market collapse and a credit crunch. This, along with record-high fuel prices at marina pumps, caused retail powerboat sales in the United States to drop to their lowest level since 1965.[9] In response, Mercury took steps to balance its supply of products with falling demand. In February 2008, nearly 50 employees in Fond du Lac took voluntary and temporary layoffs, and all manufacturing operations shut down for a week. At the time, Steve Fleming, director of communications for Mercury Marine, acknowledged that the company anticipated 2008 to be a challenging year for Mercury and the US boating industry, but dismissed the idea of a permanent closure of local facilities, stating, "We've been here for more than 60 years, and

we are aware that we are not only a leader in the industry but an important facet of this community."[10] Little did anyone know just how difficult the next two years would be.

The End of an Era

Following an announcement in January, Mackey retired as president of Mercury on March 1, 2008. (He also retired as chief operating officer of Brunswick's Marine Engines and Boats group.) "It's time to do other things," Mackey told the press, noting that he planned to return to Ireland, where he was born, and to spend more time with his wife, children, and grandchildren. "I enjoyed every single minute of this job—the production, the quality improvements, the innovation, the cooperation from employees and customers and partners. It's been a wonderful time, and I couldn't have asked for more from everyone I worked with."[11]

For more than seven years—two years longer than his original commitment—Mackey led a revival of the company, firmly establishing the Mercury brand as the unsurpassed leader of marine engines and bringing to the company unprecedented operational excellence and technological advances. At the

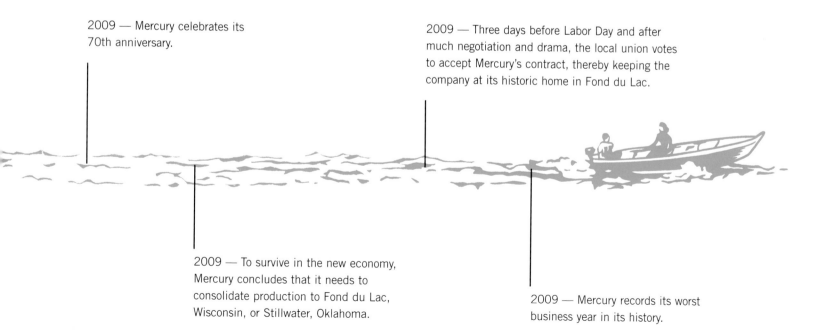

2009 — Mercury celebrates its 70th anniversary.

2009 — Three days before Labor Day and after much negotiation and drama, the local union votes to accept Mercury's contract, thereby keeping the company at its historic home in Fond du Lac.

2009 — To survive in the new economy, Mercury concludes that it needs to consolidate production to Fond du Lac, Wisconsin, or Stillwater, Oklahoma.

2009 — Mercury records its worst business year in its history.

Pat Mackey, who served as president of Mercury Marine from 2000 to 2008, is credited with repositioning Mercury Marine by revolutionizing the company's products and processes.

same time, Mackey built a reputation for developing successful relationships with dealers, boatbuilders, and other customers. "Pat has been a visionary for our industry who has championed technology, while setting new standards for customer and dealer relations," said Brunswick chairman and CEO Dustan McCoy. "I am personally grateful for all that he has done at Mercury, which faced significant challenges when he arrived. ... He gave us far more than he promised, both in terms of time and accomplishments."[12]

Mark Schwabero, president of the Outboard Business Unit; Kevin Grodzki, president of MerCruiser; and Cramer continued to lead their respective divisions and reported directly to McCoy. In addition, Grodzki added Mercury Racing and Moto-Tron to his current responsibilities, and Schwabero became responsible for Mercury Focused Businesses, Service and Parts, along with R&D. Cramer also became an administrative officer in addition to his duties as chief financial officer.[13]

After he announced his retirement, Mackey told *Boating Industry* magazine that he was proud of what Mercury had accomplished during his tenure there. In addition to the globalization of the business, Mackey stressed the fact that Mercury now had "a plethora of brand-new 21st-century products. Those are milestones," he said, "and I think some of these technologies have and will now really revolutionize boating [because they] take a lot of hassle out of boating. And forever, I will be able to look back and say, 'You know, I was there with the people who thought all that stuff up.' I take great pride in that."[14]

Chief of Staff Jim Hubbard and longtime General Counsel Joe Pomeroy would retire just a few months later, the end of another important chapter in Mercury's history.

A Stalled Economy

The worsening economy first began to take its toll on Mercury early in 2008, as first-quarter profits dropped 1 percent compared to the previous year. Its parent company, the Brunswick Corporation, fared worse, recording a 3 percent dip in sales and an 81 percent drop in operating earnings, resulting from a planned divestiture and restructuring charges. "Sales for the quarter reflected lower demand for marine products," explained McCoy, "particularly in the United States where industry retail sales were down about 17 percent in units in the first quarter."[15] Brunswick acted to stem the hemorrhaging and eliminated a number of its boat brands, which in turn adversely impacted Mercury. Despite the setback, Mercury's leadership was confident. Acknowledging the challenging times, Fleming said, "We don't feel overwhelmed by any means," adding that the company would work with dealers to ensure they carried brands equipped with Mercury engines.[16]

Business seemed to be back on track by June as the company hammered out a four-year labor contract with the local chapter of the International Association of Machinists (IAM)[17] and earned three "Best Buy" designations from *Consumer Digest* magazine (the only marine engine company to do so) for the 15-horsepower Bigfoot, the 75-horsepower OptiMax, and the 175-horsepower Verado.[18] However, the US boat market continued to cool down, prompting Brunswick to downsize further and cut costs by $300 million. Additional boat plants were closed, and at the MerCruiser plant in Stillwater, Oklahoma, 135 workers were displaced through attrition, voluntary separation, reduction of temporary work, and layoffs.[19] The continued downward trend was confirmed by the National Marine Manufacturers Association, who reported that motorboat sales were down 18 percent for the first six months of the year and that boat dealers were feeling increased pressure, with a number of them closing their doors.[20] By October, it was clear that this slump was neither temporary nor shallow. In the third quarter, Mercury's sales dropped by 21 percent from the previous year and suffered an operating loss of $8.6 million, compared to earnings of $47.5 million in 2007. Brunswick fared no better as sales within its boat division dropped 36 percent.[21] It became clear that to steer Mercury back into safe waters, a new direction was needed.

A New Path

After being part of a three-man team that led the company after Mackey retired in March, Schwabero, a 28-year veteran of the automotive and commercial vehicle industries who joined Mercury in 2004, was named president of Mercury Marine on November 6, 2008.[22] In response to the worsening recession, Schwabero instituted policies based on a simple maxim: cash is king. The company would focus on short-term goals and projects to generate the cash it needed to stay afloat during the crisis, putting most long-term projects on hold. Stephan Cloutier, vice president of global procurement, recalled that belt-tightening made managing

things paradoxically both easier and tougher: "The only thing you manage in a recession is cash. You have to conserve cash, and you have to make the right decision based on that, [asking] 'Can you afford it? No?' Bingo! Decision done. ... It was an easy time to manage, but tough though."[23] Although the immediate need to keep the business afloat was the top priority, Mercury still continued to invest in new product development, recognizing that new products would be needed for the company to thrive once the crisis had passed. "It seemed as though Mercury retained the vast majority of its engineering and even advanced programs through that period of time," said David Foulkes, vice president of engineering, product development, and racing. "I think it was very, very forward thinking and did not mortgage its future at all from the product side."[24]

Other adjustments needed to be made as well. Ray Atchinson, vice president of global parts and accessories business development, served as vice president of human resources at that time and recalled why and how the company's charitable giving strategy needed to change:

This pen is the one I used to sign severance letters for hundreds of local families who I saw at the grocery store, the gas station, and the hardware store, day after day after day. ... Fond du Lac is a

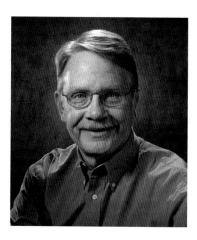

Above: David Foulkes, Mercury vice president of engineering, product development, and racing, helped the company weather the recession.

Far left: Jim Hubbard, vice president and chief of staff, retired in the summer of 2008 after a 36-year Brunswick career, with 20 years in the marine industry.

Left: Joe Pomeroy, general counsel and vice president of law, who represented Mercury for more than two decades, also retired in 2008, ending an era in Mercury history.

small town. These are people that I smiled at, shook hands with. I know their children. You have to take that personally. The textbooks say, "Don't," but I am literally standing in the line at Walmart or at Festival Foods behind them.

So we had to do a lot of things. How could we fund the arts and fishing tournaments when people who used to be part of our family are now struggling to eat? So we switched our giving to basic care, clothing, shelter, food, utilities for the local community—everything went to needs-based giving.[25]

Freefall

The year ended brutally for Mercury. In December, the company announced that an additional round of layoffs of employees in Fond du Lac would be coming.[26] Mercury also reported a 17 percent drop in sales, while Brunswick, which enjoyed operating earnings of $107.2 million in 2007, now faced an operating loss of $611.6 million in 2008, as its boat sales dropped by 25 percent. McCoy grimly acknowledged the difficult times past and those coming:

As we anticipated, 2008 proved to be a very challenging year for our businesses and we expect 2009 to also be difficult. Although we have limited visibility to a very volatile marketplace entering the year, we expect our revenues to be lower in 2009 with higher relative percentage declines occurring in the first half of the year.[27]

As the US economy continued to deteriorate in 2009, so did business for Mercury. By January, the company had a temporary shutdown to align production with decreased demand and to preserve cash. By February, the Fond du Lac plant, in addition to initiating another partial shutdown, eliminated 85 jobs entirely.[28]

At the end of the first quarter of 2009, Mercury reported a 45 percent drop in net sales from the previous year, which included a proportional drop in the previously strong international sales segment. Brunswick recorded a 52 percent drop in marine sales.[29] In response, the corporation instituted the first large-scale payment protection plan in the marine industry. Inspired by the auto industry, Brunswick's plan would cover several months' worth of loan payments in the event that the purchaser of a Mercury engine–equipped boat became unemployed, and it served as a welcome selling point for struggling boat dealerships.[30]

Mercury sales continued to tumble in the second quarter from $723.6 million the previous year to $415.2 million—a 43 percent drop. Brunswick's boat sales plunged 77 percent in the same quarter.[31] "The marine industry has become smaller and will remain that way, and Mercury Marine is preparing to be profitable in a smaller market," noted Fleming.[32] International sales fell again by 45 percent. Engine sales—especially for sterndrives—plummeted, and sales from service, parts, and accessories dropped to low single digits.[33] Something big had to happen if Mercury was to survive.

Project Big

In January 2009, what was informally known as "Project Big" was first discussed at Mercury when Mark Biznek, former director of manufacturing integration, put together a number of potential scenarios to rationalize Mercury's manufacturing capacity

Mercury's MerCruiser facility in Stillwater, Oklahoma, which built sterndrive engines, suffered numerous shutdowns and layoffs as demand dropped precipitously.

Above: Ray Atchinson, who serves as Mercury's vice president of global parts and accessories business development, had served as vice president of human resources during the worst of the Great Recession.

Right: Mark Schwabero succeeded Mackey as president of Mercury in November 2008. He soon instituted a policy of "cash is king," focusing the company on goals and projects that would keep it financially afloat.

to the new, smaller global marine market. Included as an option was the rationalization of Fond du Lac and Stillwater manufacturing. "Closing a major manufacturing facility was one. Headcount reductions was another," he recalled. "The last two were the big ones. I was waiting for people to gulp."[34]

Aware that manufacturing was far over capacity even for a postrecovery market, the company glumly realized that, to continue in the new economy, Mercury needed to consolidate production in either Fond du Lac or Stillwater and close the other plant. Atchinson, who began his career working for General Motors in Flint, Michigan, and knew what it was like when a one-company town lost its employer, summed up the cold equations of the situation:

Our challenge was this: Clearly the company's center of gravity was [here in Fond du Lac], but its costs were extraordinary. Capacity could be built [in Stillwater] and, over the long term at a lower cost base, it would pay to move.

But before making that decision, we wanted to give this location the opportunity to become

[cost competitive] with the other option, which was Oklahoma. We said that to our staff, we said that to our employees, we said that to the community leaders.[35]

Mercury announced in June its intention to consolidate its operations, prompting Fond du Lac city and county officials to study the potential impact of Mercury leaving.[36] Wayne Rollin, a community development director for the City of Fond du Lac, said that keeping the company in Fond du Lac was vitally important not just for the jobs that would leave with Mercury, but for the jobs that would be lost if the local economy became depressed with the departure of such a large employer. "There was an estimated loss of 5,900 jobs had they left," said Rollin. "We had to keep Mercury in Fond du Lac."[37] There would also be less direct but equally dramatic impacts to the community. "If Mercury had left, the estimate was that the water bill of everybody in Fond du Lac would have increased 5 percent," according to Tom Herre, retired city manager. "They were one of our biggest consumers and we'd have many fixed expenses. It'd have to be borne by other customers."[38] The city, the county, and the state began to develop incentives to encourage Mercury to stay in its decades-old home.

However, incentives alone were not enough to make staying in Fond du Lac fiscally viable. In July, after Schwabero discussed the situation with Mercury employees, contract negotiations began with IAM Local 1947. Mercury proposed a series of changes to the contract that would allow the company to emerge from the global recession more competitive and flexible. After volatile negotiations, the proposed contract went to vote and was voted down by union workers on August 23.[39]

The following day, Atchinson booked tickets to Stillwater to begin final status negotiations with the state of Oklahoma.[40]

Another Bite at the Apple

A groundswell to keep Mercury at Fond du Lac began soon after the proposed contract was rejected. More than 200 union members signed petitions calling for another vote. Members also contacted regional and national leadership. "We are fighting right to the end," said Fred Toth Jr., a 15-year Mercury employee who, along with fellow union members Rick Schmidt and Felipe Rodriguez, started the petition drive.[41] "It's definitely worth taking a look at again. Over the years, there's never been anything said about not being able to vote again on the same things," said Jim Bomier, a 25-year veteran at the plant.[42]

"If the union does vote again, and it's a 'yes' vote, we are certainly OK with remaining in Fond du Lac and continuing to produce engines here," said Fleming, but he also indicated that a 'no' vote, or the lack of a second vote, would greatly increase the likelihood of Mercury relocating to Stillwater.[43]

Community leaders backed the call for a revote as they put together an incentives package to convince Mercury to stay. "I am saddened and frustrated with the decision of the IAM, as it doesn't seem appropriate and right to not allow its members to vote again when it's clear they want to," said Brenda Hicks-Sorensen, president of the Fond du Lac Economic Development Corp.[44]

Officials from Mercury and the IAM's Midwest Territory met to "bring clarity to the communications regarding the unchanged 'best and final' proposal" soon after. Fleming flatly denied rumors that Mercury planned to move its operations to Stillwater regardless of the vote's outcome, saying, "We've said over and over prior to and during negotiations that not one decision had been made yet, and that's the absolute truth."[45]

Union workers held one more vote, scheduled just before Labor Day weekend. Mercury stated that contract approval would mean that the plant would remain in Fond du Lac, with additional work coming from Stillwater, and that Mercury's world headquarters would stay as well, saving an additional 1,000 jobs above the 850 at the manufacturing plant. "Hundreds of employees expressed a desire to voice their true feelings, and that's something we can't ignore," said Schwabero. "Obviously this is a difficult situation for all employees in Fond du Lac and Stillwater."[46]

The new proposal contained supplemental material that clarified some of the terms, and Rich Michalski, general vice president of the union's national leadership in Washington, DC, was confident that the new material "will allow our members to cast an intelligent vote." Herre agreed. "All I can say is people are much better informed on the issue this time around," said Herre. "I think that will go a long way with folks who are trying to make a decision that has far-reaching consequences."[47]

On Friday, September 4, the members of IAM Local 1947 voted to approve the proposed contract.[48] "After weeks of intense discussions and completion of the voting process, we accept the union's ratification of our contract proposal," said Schwabero in response. "As we've stated throughout this important process, comprehensive changes to wages, benefits, and operational flexibility are necessary for Mercury to effectively compete in a smaller and fundamentally changed [marine] marketplace."[49] IAM Business Representative Russell Krings echoed the sentiment: "While it was a very difficult decision, it clearly says the union workers are willing to work

STILLWATER: STILL STANDING

WHEN MERCURY CHOSE TO STAY IN FOND DU Lac, Wisconsin, it also meant that the company would be leaving Stillwater, Oklahoma. However, despite the closing of the 36-year-old MerCruiser facility and the resulting loss of nearly 400 jobs in December 2011, the community of Stillwater got a happy ending.

Not only did Mercury help with the retraining of the displaced employees[1] and offer most salaried employees a job in Fond du Lac,[2] Mercury also opened a design center in Stillwater and retained approximately 30 engineering staff who remain a vital part of the Mercury team.[3] Additionally, in 2012, the former MerCruiser facility was sold to aerospace company ASCO Industries, which turned it into a production facility with plans to create more than 500 jobs for the community—a net increase of 100 jobs at the former MerCruiser plant.[4]

with Mercury to secure a strong future for themselves, the company, and the community. This decision [was] a huge sacrifice on the part of our members."[50] Mercury Marine understood exactly how difficult the vote was. Cramer recalled a conversation he had during a flight in 2010:

Above: After contentious negotiations, union workers in Fond du Lac, Wisconsin (above), eventually voted to approve a new labor contract on September 9, 2009, that would allow Mercury to stay in its decades-old home.

Left: Steve Cramer, Mercury's chief financial officer, helped run the company when Mackey retired and was instrumental in realizing Schwabero's maxim that "cash is king."

I sat down next to a guy who looked at me and said, "Oh, you work for Mercury Marine? That's awful up there, isn't it? You know, the union problems." I said, "We don't have any union problems." He looked at me like I'm a moron because it was all in the news, right?

I went on to tell him a story. First I framed for him the economic downturn we went through: In 2008 and 2009, long before we made a decision to shutter Stillwater or Fond du Lac, we shut down five or six distribution centers around the world. We eliminated 40 percent of our salaried workforce. We put our salaried workforce through furloughs. We eliminated defined benefit pension programs. We had a portfolio of 13 companies within Mercury that we either sold off or shut down. I'm telling this guy all of this, and I said, "Listen, we were in survival mode. We were faced with a really crummy decision, and if we wanted to keep the doors open for the long term, we had to take capacity offline."

"Now," I said, "put yourself in our production and warehouse employees' shoes for a minute. [If we had] put all of our salaried employees in a room and said, 'Let's take a vote: How many of you want to give up your defined pension program? How many of you want to go on furlough? How many of

you want to have forty percent of your neighbors leave? How many of you want to...' I would put to you that they might not vote 'yes' the first time. I might not have even voted 'yes' the first time."

When I put it in that light...the fact that our production and warehouse employees struggled with the decision, I don't fault them for one minute. They had a really tough decision to make.[51]

Russ Lathrop, a 13-year Mercury employee who had been laid off eight months earlier, said, "I harbor no resentment toward the company at all. They have treated me and my family more than fairly over the years, and now they are in difficult times. I understand it's time to give back so that we can keep all of the jobs here in town."[52] The community was elated by the decision. "It's Labor Day weekend; what a great way to celebrate," said Herre.[53] The turn of events could not have come at a more urgent moment. When the recession began in late 2007, the unemployment rate of Wisconsin was 4.5 percent; at the time of the revote, it had nearly doubled.[54]

As part of an incentive package to keep Mercury in the state, the company received a $50 million, 12-year, low-interest, collateralized loan from the county, financed with a 0.5 percent county sales tax.[55] The loan was also performance based, allowing Mercury to earn credits towards repayment by retaining and creating new jobs but penalizing the company for positions lost.[56] The state of Wisconsin provided an additional $70 million in performance-based incentives that provided potential tax credits for Mercury and loans for investment in energy-saving technologies. Mercury also received $3 million from the City of Fond du Lac. The incentives were slated by Mercury to fund transitional costs, retirement incentives, capital costs, future product development, green technologies that would lower the company's energy costs, and employee training opportunities.[57]

The sales tax proposed was highly controversial, and passing it required political courage. Fortunately, the members of the county board had that. "They recognized this was the right thing to do for the community and the county," said Allen Buechel, county executive, who was instrumental in keeping Mercury in Wisconsin. "It was a tough decision in one respect but an easy decision in the other. We had to keep Mercury in Fond du Lac."[58]

Turning Around

Although Mercury's third quarter of 2009 still suggested a pessimistic outlook, with sales down 29 percent from 2008 and the company suffering an operating loss of $13.4 million, Will Sangster, sales director for Australia, New Zealand, and the South Pacific, declared in September that "the green shoots have finally begun to break through the soil."[59] He added:

There is still a long way to go. We are all still working very hard with our dealers for every sale, but there are certainly more inquiries and they're the right sort of inquiries. People are serious about buying.

Understandably, re-powers have been the order of the day with people wanting to continue the use of

AFTERMATH

THE ECONOMIC DOWNTURN POPULARLY KNOWN AS the Great Recession hammered the entire marine industry, and Mercury Marine and parent company Brunswick were no exception. Besides the closing of the MerCruiser facility in Stillwater, Oklahoma, there were a number of other consequences of the downturn:

- Brunswick ended production of its Bluewater Marine brands and closed a number of its boat plants. The company also divested itself from other businesses, including MotoTron. Additionally, Brunswick's workforce was reduced by 27 percent.[1] Ultimately, as a result of the recession, Brunswick and Mercury would sell or restructure a total of 13 businesses and facilities.
- Once a gem that provided Mercury a yearly profit in excess of $100 million, the sterndrive boat industry evaporated. Despite gaining market share in 2013, the newly consolidated manufacturing facilities in Fond du Lac produced approximately 22,000 sterndrives—a fourth of the amount from when they were produced in Stillwater.[2]
- Between June 2008 and May 2010, the number of Mercury dealers in the US fell 17 percent—totaling 816 businesses.[3] For example, in August 2009, Fountain Powerboat Industries Inc., a boat manufacturer founded in 1979, which exclusively used Mercury engines and whose customers included former president George H. W. Bush and the US Coast Guard, filed for Chapter 11 bankruptcy.[4]

All told, up to 75 percent of all marine industry jobs were lost during the Great Recession.[5]

In Mercury's Australia, New Zealand, and South Pacific region (above), increased interest in products such as the line of low-emission OptiMax outboard engines (right) signaled that the market was finally turning around.

an existing boat, but we're also seeing the start of a swing back to new boats in some regions.

People are willing to spend again if they can find the right product. For example, there has been a fantastic level of interest in low-emission products like our fuel-injected OptiMax outboards. People are still demanding value for money but not at the expense of the environment.[60]

In October, Brunswick announced that it planned to increase boat production the following year to help restock depleted dealer inventories, which in turn would reduce its losses in 2010. This would directly benefit Mercury since new boats would mean new engines from Mercury to power them.[61] Mercury, which hadn't had a layoff since September, recalled 129 employees in November.[62] The marine industry, which recorded its worst year in a half century, was turning around.

Additionally, the end of the weeks of uncertainty concerning Fond du Lac's fate brought "a great sigh of relief in the community," said Joe Reitemeier, president and CEO of the Fond du Lac Area Association of Commerce.[63] Businesses that relied on discretionary dollars and disposable income, such as those in the hospitality industry, could expect increased business now that the cloud of possible unemployment and unpaid bills no longer loomed large in the minds of their potential customers. "Things are on the way up," said Chris Rockweit, president of the Fond du Lac Credit Union on Pioneer Road. "Hopefully with the Merc situation, if it brings in jobs, we will see new opportunities."[64]

Mercury emerged from 2009 with the worst loss in the history of the company—$155 million.[65] Cramer, describing 2009 as "a stain on our record," said the way to erase such a blemish is to establish a new earnings high.[66] Consequently, the company dedicated itself to new product development, particularly in regards to new technologies to reduce emissions. As Mercury began a new chapter, the tribulations it endured revealed a silver lining. "The downturn has forced us to be very careful with how we design the product, what we target, and the functional requirements," Bass said.[67]

Jeff Stueven, director of electrical and electronics engineering, also noted that the consolidation of engineering and engineers led to increased sharing of information and innovation. "We came together with common goals, common thinking. We are a lot closer with our boat companies now, and we're a lot closer with our OEMs," said Stueven, adding that better and more cost-effective solutions can now be found.[68] As a result of this new synergy, the development of a new outboard engine—appropriately codenamed "Bedrock"— would provide the foundation for Mercury's future growth.

After years of development in a program codenamed "Bedrock," Mercury released the 150 FourStroke in 2011. The revolutionary outboard (seen here powering a boat from Buster, a Finnish boatbuilder and a strong partner of Mercury) would quickly become a best seller for the company, far exceeding expectations and prompting the hiring of additional workers to keep up with demand.

CHAPTER EIGHTEEN

SMOOTH SAILING AHEAD

[Mercury Marine's] 75th anniversary reflects their strong heritage of innovation and leadership in the marine industry and their strong roots right here in Wisconsin.

—Wisconsin State Senator Richard Gudex, 2014[1]

MERCURY MARINE WEATHERED THE Great Recession well, but it did not emerge unscathed. Not only was 2009 the worst year on record for Mercury, it was also the worst year on record for the entire marine industry. However, under the leadership of newly appointed president Mark Schwabero, who worked hard to keep morale high by frequently communicating with employees, Mercury successfully balanced the short-term need to concentrate on cash-generating efforts with long-term investments in research and product development. Mercury not only successfully charted a course out of the dire economy but also laid out a path for success that today is leading the company to new heights.

Emerging From the Storm

Although the Great Recession ended in the summer of 2009, its effects on the economy did not, as 500 workers from Mercury remained on layoff.[2] Business continued to lag for the remainder of the year but began to slowly improve, and by January 2010 fewer than 100 remained on layoff. By April, Mercury posted its first optimistic quarterly report in more than a year, as net sales jumped 30 percent compared to the same period in 2009. Mercury also reported operating earnings of $26.5 million—a welcome change from the $50.6 million operating loss the previous year. International sales, which accounted for nearly half of total segment sales, improved by 37 percent.[3] Furthermore, thanks to increased orders, the transfer of work from Stillwater, and increasing demand for outboard engines, Mercury hired an additional 150 employees for various positions throughout the company, including in assembly, machining, die-cast, trim, and warehousing.[4] By summer, Mercury was well on its way to recovery; in July, not only were no Mercury employees on layoff, but the company also hired an additional 145 hourly employees and held a job fair to fill a number of full-time positions in Fond du Lac.[5]

Brunswick Corporation reported a 22 percent increase in its third quarter revenue, compared to 2009. Brunswick also reported operating earnings of $25.2 million, a relatively modest amount but one representing a $134.6 million improvement from the previous year. Mercury reported an 18 percent increase in net sales, and international sales improved by 5 percent. The company

Mercury unveiled its 150 FourStroke outboard motor to distributors, dealers, and press in September 2011.

also posted $49 million in operating earnings, compared to an operating loss of $13.4 million the same time the previous year.[6]

The job situation also continued to rapidly improve. After working closely with state officials, in August 2010 Mercury announced that, in addition to MerCruiser castings and machining operations coming to Wisconsin, its MerCruiser engine and drive assembly operations from Stillwater would also move to Fond du Lac. This would bring 200 new assembly jobs to the community.[7] "The unique combination available in Fond du Lac of a skilled and experienced workforce, world-class processes, a solid supply base, and strong community support provides the best option for the remaining MerCruiser operations," said Schwabero, named Brunswick president and chief operating officer in May 2014 and succeeded as Mercury president by former vice president of global operations John Pfeifer. "This decision is consistent with our

Market growth and market share gains in outboards around the globe led to a significant addition to Plant 15 to accommodate new, state-of-the-art, aluminum-machining investments. *(Photo by James Dean.)*

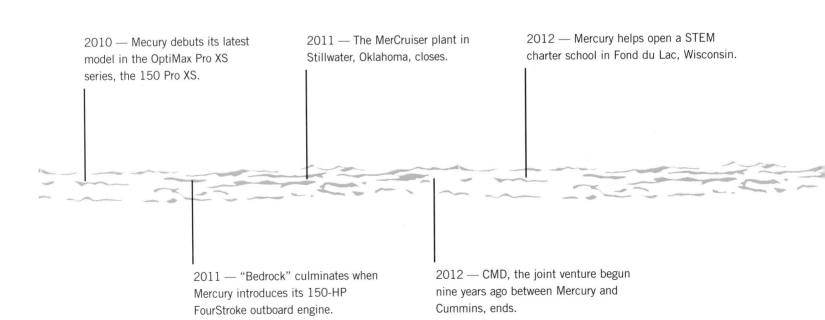

2010 — Mecury debuts its latest model in the OptiMax Pro XS series, the 150 Pro XS.

2011 — The MerCruiser plant in Stillwater, Oklahoma, closes.

2012 — Mercury helps open a STEM charter school in Fond du Lac, Wisconsin.

2011 — "Bedrock" culminates when Mercury introduces its 150-HP FourStroke outboard engine.

2012 — CMD, the joint venture begun nine years ago between Mercury and Cummins, ends.

goal to emerge from this unprecedented downturn as a stronger company, better able to compete in a new and very different marketplace."[8]

"Throughout the first nine months of 2010, we have successfully executed against our strategic initiatives," said Brunswick chairman and CEO Dustan McCoy, who added:

We continue to remain focused on meeting all of the requirements we have identified for ourselves in these difficult economic and market conditions, and subject to the state of the global economy and retail marine markets, we maintain our objective of returning to profitability in 2011.[9]

Mercury returned as a corporate sponsor of tournament fishing when it partnered with FLW Outdoors as an official outboard-engine sponsor in October 2010. "We are very pleased that Mercury has rejoined the ranks of FLW Outdoors," said Trisha Blake, president of the FLW Outdoors Marketing Division. "With our aggressive programs, we're confident Mercury will see considerable market-share growth. They're making a strong statement of support to professional fishing, and our anglers are sure to respond enthusiastically."

Mercury echoed the sentiment. "We feel Mercury represents the heart of tournament fishing," said Mike Shedivy, vice president of marketing at Mercury Marine. "We will continue to support the various species of competitive angling."[10]

Mercury continued to improve in the fourth quarter of 2010 as sales increased 17 percent over the previous year, which included a 10 percent increase in the domestic marine parts and accessories businesses, representing 21 percent of total segment sales in the quarter.[11] The recovery only began to accelerate with the new year. In the first quarter of 2011, Mercury saw net sales increase 17 percent to $520.5 million, with operating earnings nearly doubling to $51.6 million compared to the previous year. Net sales for Brunswick increased 17 percent to $985.9 million.[12] McCoy expressed cautious optimism:

We continue to believe that our 2011 net income will benefit from our previously announced marine plant consolidations, lower restructuring costs and reductions in net interest, depreciation, and pension expenses.[13]

His positive assessment would prove accurate. By July 2011, when Mercury held another job fair

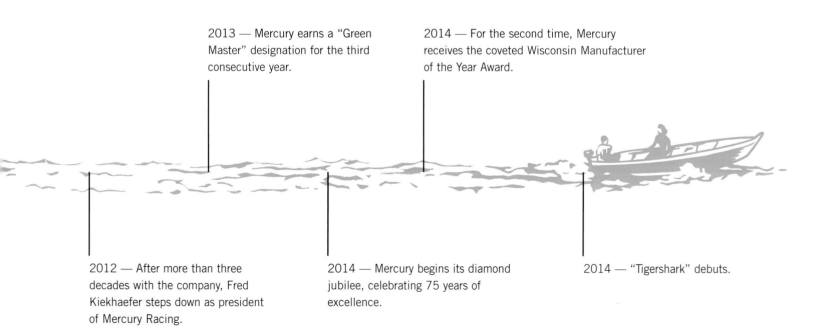

2013 — Mercury earns a "Green Master" designation for the third consecutive year.

2014 — For the second time, Mercury receives the coveted Wisconsin Manufacturer of the Year Award.

2012 — After more than three decades with the company, Fred Kiekhaefer steps down as president of Mercury Racing.

2014 — Mercury begins its diamond jubilee, celebrating 75 years of excellence.

2014 — "Tigershark" debuts.

Sales of Mercury products to law-enforcement organizations at the state and federal level help fuel Mercury's recovery.

in Fond du Lac to add 150 workers, the company had already hired nearly 300 employees.[14] About 38 percent of Mercury's sales came from overseas, helping offset sluggish business in North America, and Brunswick had cleared out millions of dollars in excess boat inventory.[15] Sales of Mercury products to such organizations as the Coast Guard,[16] the New Hampshire Department of Safety,[17] the US Department of Defense Special Operations Command,[18] the Department of Homeland Security,[19] the US Naval Supply Systems Command,[20] and the Alabama Department of Finance[21] helped improve the company's domestic market share.

Making the Good Even Better

Mercury had plenty of reason to keep its employees busy and hire new workers in 2011. In the spring of the previous year, the company debuted its latest model in the OptiMax Pro XS series, the 150 Pro XS. Featuring a new exhaust

tuner to increase torque at liftoff, the 150 Pro XS had a top speed nearly 5 mph faster than competitors, and still delivered a 3-Star emissions rating from the California Air Resources Board.[22] The series' reputation for quality received validation when, at every major B.A.S.S. event in 2010—including the B.A.S.S. Elite tournaments and the 2010 Bassmaster Classic—all the winning anglers used Pro XS engines. The Pro XS had been a favorite choice among anglers on the B.A.S.S. Elite trail for some time because of its strong hole shot, acceleration, top-end speed, fuel efficiency, and dependability.[23] "I know I can count on my Mercury, and that gives me confidence in my ability to win," said Kevin Vandam after winning the 2010 Bassmaster Angler of the Year title and becoming the second person ever to claim the Bassmaster Classic and Angler of the Year titles in the same season.[24]

Mercury's other offerings proved themselves no less capable. On the strength of such products as MerCruiser's Alpha One and Bravo series and Mercury Racing's 525 EFI, the company won the Favorite Sterndrive Manufacturer category in *Powerboat* magazine's inaugural Readers Choice Awards in August 2010. "[Mercury] offers brawny MerCruiser and Mercury Racing drives that are found on the transoms of a majority of performance boats across the country, and they keep getting better," the magazine said. In addition, Mercury Racing also won Favorite Engine Builder and received an honorable mention for Favorite Propeller Manufacturer. "It is always a joy to have your engine, sterndrive, and propeller creations warmly embraced by enthusiasts," said Fred Kiekhaefer, then president of Mercury Racing. "*Powerboat* readers have a passion for excellence and we sincerely appreciate their endorsement."[25]

In the beginning of 2011, Mercury introduced the Verado 250 Pro, the latest addition to the popular Verado series long regarded for its reliable and sophisticated four-stroke propulsion systems. Featuring calibration that improved torque and power by a more performance-oriented boost-control strategy, the 250 Pro boasted quiet and virtually vibration-free performance, as well as supercharged technology that allowed for precise, programmable control over not only fuel use but also air intake to an unparalleled degree of precision.[26]

Mercury further enhanced the Verado by engineering a more robust gear case, delivering even greater durability and reliability. With strengthened internal components, hydrodynamically designed and featuring Mercury's patented XK 360 Alloy for superior corrosion protection, the new gear box was 14 percent larger and came standard with most six-cylinder Verados from 200–300 horsepower. Mercury also offered a special heavy-duty version for heavy commercial applications, and made sure that the new 5.44-inch gear case was designed to work with all of Mercury's existing propellers suitable for six-cylinder engines.

The change came in response to customer trends, said Nicholas Webb, Mercury's director of marketing and outboard product, ANZP Brunswick Asia Pacific Group. "At that larger end of the outboard market, we've noticed a trend with buyers opting for heavier boats in which they can go further and in bigger wave conditions," he said. "That can put more strain on the gear case so, of course, we've reacted. Not only is the gear case stronger but it will also provide additional lift. The Verado is simply the world's best four-stroke outboards, and we're going to make sure it stays right on top of the pack."[27]

Although committed to the improvement of its higher-horsepower engines, the company also remained dedicated to its much smaller machines. Mercury upgraded its smaller four-stroke engines, with its new 4-, 5-, and 6-horsepower models featuring four major improvements: a change to a front-mounted shift lever to make the engines easier and more comfortable to use; the addition of an integral fuel tank to save space and make the engines more portable; a longer tiller handle for improved control and maneuverability; and redesigned engine cowls for better protection and durability.[28]

The drive to improve evolved from monthly quality summits that began in 2010 as Mercury created benchmarks for improvement. One goal was to improve Mercury's warranty rate, the percentage of sales dollars put away to pay for warranty service on the life of the engine. When the summits began, Mercury's rate hovered between 2.5 and 3 percent of sales. Within three years, thanks to quality improvements to the Optimax air compressor

In 2010, Mercury debuted the latest addition to its popular OptiMax Pro XS series, the OptiMax Pro XS 150. That same year, every winning angler at every major B.A.S.S. event had used Pro XS motors.

and the Verado's gearcase, that rate shrank to 1.3 percent, with the savings going directly to the bottom line. This renewed dedication to quality boosted morale, according to Jeff Stueven, director of electrical and electronics engineering and the co-chairman for Mercury's extreme reliability initiative:

> *I am proud to work for Mercury and its quest for a high-quality environment. I've had a lot of fun because people want to improve quality. Everyone has really chipped in to make this happen. The last few years have been really rewarding.*[29]

Hand-in-hand with this heightened focus on quality came an increased attention to efficiency. Dealers and boatbuilders throughout the world were no longer willing to carry the levels of inventory they had previously. This change caused Mercury to become more resilient and flexible in its manufacturing operations and supply chain.[30]

Mercury's efficiency and quality not only reduced the amount of time a sterndrive took to be delivered to potential customers, it also earned the company *Powerboat* magazine's first-ever Reader's Choice Award for Favorite Sterndrive Manufacturer.

Innovation and Investment in the Environment

Mercury's decision to continue investing in research and development during the economic downturn, especially with regard to fuel efficiency, proved wise. In February 2010, out of a field of more than 40 entries, a panel of judges most appreciated the ability of Mercury's MercMonitor with ECO-Screen to automatically calculate the best fuel economy settings for boaters, as well as continuously monitor engine rpm, boat speed, fuel consumption, and engine trim. The device earned West Marine's Green Product of the Year Award grand prize of $10,000. Mercury used the prize money to launch the Mercury Marine Conservation Fund, which, in cooperation with the Fond du Lac Area Foundation, supports local initiatives to improve and maintain the health of the community's aquatic environment. "We have deep roots in this community," said Mike Shedivy, head of company operations in Europe, the Middle East, and Africa. "It's a beautiful place to live and to raise our families. Through this fund, Mercury is playing a greater role in keeping it that way for generations to come."[31] Sandi Roehrig, foundation executive director, added: "Mercury Marine has been such an important part of the vitality of this community

TAKING CARE OF DEALERS

ERCURY MARINE'S DEALERS STRUGGLED during the Great Recession. Between June 2008 and May 2010, Mercury lost 816—17 percent—of its US dealerships.[1] In response, Randy Caruana, vice president of sales and marketing, launched the Power of Choice program in 2009, which incentivized US dealers to take advantage of the entire suite of Mercury, Attwood, and Land 'N' Sea product offerings to enhance customer service and profitability. Caruana recalled the rollout of the program:

> During the downturn, it was very difficult to walk into a dealer and try to plan for his business or plan for growth when he had to plan for his survival. So, we got our staff together and we said, "We're going to approach things a little differently. Rather than go in and drive the dealer to buy 20 outboards, talk about

the program. Focus on trying to make a healthier dealer."

All of a sudden, the dealers' guard came down: "Wow! You guys are really listening!" And then conversations started happening. ... And so, because our approach changed, we weren't treated like a vendor—we were treated like a partner.[2]

Struggling dealers also benefited when Brunswick offered its Dealer Advantage program to all dealers in 2011, giving them Gold- and Platinum-level benefits on a temporary basis.[3]

The new approach has clearly paid off. In *Boating Industry*'s 2013 list of the top 100 dealerships, Mercury dealers took the top 10 spots, with more than 80 Mercury dealerships making the list. In addition, seven dealers also were recognized with "Best in Class" awards.[4]

throughout the years. I am very happy that Mercury has chosen to establish this fund that further demonstrates their continued commitment to the Fond du Lac area."[32]

Mercury also benefited from Wisconsin's Focus on Energy industrial grant program, receiving $270,000 to install centralized air collection systems that allowed clean, filtered air to be recycled inside the facility. The program conserved enough energy to power more than 300 homes for a year and saved Mercury Marine more than $200,000 in annual energy costs. "Wisconsin is working hard to help our manufacturers invest in energy efficiency technologies that reduce energy costs, improve their bottom line, and create and retain jobs," said then-Governor Jim Doyle. "Through these investments, we'll help some of our biggest manufacturers invest in energy efficiency that will help them compete."[33] The investment proved sound in light of an independent evaluation that showed that Wisconsin's Focus on Energy clean energy program added more than 5,000 jobs and

$1.4 billion to Wisconsin's economy since its inception in 2001.[34]

At the 2010 Miami Boat Show, Mercury further demonstrated its environmental savvy with a hybrid electric/solar/diesel concept boat. In its April issue, *Motor Boating* magazine described the test-drive experience:

> As we pulled out of Sea Isle Marina, maneuvering around the other boats in the busy fairway, the boat handled just like any other 42-foot cruiser with Zeus joystick drives and twin diesels. We then turned north, up the Intracoastal Waterway, at eight knots or so. All this was perfectly normal—except that we weren't burning a single ounce of fuel. We were in full-electric mode. No fossil footprint, no exhaust, no noise other than that of the hull sliding through the water.
>
> [Mercury] showed what can be done with existing hull technology. [The boat] had two 100-HP electric motors built into the transmissions, solar panels on the hardtop and under the sun pad on the bow, plus

a bank of high-capacity lithium-ion batteries under the salon sole. ... In this experimental concept boat, you can cruise around the docks, troll offshore, or simply head off for a picnic and run in full-electric mode (under 10 mph) for two or three hours under battery power. Then you either need to start the diesels or, if you're back at the dock or at anchor, wait for the solar system to recharge the batteries.[35]

The whole hybrid system would add 5 to 7 percent to the total cost. "But that's not much," noted Dan Balogh, head of the hybrid program for Mercury, "when you consider the potential fuel savings—and how you're helping the planet."[36]

The magazine also lauded Mercury for "thinking ahead, pushing the envelope, trying to create something new down the road," especially when, considering the existing economic environment, the urge would be to play it safe.[37] This willingness to push the boundaries would be demonstrated again when Mercury unveiled the result of one of its most anticipated development programs: the 150 FourStroke outboard engine.

"Bedrock": The Foundation for Mercury's Future

In September 2011, Mercury announced that the company had invested in the industry's future during its historic downturn and was ready to take advantage now that the market was coming back. The proclamation to distributors, dealers, and press in Genoa, Italy, came in the form of the debut of the 150 FourStroke outboard motor.

The journey to Italy began several years prior when Mercury began developing a new engine based on a

The 150 FourStroke's revolutionary design not only made it significantly lighter than competing engines, it allowed it to be the most powerful engine in its class. *(Photo by Jeff Lendrum.)*

simple idea: listen to what boaters were asking for, and then build the ultimate 150-horsepower outboard. "We particularly focused our attention on being a standout in the areas that our customers told us really matter to them: quality and reliability, smooth operation, a great torque curve, low weight and compact size, excellent fuel economy, and easy maintenance," said David Foulkes, vice president of engineering, product development, and racing at Mercury. "We started our engineering efforts by listening hard to our customers, and then we executed the most effective possible design to meet their needs."[38] The program to build such an engine, codenamed "Bedrock," had been in danger of cutbacks during the Great Recession as the company needed to conserve cash. Fortunately, investment in the future remained a priority and, with the partial help of the loan Mercury received from Fond du Lac County in 2009,[39] development of "Bedrock" continued, using lessons learned from the now-ongoing quality summits. Tim Reid, director of engineering design and development, described the thought process behind its design:

How do you create a low-cost engine? By making it simple, because less parts equals less cost. We did a lot of really goofy brain-storming sessions where we questioned things. On "Bedrock" there would be four injectors, but we asked ourselves, "Why can't there be two? It's less complexity. Why can't it be one?" There are a lot of engineering reasons why not, but in asking those questions and pushing everybody to think about it, something hit the table that made sense. And through that critical thinking and questioning of why we do things and how we do them, we came up with things like the fuel system on "Bedrock." It does everything it has to do but it's much simpler.

Designing simple engines is very challenging, and that drove the engineering team. We would sit and look at the block and say, "Why is that block that big? Why is

FOND DU LAC:
PAYING BACK, GIVING BACK

IN 2010, FOND DU LAC COUNTY PROVIDED Mercury Marine a $50 million low-interest loan to assist Mercury in consolidating operations from Stillwater, Oklahoma, and to develop the new 150 FourStroke outboard. The successful pursuit of these goals led to the creation of full-time jobs in Fond du Lac, with Mercury's workforce nearly doubling from 1,526 in 2009 to almost 3,100 by the end of 2013. "I'm very pleased with what Mercury has been able to accomplish in the last three years," Fond du Lac County Executive Allen Buechel said. "It's what we hoped would happen."[1] In return, Mercury is both repaying the loan and giving back to the community.

In 2010, in cooperation with the Fond du Lac Area Foundation, the company launched the Mercury Marine Conservation Fund, which supports initiatives to improve and maintain the health of the community's aquatic environment.[2] Two years later, in partnership with the Fond du Lac School District, Mercury opened the Fond du Lac STEM Academy, an elementary charter school whose mission is to "develop innovative, passionate learners by providing a rigorous and challenging project-based curriculum grounded in science, technology, engineering, and mathematics [STEM]" and to "encourage ingenuity and creativity using real-world, hands-on experience."[3] Mercury offered its resources and facilities for class projects.[4] The company also supports community organizations such as the Fond du Lac Children's Museum, the Fond du Lac Partnership for Young Children, the Boys and Girls Club of Fond du Lac, and the United Way, to which Mercury donates more than $180,000 annually. Mercury also holds community events such as the "Fill the Boat to Cast Out Hunger" food drive, the "Mercury Recycling Challenge," and "Support the Troops." Mercury employees volunteer for local organizations and serve on their boards.

Mercury's community involvement extends to Juárez, Mexico, where employees donate school supplies and paint classrooms, and to Suzhou, China, where employees work with the Wuzhong orphanage.[5]

---

that billet that big? Why can't we pull a little bit of weight out of here? Let's take this out. Why is that even there? Move the parting line there." It gets to a level of discipline where you are looking at every gram of aluminum and asking, "Why is it on here?" because every gram is money and weight.[40]

Reid also emphasized the importance of simplicity of engine design in general:

Our engines serve many different customers, from back in the woods in the tropics to owners of sport fishing yachts. And we joke about how you've got to be able to fix them with a coconut; you've got to keep it simple. Many of our dealers are in remote parts of the world. Many do not have computer systems to diagnose issues. You have to keep those customers in mind as well.[41]

With that in mind, designers made user-friendly maintenance of the motor a priority. "We put an enormous amount of effort into trying to make it simple for the end user," said Randy Poirier, director of drives and propulsion engineering. "It looks very clean underneath the cowling. All the service points are really thought out."[42]

Designed on five product pillars—smallest, lightest, easiest to maintain, most versatile, and most durable—the result of the "Bedrock" program was a home run. Despite having nearly 20 percent fewer parts than competitors' models and being the lightest 150-HP engine on the market—just 24 pounds more than the OptiMax 150 direct-injected two-stroke—the 3.0-liter, four-cylinder, 150 FourStroke offered more displacement than any other 150-HP engine. Thousands of hours of severe, real-world field-testing guaranteed that the 150 FourStroke would be the most reliable and durable engine on the planet, allowing everyday owners of mid- and entry-level vessels and premium boats to enjoy an easy-to-maintain, long-lasting, and worry-free outboard motor suitable for both recreational and commercial applications.

The engine's unique components included a 4.9-inch gearcase that not only met durability requirements for an engine with twice the horsepower, but also sported an ultra-efficient hydrodynamic profile superior to smaller gearcases. The engine also featured a focus mount system that reduced the mount's temperature, increased its durability, cut boat vibration, and simplified inspection and service; stainless steel latch components, heavy-duty transom brackets, and balance shaft gears produced from bulletproof, high-grade steel; a lightweight thermobonded SMC top cowl made from commercial-grade bonded composites; and a simplified engine flushing system.

Additionally, the 150 FourStroke featured a marine-hardened, automotive-style, 60-amp alternator that was considerably lighter, fully regulated, and supplied current only on demand. It generated two-thirds of its output at only 1,000 rpm and was designed to minimize power drain and heat build-up. An idle exhaust relief system using a low-pass acoustic filter dramatically managed sound. Mercury's SmartStart ignition technology eliminated the possibility of grinding the starter gear. Finally, the 150 FourStroke was configured for quick, easy, intuitive, and hassle-free rigging and repowering. Designed to connect with any steering system, the engine was compatible with standard mechanical cables, dual cable or hydraulic steering, optional power steering on dual-engine setups, standard analog or full SmartCraft instrumentation, and

Mercury's innovative Big Tiller system.[43] Despite all these amenities, the 150 FourStroke cost about $2,500 less than competing 150-HP engines.[44]

The 150 FourStroke's revolutionary design attracted immediate attention and received a very warm welcome from dealers. Pfeifer recalled its unveiling in Italy:

> So this is 2011. Europe's still in bad shape, right? The market's not doing well. From the United Kingdom down to Italy, the market's bad. I think it was an event that gave our channel partners a lot of hope. From day one we were in an oversold situation on that engine. So many, many dealers. We thought we had a pretty good forecast when we designed and developed the product. But I think we oversold our forecast on an annual basis by up to 75 percent, which is enormous. We had dealers that were immediately jumping onboard with it.[45]

A month later, in October, the engine received an innovation award at the International Boatbuilders Exhibition and Conference (IBEX). "Mercury found a way to trim 24 pounds off their new 150 FourStroke, while helping to satisfy the growing need for superb fuel efficiency and performance," said IBEX innovation awards judge Zuzana Procheska.[46] The public responded with equal enthusiasm: Mercury assumed that it would produce 6,500 units in the first year, but the company surpassed that number within six months.[47] "The 150 FourStroke showed the world that we are a world-class engine manufacturer," said Marty Bass, vice president of category management. "But I think it also showed the world that we can listen to our customer requests and make those actionable, and that's really in my mind where that product shined. We knew that we had the lightest, fastest, easiest to maintain 150-HP motor. That's what we delivered and there were no compromises on that engine. It has just blown us out of the water on capturing market share and sales."[48]

The 150 FourStroke proved to be not only a commercial success for Mercury, but also a much-needed morale booster, according to Kevin Grodzki, vice president of Brunswick and president of global sales and marketing at Mercury:

The 150 FourStroke accomplished all the goals that we set out to achieve in terms of the reputation for Mercury Marine, the performance in the market-place, the ability to enter and penetrate some new markets. And quite frankly it was a big shot in the arm for our organization at the same time. When there was so much bad news that was going around, knowing that we could deliver something like this was a big rallying point for the organization, whether it be in manufacturing, engineering, sales and marketing, finance, wherever. It was a true team effort, and seeing that chalked up to the win column was a big plus for everyone.[49]

Transitions

The transition of MerCruiser operations from Stillwater to Fond du Lac began quickly and quietly

The "Bedrock" development program culminated in Genoa, Italy (below), as Mercury debuted its newest 150 outboard motor, the 150 FourStroke (right), to popular acclaim.

in 2011. A subtle change included the addition of a large door at the loading dock of Plants 4 and 17. The door was meant to accommodate two castings-related machines from Stillwater, one of which included a 16-foot-diameter bowl. Bearing-carrier machining cells, which contain four machines (two lathes, one vertical drill, and one media finisher), also moved. "We're more than 50 percent finished moving the castings-related components," said Gary Smet, retiring vice president and executive project manager. "While it might not be obvious to those driving by our plant, many significant changes have already taken place, and additional movement will happen on an ongoing basis."[50]

More noticable changes began later that year in November as construction began on a 33,000-square-foot expansion project to support consolidation of Stillwater operations at Plants 3 and 15 in Fond du Lac. The project would build the main receiving dock for Mercury in Fond du Lac, as well as the receiving area and component storage site for Mercury MerCruiser manufacturing. Wayne Rollin, the City of Fond du Lac's community development

Mark Schwabero (far right, third row) and the team behind project "Bedrock" stand next to the first 150 FourStroke. The motor was designed to be the smallest, lightest, easiest-to-maintain, most versatile, and most durable 150-HP outboard on the market.

director, said, "A year and a half ago, we thought the company might not be here at all. So this is definitely good news for the community. It's not a major expansion, but any expansion is a good thing."[51]

The transition came to a bittersweet end in early December 2011, as Stillwater closed its doors. According to Lawrence Robinson, Stillwater's director of operations, workers averaged 50 years of age and 25 years of service, and he praised the remaining workers' professionalism and composure in keeping the plant running despite the announcement of its eventual closing more than two years before. Many workers expressed gratitude for Robinson and Joe Payne, the Stillwater plant's director of human resources. Diann Wingfield, one of 14 employees who retired as the plant closed, said the toughest part would be saying goodbye to friends. "There are lots of good people here," Robinson echoed. "It's not just a group of employees—it's a group of family and friends."[52]

Grodzki said:

Our goal was to emerge from the downturn a strong company that is better able to compete in a new market environment, and this program is a strong step in that direction. This was a complex operation that was very well-managed by teams here in Fond du Lac and in Stillwater. More than 80,000 discrete parts were moved and requalified in the new Fond du Lac facility. Throughout the process, we had excellent cooperation by members of the teams in both cities, with employees sharing decades of invaluable experience, knowledge, and know-how.[53]

Cummins MerCruiser Diesel Marine (CMD), Mercury's 9-year-old joint venture with Cummins, Inc., also ended. Announced in December 2011, the dissolution of the joint venture was completed by the following April. The partnership came to a natural end, said Steve Fleming, director of communications: "Joint ventures typically aren't forever. That's the course here. In nine years, it seems to have done its job. Was it successful? Absolutely."[54]

Despite the breakup of the joint venture and the subsequent retirement of the Cummins MerCruiser brand, the two companies continued to work together, switching to a strategic supply arrangement to better serve customers in the global diesel marine market.[55] Cummins would continue to use parts from Mercury—including propulsion systems, rigging accessories, and engine controls—and focus on the mid-range and heavy-duty diesel engine business, while Mercury pursued

Global market growth and market share gains in outboards required a significant addition to Plant 17 to accommodate new high-tonnage, high-pressure die-cast investments. *(Photo by James Dean.)*

smaller, high-speed engines, integrating CMD's High Speed Diesel range into its product portfolio.[56]

Sharing the Fruits of Success

In December 2011, Mercury gave about 1,200 hourly employees a special one-time bonus as a "thank you" for their work helping the company achieve solid growth despite a challenging year. "We want our employees to know that their dedication and extraordinary efforts in 2011—and the results of those extraordinary efforts—were greatly appreciated by the company, and we're glad to be able to show that appreciation with a monetary bonus to our hourly employees," said Schwabero.[57] "New product launches, in addition to transition activities associated with our plant consolidation, required extra effort," said Denise Devereaux, vice president of human resources. "We wanted to recognize those efforts by providing an award that would be meaningful [and] hope this will enable them to celebrate with their families."[58] Mark Zillges, president of the local chapter of the International Association of Machinists, expressed appreciation for the action: "I think it's a nice gesture. It's a step in the right direction."[59]

The bonus served as a cap to a successful year that included the consolidation of Stillwater, a record-setting performance by Land 'N' Sea, the launch of a sustainability program, and achieving Green Master certification. The launch of the new 150 FourStroke outboard and the introduction of a fuel system by Attwood Marine, both of which earned innovation awards at the 2011 International Boatbuilders Exhibition and Conference, topped off the achievements. Foreign markets saw a 12 percent increase, driven by commercial marine market sales, in the first nine months of 2011. Domestic sales increased 8 percent.[60]

Parts and Accessories and Service: Continuing to Keep Mercury Afloat

During the Great Recession, consumers opted against purchasing new products in favor of upgrading and maintaining their current engines, and Mercury business units Attwood Marine and Land 'N' Sea, which sell the company's parts and accessories, benefited from this trend. According to Tom Schuessler, president of Land 'N' Sea, sales only fell by "single digits for a couple of years."[61] At Attwood, which now enjoys annual sales close to $125 million, diversification into aftermarket sales proved a boon, said company president Chris Drees:

When I joined in 2007, we wanted to diversify our market mix, and we really targeted the after-

In November 2011, expansion of facilities for MerCruiser manufacturing at Plant 3 and Plant 15 (below) commenced. *(Photo by James Dean.)*

Mercury's commercial marine sales overseas in regions such as South America (above) contributed to the company's growing success in foreign markets.

market to grow and expand. That was great timing because the OEM market began declining in 2008 and 2009. Our aftermarket sales were really doing extremely well. It was very fortuitous for us that our sales continued to grow throughout the downturn because our aftermarket business was expanding faster than the OEM market was contracting.[62]

As a consequence, sales of parts and accessories helped Mercury weather the recession. "Right now, parts and accessories are booming," Fleming said. "People are not buying as many new boats—they're replacing parts on their old boats."[63]

Mercury's superior propeller technology also helped secure business in the aftermath of an environmental disaster. Unlike other manufacturers whose propeller hubs are made of rubber, which are prone to deterioration when exposed to oil, Mercury's Flo-Torq hub system uses Delrin, an oil-impervious resin from DuPont. Mercury had been using Flo-Torq, whose durability made them

particularly appealing to racers, since 1995, and its oil resistance led to the company receiving an order of 90 engines for boats sent to clean up after the 2010 BP oil spill in the Gulf of Mexico.[64]

Mercury continued to innovate and improve its propellers. In August 2011, Mercury Propellers introduced the Spitfire, its first four-blade aluminum performance propeller designed for 25-HP to 125-HP outboards, which included designs that addressed the unique needs of pontoon boats. Its design increased blade area while decreasing diameter and borrowed from Mercury's stainless steel Fury and Enertia propellers. The propeller dramatically improved acceleration—25 percent faster from 0 to 30 mph than Mercury's best-selling Black Max. The Spitfire used an extra cup design coupled with a straight trailing edge to hold the water, with a goal of being the best-handling aluminum propeller on the market.[65]

With the growth of ultraquiet motors, Mercury introduced a Moving Propeller Alert safety-warning light system for its SmartCraft range of engines in April 2012. Designed to fit on the transom at the boarding location, the alert features six highly visible synchronized LED lights that move when the prop is rotating to indicate when the boat is safe to board or exit.[66]

In October, the company introduced seven new propellers to its Enertia and Revolution 4 propeller lineups, which complemented the 150 FourStroke and the new Verado gearcase.[67] The following spring, Mercury introduced a new line of Bravo Three propellers designed for heavier boats using higher-horsepower diesel engines. "Today's pressure-charged diesel engines generate a lot of torque at very low rpm," said Dirk Bjornstad, category director for Mercury Propellers. "The high rake and extra cup on the Bravo Three Diesel propellers capture that power and hold the water, resulting in faster time to plane and superior cavitation and ventilation resistance on diesel-powered boats. They also provide more bow lift."[68]

Mercury launched a new website to support its Quicksilver retail brand of marine parts and accessories, www.quicksilver-products.com, in July 2012. "Only a small population of the boating community knows that Quicksilver is part of the Mercury Marine family," said Heidi Stark, manager of aftermarket products at Mercury Marine. "This website will make consumers aware that Quicksilver is the Mercury Marine retail brand that can be found in aisles at many of the nation's largest retail stores."[69]

In February 2013, Mercury released the new VesselView 4 and VesselView 7 engine displays for its SmartCraft-ready outboards, MerCruiser engines,

SAFETY ALWAYS FIRST

DESPITE THE TURMOIL SURROUNDING THE GREAT Recession, employee safety never took a back seat at Mercury Marine. Even during the challenging time afterwards when the number of new hires meant on-boarding employees unfamiliar with manufacturing safety procedures, training and emphasis on working safely remained a priority and have become a tradition. In April 2010, three Mercury plants in Fond du Lac staffing more than 500 employees recorded 1 million consecutive hours without a lost-time injury. In 2011, 2012, and 2013, Mercury Racing earned the annual Brunswick Chairman's Safety Award for the highest level of safety performance by a Brunswick Corporation facility, which was created to encourage and reward employees and facilities for outstanding safety and health performance,[1] and in 2013, eight Mercury plants earned Brunswick's Distinguished Safety Award.[2]

Tom Baumgartner, Mercury's environmental health and safety director, credited the regular audits of plant safety practices and employee safety education programs. "These milestones reflect the diligent efforts of Mercury employees to maintain safety as one of our core values," he said in 2010. "Their leadership and commitment have made significant progress toward building awareness and achieving sustainable safety practices in their workplace."[3] Baumgartner himself was honored with a Lifetime Achievement Award—established to honor those individuals who have devoted their lives to the safety of others—by the Wisconsin Safety Council and the Wisconsin Department of Workforce Development in April 2013.[4]

In their efforts to prevent injuries and improve employee health, Mercury also implemented a number of additional strategies. Employees were taught pre-shift stretching exercises, and certain job stations were ergonomically redesigned. The company also added physical fitness coaching to complement its ongoing biometric screening, health risk assessment, and tobacco-cessation programs.[5]

Mercury Racing engines, and Mercury Diesel engines. The new VesselView models displayed more than 30 engine parameters in 16 languages, could monitor up to four engines, and sported such features as the ECO-Screen, Smart Tow, and Troll Control.[70] That same month, the company also introduced Joystick Piloting for Outboards, which allows an operator to move a multi-engine outboard-powered boat sideways, diagonally, or spinning on its own axis with a simple push or twist of a joystick. Developed for the Verado, the system was designed to take the stress out of docking, maneuvering in tight spaces, and operating in less-than-ideal environments. The system also features Mercury's Skyhook virtual anchor, VesselView integration, and Auto Heading and Waypoint Sequencing autopiloting.[71]

Of course, servicing products is no less important, and that fact is part of any development project. Mike Gyorog, vice president of global service and marine parts and accessories, said:

> *When we do new product programs, one of the first considerations that goes along with developing a concept for a new engine is how are we going to take care of and service this product. From a service and parts and accessories perspective, we are heavily involved from the very beginning of every program. We have people on my team who are part of the engine product development team.[72]*

He also discussed Mercury's commitment to technician training:

> *Training is a huge component of what we do. We have a training curriculum which is more extensive than any other marine engine manufacturer, and making sure that training supports all of our new engines is a very important piece of our responsibilities. We have more than 20,000 ID numbers assigned to technicians in our learning system just in North America. We have service schools all over the globe, and there's a customized curriculum technicians go through in their local language. We offer a wide curriculum of online learning classes, and a technician can learn about a particular topic in either an instructor-led, hands-on fashion, or via the Internet.[73]*

Above: The parts and accessories business helped Mercury weather the Great Recession, and strong parts and accessories sales of items such as the Bravo Three propeller continue to bolster Mercury's bottom line today.

Below: Mercury's high-tech VesselView 4 and VesselView 7 displays not only monitor a host of engine parameters, they also feature a number of Mercury innovations, including the Skyhook virtual anchor, Auto Heading and Waypoint Sequencing, and the award-winning ECO-Screen.

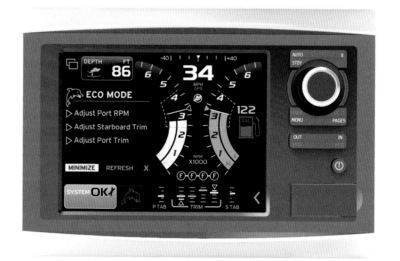

Gyorog added that the most important focus is the customer:

We answer our phones within 30 seconds 97 percent of the time. We don't want people waiting for somebody to call them back. We're committed to making sure we have knowledgeable agents on the phone who have the training they need on our products, so that when somebody calls us and needs help, they are going to get that help quickly.[74]

Expansion and Growth

Business continued to improve, and Mercury reported increased operating earnings and sales for the second quarter of 2012, with higher sales in parts and accessories and outboard engines in the United States. US retail growth in the aluminum and fiberglass outboard marine markets helped Brunswick achieve a 21 percent increase in profits.[75]

Mercury's dedication to quality continued to pay dividends. In June, Mercury repeated its hat trick from four years earlier by once again being the only marine engine manufacturer to receive three "Best Buy" designations from *Consumer Digest*, for the 9.9-horsepower BigFoot, the 75-horsepower OptiMax, and the 150-horsepower FourStroke, respectively.[76] The company also later received Marine Industry Customer Satisfaction Index Awards in the outboard, sterndrive, and inboard categories from the National Marine Manufacturers Association—the only engine manufacturer to win awards in multiple categories. "Mercury Marine is honored to be recognized for customer satisfaction," said Schwabero. "Mercury Marine continually focuses on improving the boating experience for our customers by manufacturing innovative and reliable products, while providing personalized customer service."[77]

Mercury's expansion continued in earnest as it embarked on a $20 million construction project in August 2012 to expand product development and engineering.[78] "It's all about growth and commitment

Mike Gyorog, Mercury vice president of global service and marine parts and accessories, emphasizes the important role parts and accessories teams play in the development of new technology.

to technology and product development," Schwabero said at the ceremonial groundbreaking, when a shovel preserved from the original groundbreaking nearly 50 years ago again saw use. He hinted at continued growth, adding, "If everything is going as planned, maybe we can keep the cranes on site. ... It's good to see new employees walking through the doors."[79]

The company had real reason for optimism: Mercury's third quarter showed an 11 percent rise in sales and a 41 percent growth in operating earnings compared to 2011, driven by increased sales in outboard engine and parts and accessories businesses, but partially offset by declines in sterndrive engines.[80] US sales of recreational boats, accessories, and marine services increased 6 percent in 2011, the first increase in retail sales since 2006, according to the National Marine Manufacturers Association.[81]

Thanks to an increase in demand for its most popular engines, in November 2012 Mercury announced it would hire about 170 additional workers, mostly for manufacturing positions.[82] "Mercury Marine continues to see unprecedented demand in many of its most popular outboards, such as the new 150-horsepower FourStroke," said Devereaux, who has seen the effects in her human resources position. "In order to meet that demand, Mercury is focused on attracting and hiring quality employees by offering a competitive salary and benefits package, as well as a variety of work shifts."[83] In anticipation of the upcoming production, Mercury offered a new full-time shift schedule that would be particularly attractive to college students, parents wanting to balance a home life with a career, or those with a home-based business: 12-hour shifts on Friday, Saturday, and Sunday, with another four hours of pay thrown in for a total of 40 hours of compensation.[84]

The year ended strong, as sales grew 12 percent and operating profits more than doubled in the fourth quarter, compared to 2011, with nearly $2 billion in sales in 2012.[85] "Our goal was to take the steps necessary to emerge from the industry downturn a stronger company, better able to compete in a new and different market," said Schwabero. "Market conditions remain fragile, but there are areas of growth that we are taking advantage of and Mercury is growing. Our 2012 performance reinforces that we took the right actions at the right time to position ourselves to meet our goals."[86] The decision to invest in the future and to develop the 150 FourStroke proved to be one of those right actions. In February 2013, Mercury again expanded production and hired 80 new workers to keep up with demand for the company's most popular engines.[87] In particular, Kurt Langel, human resources director, credited "the phenomenal success of the 150 [FourStroke] in the marketplace."[88]

Another Chapter Closes

In December 2012, Fred Kiekhaefer, the son of Mercury founder Carl Kiekhaefer and a veteran with more than three decades' experience in the industry, announced he would step down as president of Mercury Racing, ending his 22-year career with the company. Schwabero praised Kiekhaefer, saying:

The achievements of Fred Kiekhaefer have been integral to the success of Mercury Marine for two decades and, more specifically, to Mercury Racing. Fred's genetic association to boating was strengthened by an impressive education and a powerful desire and commitment to create the best-performing marine engines.

Fred has brought many key innovations to Mercury, and his influence will be felt here and throughout the world of boating for many years.

On behalf of all Mercury employees, I'd like to thank Fred for his important contributions and wish him the very best in all future endeavors.[89]

Among those contributions was project "Mesa," which developed Mercury Racing's quad-cam, four-valve, 9.0-liter engine—the QC4v. Designed to provide ultimate torque capacity, the QC4v also offered an unheard of level of reliability and was capable of going up to four seasons before requiring any

Along with expansions of manufacturing facilities came expansions to Plant 15's workforce as production increased.

Erik Christiansen, a Mercury veteran who served as chief engineer on a number of projects for Mercury Racing, became general manager of the independent business unit after Fred Kiekhaefer stepped down as president of Mercury Racing.

rebuild work. The new engine not only allowed Mercury to recapture its market, it became virtually essential to it. "Some companies told us they couldn't sell a boat if it did not have a QC4v in it," said Kiekhaefer. "It literally took over the high end of the marine industry. Performance boats just were not able to be sold without them."[90]

After Kiekhaefer's departure, the company appointed Erik Christiansen general manager. A 15-year veteran who had been serving as director of engineering at Mercury Racing, Christiansen led teams that created many of the company's most notable high-performance engines. He worked on the design team for the Verado and acted as chief engineer of a 25-person team that designed and developed Mercury Racing's QC4v 1100- and 1350-horsepower propulsion systems, as well as the company's 850-, 1075-, and 1200-horsepower high-performance sterndrive engines. "Erik's rich experience and intimate knowledge of the programs and market

needs will ensure the continuity of Mercury's leadership in the global high-performance market," said Schwabero.[91]

Under Christiansen, Mercury Racing continued a long-held tradition: winning. "We did Rouen [the annual 24-hour race held in France] in 2013," said Christiansen, "and won first through eighth."[92]

Cruising Along

Mercury began to invest in earnest. In July 2013, as its new research and development facility neared completion, Mercury broke ground on another $20 million expansion project at Plants 15 and 17 in Fond du Lac, adding 38,000 square feet of increased manufacturing capacity. The project, which included the installation of horizontal machining equipment and high-pressure die-cast machines, also planned for future equipment installation through 2015. According to Pfeifer, who was named Mercury president in May 2014, the expansions were necessary in part because of increased technology and emissions requirements, along with the company's increased focus on sustainability. Pfeifer also noted that Mercury was taking on a significant amount of commercial and government work. "This is another statement of the success that we have at Mercury Marine and our continued commitment to the community and employees in Fond du Lac," said Schwabero.[93] Smet added, "This year, we're going to spend more capital in a single year than we ever have in our history."[94] As with Mercury Marine's earlier expansion, companies based in the Fond du Lac area of Wisconsin did approximately 90 percent of the project work, prompting state representative Jeremy Thiesfeldt (R-Fond du Lac) to say, "I think it shows that Mercury Marine is dedicated to the promises to its employees and the county and city that they intend to stay in Fond du Lac and hope to continue profitable operations in the community."[95]

High Performance

The company also continued to expand its product portfolio with innovation in 2013. In August, Mercury Racing debuted the 520, the newest member in its family of high-performance sterndrives. Intended as a low-cost, high-tech alternative for recreational boaters, the 520 featured an increased cylinder bore size for enhanced torque and horsepower; aluminum cylinder heads featuring optimized valve angles for improved air flow; a digital throttle and shift utilizing Mercury Racing's exclusive Engine Guardian System, a "smart" technology that helps prevent engine damage; one-touch Smart Start and automatic throttle synchronization; and ergonomic Zero Effort Digital controls.[96]

The following month, Mercury debuted the Enertia ECO propeller, an environmentally conscious alternative designed specifically for high-horsepower outboard-powered boats. "Mercury Marine already produces fuel-efficient engines, as well as driver aids such as the ECO Screen display," said Jared Reichenberger, brand manager for Mercury Propellers, as he explained the new propeller's genesis. "As marina gasoline prices have continued to rise, customers are increasingly focused on fuel economy. We realized an appreciable fuel economy gain could be found in the design of the propeller itself."[97] Made from Mercury's proprietary X7 stainless-steel alloy, the Enertia ECO drag-reducing design matched the performance of other Mercury propellers while providing a 10 percent increase in fuel economy at cruising speeds, saving the average offshore boater nearly $600 annually in fuel costs.[98]

By November, Mercury had nearly 3,100 employees at Fond du Lac, up from about 1,500 in 2009.[99] Since 2009, Mercury had added 2,000 members to its global workforce, employing a total of 5,300 people worldwide.[100] As the year drew to a close, the company was unrecognizable from its struggling self of four years earlier. Thanks in part to active business in outboard engines and parts and accessories, Mercury's fourth quarter saw a 5 percent increase in net sales, allowing the company to boast total sales in excess of $2 billion in 2013—one of the best years in its history.[101]

Making a Difference

Mercury demonstrated its commitment to sustainability by earning a "Green Master" designation from the Wisconsin Sustainable Business Council for the third consecutive year by scoring 442 total points in 2013, well above the program average of

HELPING OUR VETS

MERCURY COMMITTED ITSELF TO THE COUNTRY'S veterans by signing an agreement with the US Army Recruiting Command in September 2013, giving priority interview status to qualified soldiers participating in the Army's Partnership for Youth Success (PaYS) program. "The Partnership for Youth Success program is a unique opportunity for not only the US Army and Mercury Marine but for our transitioning soldiers as well," explained Lieutenant Colonel Daryl Collins, commander of the US Army Recruiting Battalion Milwaukee. "Through this program, PaYS partner companies gain employees who have developed professional work habits and have been held to the highest standards of conduct. Our soldiers are given an opportunity for employment with established reputable companies."[1]

With more than 150 veterans already employed at Mercury, not only did the company become a proud sponsor of PaYS, but it also formed a Veteran Employees Network, which assists veterans transitioning out of the military and into civilian life.[2]

Above: Technology and emissions requirements—along with an increased focus on sustainability—prompted the construction of new facilities in Fond du Lac. *(Photo by James Dean.)*

Below: After recording more than $2 billion in annual sales—one of its best years ever—Mercury Marine kicked off its diamond anniversary in 2014 at its headquarters in Fond du Lac.

for the third consecutive year by scoring 442 total points in 2013, well above the program average of 259 points. Schwabero expressed Mercury's pride for the recognition:

> *We continue to strive to have sustainability at the core of our culture. From our product designs and manufacturing facilities to employee wellness initiatives and community education and support, we remain committed to making Mercury the most sustainable company it can be.*[102]

The Green Master program measures a broad spectrum of sustainability issues, ranging from energy and water conservation to waste management, community outreach, and education. Since 2011, measures implemented at Mercury have saved 41 billion BTUs of energy annually and nearly a quarter-million gallons of water.[103] Grodzki elaborated on why Mercury will continue to champion sustainability efforts:

> *Taking a leadership role on this matter makes sense because when you think about it, boating is all about enjoying clean water and clean skies, and a marine company like Mercury is ideally suited to promote making dedicated efforts towards sustainability.*[104]

Celebrating the Past, Preparing for the Future

Mercury kicked off its diamond anniversary on January 22, 2014, celebrating 75 years of business. The company promised to make the milestone a memorable one. "We will conduct events in locations around the world that will engage our customers, suppliers, employees, and communities and will recognize the roles those people and entities have played in establishing the foundation of our business and our future," said Schwabero. "We're excited about sharing this celebration with those who have helped us grow and succeed."[105]

That celebration included the opening of a museum chronicling the company's rich history. Located inside the Children's Museum of Fond du Lac, the exhibits and interactive displays opened on April 3, 2014. Schwabero joined community leaders in the official launch of the museum, which also showcases snowmobiles, chainsaws, and drone engines once made by Mercury. Other exhibits include the first engine Kiekhaefer built and a glimpse into the mystery-shrouded Lake X[106], a 1,400-acre lake in central Florida surrounded by woods and swampland that Kiekhaefer scouted out in 1957 on a search for a secluded testing site. Teams of workers from Fond du Lac have spent months at Lake X, building seawalls and boat launches.[107]

Admission to the Mercury Marine museum is $1, and proceeds will be donated to a different charity each month.[108]

"Mercury Marine has such a rich history, and it will be a joy to share that with folks across the state of Wisconsin and around the world as they visit our museum," Schwabero said in a press release.[109]

Community leaders echoed Schwabero's thoughts. "Mercury Marine has been one of the

Left and below: The new Mercury Marine Museum in Fond du Lac opened in Spring 2014 and features numerous artifacts from Mercury's storied history.

mainstay employers in the Fond du Lac area for decades. The recent expansions have been a real boon for the economy," said Paul Stelter, director of the Fox Valley Workforce Development Board. "The growth has been very impressive and speaks well both to the efforts of employees and management."[110]

"We would have been happy if we had retained 2,900 jobs," said Steve Jenkins, president of the Fond du Lac County Economic Development Corp. "But we are well beyond that now, and I am sure more jobs will be coming."[111]

With the success of existing products such as Axius, SeaCore, and the 150 FourStroke, and myriad new Mercury projects and products, there seems to be no worry that more work will be coming. When General Motors stopped making the engine blocks MerCruiser used for its sterndrive assembly, the company adapted. "We're going to make our own short blocks [engine subassemblies] in the near future," said Smet. "We created open floor space, had to move some machines and equipment and get them up and running, and we actually brought back some knowledgeable and experienced retirees to help us with that."[112]

"There are a lot of things going on in the automotive industry that make sense for cars; there is technology they need to bring to their power sources that just don't make sense for marine applications," Schwabero said. "As we

THE INTERNATIONAL MARKET

THE GREAT RECESSION DIDN'T AFFECT JUST US markets. Nations worldwide suffered economic downturns. However, as international markets recover, business overseas promises to become an important piece of Mercury Marine's continuing success.

According to William Gress, president of Mercury in South America, Mercury is well represented in that market, which represents approximately $120 million in sales. Brazil, with its very active boat-building industry and where Mercury enjoys an 80 percent share of the inboard and outboard market, is especially prof-

itable and accounts for two-thirds of Mercury's regional business.[1]

In Australia, New Zealand, and the Pacific region, "We have a lot of customers such as hotel groups that have water skiing and parasailing franchises," said John Temple, general manager for the region, which includes island nations from New Guinea to Tahiti. Mercury also supports indigenous people who primarily use Mercury products for fishing. "They travel 30 and 40 miles between some of these islands," Temple said. "Reliability of our product is very, very important in the South Pacific."[2]

With the upcoming introduction of its "Tigershark" series of 75-, 90-, and 115-HP four-stroke outboards, Mercury is poised to increase its international market share, especially among small commercial boats that typically use lower-horsepower motors.

marinize engines today, you start with something that is not optimal. We think we can bring a purpose-built engine to a marine application that lets us bring some technology that can be unique to the marine application."[113] The resulting sterndrive—a purpose-built marine engine rather than a marinized automotive one, codenamed "Brizo" after the Greek goddess of mariner protection—debuted in 2014.

Mercury's investment in environmental technology and its drive to innovate dovetails with the biggest event the company plans during its 75th anniver-

sary: the launch of a new line of 75-, 90-, and 115-HP four-stroke outboards, codenamed "Tigershark."

Although based on the work of the "Bedrock" program that developed and designed the revolutionary 150 FourStroke, "Tigershark" is not simply a duplication of "Bedrock," according to Poirier:

Even though we had just completed "Bedrock," we still went out and listened to customers to try to find out key attributes somebody really wants in a 75-, 90-, or 115-HP product. Along with that, just like on "Bedrock," we did a lot of benchmark-

Closer to home, Mercury's transition from two-stroke to four-stroke motors has helped the company capture more than half the Canadian market share four years in a row, according to Georges Jalbert, general manager in Canada.[3]

Europe presents a unique challenge for Mercury. Not only did the continent suffer a double-dip recession and is still essentially in an economic downturn, the disparate cultures also create their own marketing problems. "There is no such thing as Europe," explained Ray Atchinson, vice president of global parts and accessories business development. "Europe is lots of languages and lots of currencies and lots of little markets and lots of different kinds of boating. ... Everything you publish has to be done in 14 languages."[4] Yet despite the current economic climate and complexity, Mercury has increased its market share by 7 points,[5] thanks in part to dedicated distributors such as Demetrius Staphio in Greece who, despite that country's particularly difficult problems, managed to nearly double his market share from 24 percent to 46 percent.[6]

Capturing a larger international share will require a new focus, however. Currently, "Mercury product is basically designed to meet the needs of the North American and European leisure markets, but we're selling all over the world. The customers in the rest of the territories are commercial markets," said Bill McEathron, general manager in Asia. "Over 90 percent of my customers use our product for a living."[7]

Fortunately, Mercury's recent innovations—particulary the 150 FourStroke—are perfectly poised to drive Mercury's future growth overseas in the commercial market. "The 150 FourStroke has done well in South America," said Gress. "It's best known currently in the Amazon River region. It's a significant product used by the water taxis. It's becoming a workhorse for them."[8] John Pfeifer, then vice president of global operations and now Mercury president, provided a dramatic example of the FourStroke's acceptance in the global commercial market:

I was with our distributor in South Korea, which is a bit more of a commercial market. Initially, he had bought maybe half-a-dozen 150 FourStrokes when it first launched. About a year later, he said, "You know, we were cautious about this at first because if you put an engine on a commercial operator's boat and then you have problems with it, it can really hurt you. We wanted to make sure that this is going to work. ... Now we are sure this is going to work." So his orders after the first year skyrocketed.[9]

Even with the FourStroke's overwhelming success overseas, the upcoming "Tigershark" line of 75-, 90-, and 115-horsepower four-stroke engines promises to be even more popular. "'TigerShark' hits the heart of where our weaknesses were at Mercury in the four-stroke market," enthused Gress. "We expect that we'll have great results with it."[10]

ing. ... The displacement of the engine is going to provide extremely good low-end torque. It's going to provide the power that's desired at the higher horsepower nodes.[114]

The "Tigershark" engines—which weigh less than comparable two-stroke engines—promise to be even bigger game-changers than the 150 Four-Stroke. Pfeifer said:

Our engineers are good and they have improved upon what they learned when they designed and

developed the 150 FourStroke, so you've got what I believe to be an even better product. The design validations that we've run right out here in the plant have been some of the smoothest validation launches we've ever done.

Like the 150 FourStroke, "Tigershark" also has commercial applications, but the 75- to 115-horsepower range is an even more important commercial engine category in terms of volume. Lots and lots of workboats and fishing boats in the world use that type of engine. So, for example, we can take it to the Chinese market, which is becoming more emissions

Above: Mark Schwabero, Mercury's president from 2008 to May 2014, orchestrated the company's bounce back from the Great Recession. Schwabero was promoted in May 2014, becoming Brunswick's president and chief operating officer.

Right: Mercury's transition from two-stroke to four-stroke motors allowed Georges Jalbert, general manager of Canada, to capture a majority of Canada's market share for four consecutive years, and he looks forward to "Tigershark" helping him continue that trend.

conscious, and say, "We've got a product now that is better in terms of its emissions and environmental friendliness, and it can work in so many of these commercial operations that are growing in this region." I think it's going to be fantastic.[115]

Georges Jalbert, general manager of sales in Canada, is even more enthusiastic about the prospects of "Tigershark" and what it means for the industry and the company:

It's the next step forward. It's another game changer and a first in the industry when you take a look at what we've done. "Tigershark" is just going to be another gangbuster for us.[116]

Just as important as producing revolutionary products is the recruitment and development of the talent that designs and builds them, and Mercury remains dedicated to that goal. Mercury's internal culture makes it an attractive employer for enthusiastic engineers. Stuart Halley, director of product planning and program management, said, "The culture is a can-do culture. Your voice can easily be heard. With any ideas you would have there is always a mechanism to get those ideas out and for review."[117] Reid agreed, adding:

We give a lot of opportunity for technical professional growth. You have a lot of impact on the product and it's a diverse interesting product line-up. You are not just going to make an alternator bracket and that's what you are going to do for your career. You're going to be able to move around and actually have a strong impact on what we make and why we make it.[118]

Devereaux also noted that Mercury can provide a fulfilling career to those without a college background:

We have the capability to offer people a full lifetime of employment and growth. We can take somebody with very limited background and skills, and we will teach them a trade. We have the opportunity to help people grow.

We have a very robust apprenticeship program, so if they want to become a skilled tradesperson,

we can help them with that. And if they want to even go into a professional occupation with us, we can help them do that, as well. I'll give you an example. One of the things that we launched in 2011 was an accelerated college degree program. We work with a partner company that can actually help them get college credit for that life experience, so they can start with college credits versus having this four- to five-year, daunting bachelor's degree timeline in front of them.[119]

Despite the economic landscape being altered, the future looks bright for Mercury—named the 2013 Wisconsin Manufacturer of the Year—as it continues to adapt to the new normal. The lessons learned during the recession will drive the company's future decision-making, Pfeifer said.[120]

"When going through a big restructuring, because you're in a crisis situation, you have to really pull back to your core competencies and rally around those areas that are most important to your customer base," Pfeifer said soon after being named Mercury's new president. "That is probably the biggest lesson we got, in general, from the recession—getting back to what we were good at."[121]

The National Marine Manufacturers Association, a Chicago-based trade group, estimated that

Above: John Pfeifer, formerly vice president of global operations, was named president of Mercury Marine in May 2014, replacing Mark Schwabero, who became Brunswick's president and chief operating officer.

Left: Denise Devereaux, vice president of human resources, says Mercury can provide fulfilling, lifelong careers for anyone with the capability and drive to succeed, regardless of educational background.

nearly 37 percent of US adults participated in some type of boating activity in 2013, the second-highest rate on record.[120] Mercury aims to remain a leader in the renewed growth of the marine industry by continuing to strengthen its global position while making sure all its customers enjoy fun, easy-to-use boating equipment, Pfeifer said. "We want [boating] to be as easy as operating an iPad," he said.[122]

Ultimately, it is Mercury Marine's drive to create and innovate that will ensure it maintains its present profitable course. One thing seems clear as it celebrates its diamond anniversary: the legacy of Carl Kiekhaefer—and the legend of Mercury—is secure and prepared to achieve another 75 years of success.

NOTES TO SOURCES

Chapter One

1. Letter from E.C. Kiekhaefer to Luther Evans of *The Miami Herald*, 9 December 1964.
2. Herman Stieg, interview by Jeffrey L. Rodengen, audio recording, 17 January 1987, Write Stuff Enterprises, LLC.
3. From an E.C. Kiekhaefer speech, "Getting the Job Done," made at a Mercury sales conference on 8–9 August 1966.
4. Herman Stieg, interview by Jeffrey L. Rodengen, audio recording, 17 January 1987, Write Stuff Enterprises, LLC.
5. Letter from Elmer Kiekhaefer to his mother, Clara Kiekhaefer, 12 August 1955.
6. *Ibid.*
7. Charles D. Strang Jr., interview by Jeffrey L. Rodengen, audio recording, 20 May 1987, Write Stuff Enterprises, LLC.
8. From an E.C. Kiekhaefer speech, "Getting the Job Done," 8-9 August 1966.
9. E.C. Kiekhaefer speech to close the Kiekhaefer Mercury Atlanta dealers' meeting, 10 October 1960.
10. *MerComment*, 1979 Special Issue, on the 40th anniversary of Mercury Marine.
11. From the first Kiekhaefer Corporation Thor Motor brochure, written and published in February 1939.
12. *Ibid.*
13. Letter from J.A. Allan, Kiekhaefer's consulting engineer for government contracts, 8 September 1942.
14. From an E.C. Kiekhaefer speech, "Getting the Job Done," 8–9 August 1966.
15. *Ibid.*
16. *Ibid.*
17. From the March 1939 flier to Thor dealers announcing "Red" Parkhurst representing the New Thor Line of Outboard Motors.
18. Transcribed interview between E.C. Kiekhaefer and Bob Brown of *Powerboat* magazine, 8 July 1981.
19. From an E.C. Kiekhaefer speech, "Getting the Job Done," 8–9 August 1966.
20. *Ibid.*
21. From the 1934 Silver Anniversary Outboards brochure prepared by the Elto-Evinrude divisions of Outboard Motors Corporation.
22. From an E.C. Kiekhaefer speech, "Getting the Job Done," 8–9 August 1966.
23. *Ibid.*
24. From the 1941 Mercury Outboard Motors brochure.
25. *Ibid.*
26. From the first Kiekhaefer Corporation dealer newsletter, the *Mercury Outboard Motor News*, published in March 1941.
27. *Ibid.*
28. *Ibid.*

Chapter Two

1. *Mercury Outboard Motor News*, July 1941.
2. Letter to Mr. William C. Naker Jr., Captain, Army Corps of Engineers, War Department, Fort Belvoir, Virginia, from E.C. Kiekhaefer, 10 August 1940.
3. Letter to Charles Hoge, Priorities Division, Washington, DC, from E.C. Kiekhaefer, 7 April 1941.
4. Letter to E.C. Kiekhaefer from Major C. Rodney Smith of the Army Corps of Engineers, Fort Belvoir, Virginia, 10 April 1941.
5. *Ibid.*
6. *Ibid.*
7. Letter to Mr. C. W. Gallagher of the Reed-Prentice Corporation, Worcester, Massachusetts, from C. Rodney Smith, Major, Corps of Engineers, Assistant Executive Officer, War Department, the Engineer Board, Fort Belvoir, Virginia, 20 June 1941.
8. Letter to Mr. F.W. McIntyre, vice president and general manager, Reed-Prentice Corporation, Worcester, Massachusetts, from E.C. Kiekhaefer, 7 October 1941.
9. Letter to Mr. C.S. Colby, Office of Production Management, Aluminum Division, Washington, DC, from E.C. Kiekhaefer, 22 November 1941.
10. *Ibid.*
11. *Ibid.*
12. Letter to F.R. Erbach, Facilities Staff, War Production Board, Washington, DC, from E.C. Kiekhaefer, 25 July 1942.
13. *Ibid.*
14. From the Kiekhaefer Corporation brochure titled, "It's a Great Place to Work," published and distributed 1942–45.
15. *Ibid.*
16. Notes to the 1942 Kiekhaefer Corporation financial balance sheets.
17. Letter to Col. John S. Seyboldt, Chief Contracting Officer, Army Corps of Engineers, Washington, DC, from E.C. Kiekhaefer, 20 October 1942.
18. *Ibid.*
19. Letter from Robert P. Patterson, Under Secretary of War, Washington, DC, to "The Men and Women of the Kiekhaefer Plant," 2 October 1943.
20. In a proclamation signed by H.A. Zuernert, mayor of Cedarburg, 25 October 1943.
21. Special edition of the Ozaukee County Wee Wonder, *Cedarburg News*, on Wednesday, 27 October 1943.
22. Text of Col. C. Rodney Smith's Army-Navy E Award speech, 30 October 1943, contained in its entirety in a letter from E.C. Kiekhaefer to H.E. Pollock, Adjustment Section, War Department, Office of Division Engineer, Great Lakes Division, Chicago, Illinois, 15 July 1944.
23. *Ozaukee Press*, Thursday, 18 November 1943.
24. Letter to the Kiekhaefer Corporation from the legal firm of Schanen & Schanen, 11 November 1943.
25. Letter to Schanen & Schanen from Guy S. Conrad, attorney for the Kiekhaefer Corporation, 16 November 1943.
26. Letter to the Kiekhaefer Corporation, attention Guy S. Conrad, by Schanen & Schanen, of Port Washington, Wisconsin, 17 November 1943.
27. Letter to the *Cedarburg News* by E.C. Kiekhaefer, 20 November 1943.
28. In the "Memorandum Report from the Army Air Forces Air Technical Service Command" concerning testing of the new "OQ-17 Radio Airplane Target," prepared by Capt. J.H. Jacobsen, 11 August 1945.
29. From the "Summary of Consolidated Profit and Loss for the Year Ended 30 September 1944 of Outboard Marine Corporation," a report to stockholders, 11 December 1944.

Chapter Three

1. In a "Memo to All Executives and Office Employees" from E.C. Kiekhaefer, dictated 25 December 1944 and dated 26 December 1944.
2. Letter to the War Department, Office of Division Engineer, Great Lakes Division, Chicago, Illinois, from E.C. Kiekhaefer, 7 August 1943.
3. Letter to the War Production Board, Automotive Division, Washington, DC, signed by Guy S. Conrad for E.C. Kiekhaefer, 16 September 1944.
4. *Mercury News*, July 1945.
5. Memo to E.C. Kiekhaefer from Fred L. Hall, 6 July 1945.
6. Herman Stieg, interview by Jeffrey L. Rodengen, audio recording, 17 January 1987, Write Stuff Enterprises, LLC.
7. *Commonwealth Reporter*, Saturday, 6 July 1968, on the occasion of the razing of the Corium Farms barn, after more than 1 million outboard motors had been assembled in 20 years. The article was based on interviews with Dirk S. Van Pelt, Clarence Sheridan, and R.W. Mills, and from letters and records of F.J. Rueping.
8. Herman Stieg, interview by Jeffrey L. Rodengen, audio recording, 17 January 1987, Write Stuff Enterprises, LLC.
9. In a transcribed telephone interview of E.C. Kiekhaefer with Bob Brown of *Powerboat* magazine on Wednesday, 18 July 1981.
10. Letter to Jack F. Reichert, president, Mercury Marine, division of Brunswick Corporation, by E.C. Kiekhaefer, April 18, 1977.
11. Bob Stuth, interview, 29 July 1987.
12. In a transcribed telephone interview of E.C. Kiekhaefer with Bob Brown of *Powerboat* magazine on Wednesday, 18 July 1981.
13. Herman Stieg, interview by Jeffrey L. Rodengen, audio recording, 17 January 1987, Write Stuff Enterprises, LLC.
14. Carl Kiekhaefer admitted the true horsepower of the 25-hp Thunderbolt was 40-hp in the "Background History of the Kiekhaefer Corporation" written as a pre-merger document for Brunswick Corporation analysis, 1960.
15. In a marketing summary called "Interesting Facts About The Mercury 25 With The Thunderbolt Engine," undated, written before the release of the Thunderbolt prototype for production by E.C. Kiekhaefer.

Chapter Four

1. Letter to Otis E. Johnson of Western Auto Supply Company, from E.C. Kiekhaefer, 24 January 1951.
2. Letter to J. Paxton Hill, the Utility Racing Secretary of the American Power Boat Association from E.C. Kiekhaefer, 20 February 1951.
3. "Ozaukee County Wee Wonder," *Cedarburg News*, 11 October 1950.
4. Letter from Charles D. Strang Jr., Department of Mechanical Engineering, Massachusetts Institute of Technology, to E.C. Kiekhaefer, 20 November 1950.
5. Charles D. Strang Jr., interview by Jeffrey L. Rodengen, audio recording, 20 May 1987, Write Stuff Enterprises, LLC.
6. *Ibid.*
7. Letter to E.C. Kiekhaefer from Charles D. Strang Jr., from the Carlton Hotel, Nurnberg, Germany, 30 July 1951.
8. Ted O. Jones, interview by Jeffrey L. Rodengen, audio recording, 13 March 1987, Write Stuff Enterprises, LLC.
9. *Ibid.*
10. *Ibid.*
11. James R. Wynne, interview by Jeffrey L. Rodengen, audio recording, 17 October 1987, Write Stuff Enterprises, LLC.
12. *Ibid.*
13. *Ibid.*
14. Charles Alexander, interview by Jeffrey L. Rodengen, audio recording, 1 December 1986, Write Stuff Enterprises, LLC.
15. *Ibid.*
16. *Ibid.*
17. *Ibid.*
18. *Ibid.*
19. *Ibid.*
20. Charles D. Strang Jr., interview by Jeffrey L. Rodengen, audio recording, 20 May 1987, Write Stuff Enterprises, LLC.
21. In a press release issued by E.C. Kiekhaefer, June 7, 1957.
22. James R. Wynne, interview by Jeffrey L. Rodengen, audio recording, 17 October 1987, Write Stuff Enterprises, LLC.
23. Charles Alexander, interview by Jeffrey L. Rodengen, audio recording, 1 December 1986, Write Stuff Enterprises, LLC.
24. Charles D. Strang Jr., interview by Jeffrey L. Rodengen, audio recording, 20 May 1987, Write Stuff Enterprises, LLC.
25. Fred "Fritz" Shoenfeldt, interview by Jeffrey L. Rodengen, audio recordng, 31 July 1987, Write Stuff Enterprises, LLC.

Chapter Four Sidebar: Carl's Obsession

1. Jonathan Ingram, "Carl Kiekhaefer: A Grand National Giant," *Stock Car Racing*, July 1985.
2. Letter to Mr. Edward T. Clapp, 22 May 1957.

Chapter Five

1. Handwritten entry contained in Jim Wynne's Lake X endurance run log book, 21 September 1957.
2. Charles D. Strang, Jr., interview by Jeffrey L. Rodengen, audio recording, 20 May 1987, Write Stuff Enterprises, LLC.

3. James R. Wynne, interview by Jeffrey L. Rodengen, audio recording, 17 October 1987, Write Stuff Enterprises, LLC.
4. Memo to E.C. Kiekhaefer from C.D. Strang on Kiekhaefer Aeromarine Motors stationery, 8 July 1957, titled "Organization of 40 Day Run."
5. Wayne and Mildred "Millie" Meyer, interview by Jeffrey L. Rodengen, audio recording, 28 September 1987, Write Stuff Enterprises, LLC.
6. *Ibid.*
7. Letter to Jim Wynne from Duane Carter, USAC director of competition, 21 August 1957.
8. James R. Wynne, interview by Jeffrey L. Rodengen, audio recording, 17 October 1987, Write Stuff Enterprises, LLC.
9. Handwritten entry contained in Jim Wynne's Lake X endurance run log book, 21 September 1957.
10. Kiekhaefer's contributions to the St. Cloud Hospital began in 1961, as the hospital was financially unable to complete plans for expansion and modernization.

Chapter Six

1. Letter to Jim Martenhoff, boating journalist, from E.C. Kiekhaefer, 15 May 1962.
2. Fred Hauenstein, interview by Mike Koretzky, 27 May 1998.
3. Larry Lohse, interview by Jeffrey L. Rodengen, audio recording, 11 June 1998, Write Stuff Enterprises, LLC.
4. Hank Bowman, "US Outboard Title Can't Last," *Little Rock Gazette*, 6 July 1958.
5. Letter to George Trimper from E.C. Kiekhaefer, 17 January 1967.
6. Memo from Armand A. Hauser to E.C. Kiekhaefer titled "Competitive Activity," undated, but drafted during the late summer of 1967.
7. Dick Snyder, interview by Alex Lieber, audio recording, 10 July 1998, Write Stuff Enterprises, LLC.
8. John Crouse, *Searace — A History of Offshore Powerboat Racing.*
9. *Ibid.*
10. Earl Bentz, interview by Alex Lieber, audio recording, 15 October 1998, Write Stuff Enterprises, LLC.
11. *Ibid.*
12. Associated Press, 31 July 1985.
13. John Crouse, *Searace — A History of Offshore Powerboat Racing.*
14. Gerry Celichowski, interview by Mike Koretzky, 10 June 1998.
15. Dennis Banks, interview by Mike Koretzky, 27 May 1998.
16. In a Mercury Marine press release, 22 October 1996.
17. Earl Bentz, interview by Alex Lieber, audio recording, 14 October 1998, Write Stuff Enterprises, LLC.

Chapter Six Sidebar: Award From "The Enemy"

1. *Dock Lines*, newsletter of Evinrude Motors, 19 March 1976.
2. From the speech by Charles D. Strang delivered at the Ole Evinrude Awards ceremony, 22 February 1976.
3. Letter to Ralph Evinrude from E. C. Kiekhaefer, 9 March 1976.

Chapter Seven

1. In a press release issued by E.C. Kiekhaefer, 8 February 1961.
2. Rose Smiljanic, interview by Jeffrey L. Rodengen, audio recording, 14 August 1986, Write Stuff Enterprises, LLC.
3. Letter, never mailed, to The Honorable Senator Alexander Wiley, United States Senator for the State of Wisconsin, 18 May 1957, from E.C. Kiekhaefer.
4. *Ibid.*
5. Donald E. Castle, interview by Jeffrey L. Rodengen, audio recording, 4 August 1987, Write Stuff Enterprises, LLC.
6. *Ibid.*
7. Charles D. Strang Jr., interview by Jeffrey L. Rodengen, audio recording, 20 May 1987, Write Stuff Enterprises, LLC.
8. In a draft of a letter never mailed to R.C. Ingersoll, chairman of Borg-Warner Corporation, from E.C. Kiekhaefer, 9 October 1957.
9. *Time*, "Diversified Success," 19 May 1961.
10. Rick Kogan, *Brunswick, The Story of an American Company from 1845 to 1985*, (Brunswick Corporation, 1985).
11. *Ibid.*
12. Letter from Brunswick President B.E. Bensinger to E.C. Kiekhaefer, 10 September 1958.
13. *Ibid.*
14. Rick Kogan, *Brunswick, The Story of an American Company from 1845 to 1985*, (Brunswick Corporation, 1985).
15. *Ibid.*
16. *Ibid.*
17. From transcribed telephone conversations between Willis Blank and B.E. Bensinger, 2 November 1960 and 8 November 1960.
18. Robert C. Anderegg, interview by Jeffrey L. Rodengen, audio recording, 23 February 1987, Write Stuff Enterprises, LLC.
19. In a press release issued by E.C. Kiekhaefer, 8 February 1961.
20. Letter from F.E. Troy, vice president of Brunswick Corporation to E.C. Kiekhaefer, 13 March 1961.
21. Charles D. Strang Jr., interview by Jeffrey L. Rodengen, audio recording, 26 January 1989, Write Stuff Enterprises, LLC.
22. Letter from Arthur A. Burck of McClellan & Burck, Inc., consultants, to E.C. Kiekhaefer, 1 August 1961.
23. Alan Edgarton, interview by Jeffrey L. Rodengen, audio recording, 30 July 1987, Write Stuff Enterprises, LLC.
24. Robert C. Anderegg, interview by Jeffrey L. Rodengen, audio recording, 23 February 1987, Write Stuff Enterprises, LLC.
25. Ian Edgarton, interview by Jeffrey L. Rodengen, audio recording, 30 July 1987, Write Stuff Enterprises, LLC.
26. Robert C. Anderegg, interview by Jeffrey L. Rodengen, audio recording, 23 February 1987, Write Stuff Enterprises, LLC.
27. *Ibid.*
28. *Ibid.*
29. Memorandum from B.E. Bensinger to E.C. Kiekhaefer, 30 August 1961.
30. Emil A. Schneider, *Milwaukee Journal*, 13 October 1961. Carl would confirm the accuracy of the final amount

received from the Brunswick shares in a letter to Schneider, 18 October 1961.

31. In a telegram mailed to all US and Canadian distributors and branch managers by Tom King, about 15 August 1961.

Chapter Seven Sidebar: Lining Up to Get Fired

1. Unedited version of this story appeared in *Boy's Life*, written by P. Reidy. Reprinted by *Reader's Digest*, March 1990.
2. Ted Karls, interview by Jeffrey L. Rodengen, audio recording, 6 August 1987, Write Stuff Enterprises, LLC.

Chapter Eight

1. Charles D. Strang Jr., interview by Jeffrey L. Rodengen, audio recording, 20 May 1987, Write Stuff Enterprises, LLC.
2. Flier produced by the Johnson Motor Company titled, "Outboard Motors and Boats by Johnson," with text by Warren Ripple, president, 1930.
3. *Ibid.*
4. James R. Wynne, interview by Jeffrey L. Rodengen, audio recording 17 October 1987, Write Stuff Enterprises, LLC.
5. Ann Adams, "Sterndrive Charts Prosperous Course," *Go Boating*, August 1973.
6. Dick Porter, "Elder Statesman: James R. Wynne," *Boating Industry*, October 1989.
7. James R. Wynne, interview by Jeffrey L. Rodengen, audio recording 17 October 1987, Write Stuff Enterprises, LLC.
8. Charles D. Strang Jr., interview by Jeffrey L. Rodengen, audio recording, 20 May 1987, Write Stuff Enterprises, LLC.
9. *Ibid.*
10. Letter to Robert H. Soelke of Miami Outboard and Sport Sales, from E.C. Kiekhaefer, 10 March 1958.
11. Charles D. Strang Jr., interview by Jeffrey L. Rodengen, audio recording, 20 May 1987, Write Stuff Enterprises, LLC.
12. James R. Wynne, interview by Jeffrey L. Rodengen, audio recording 17 October 1987, Write Stuff Enterprises, LLC.
13. Harald Wiklund, interview by Jeffrey L. Rodengen, audio recording, 13 December 1990, Write Stuff Enterprises, LLC.
14. Charles D. Strang Jr., interview by Jeffrey L. Rodengen, audio recording, 20 May 1987, Write Stuff Enterprises, LLC.
15. Harald Wiklund, interview by Jeffrey L. Rodengen, audio recording, 13 December 1990, Write Stuff Enterprises, LLC.
16. Memo to C.D. Strang and T.B. King, 30 January 1960, from E.C. Kiekhaefer.
17. Letter to Thomas B. Fifield of the legal firm of Foley, Sammond & Lardner, from Willis Blank, 22 June 1960.
18. Harald Wiklund, interview by Jeffrey L. Rodengen, audio recording, 13 December 1990, Write Stuff Enterprises, LLC.
19. James R. Wynne, interview by Jeffrey L. Rodengen, audio recording 17 October 1987, Write Stuff Enterprises, LLC.
20. Harald Wiklund, interview by Jeffrey L. Rodengen, audio recording, 13 December 1990, Write Stuff Enterprises, LLC.

21. In notes assembled by E.C. Kiekhaefer, titled, "Questions Re Mercury-Volvo Agreement," 30 June 1960.
22. Harald Wiklund, interview by Jeffrey L. Rodengen, audio recording, 13 December 1990, Write Stuff Enterprises, LLC.
23. *Ibid.*
24. List of 12 points to be covered by E.C. Kiekhaefer at the 1960 sales and marketing conference.
25. In a speech delivered by E.C. Kiekhaefer to the Kiekhaefer Mercury distributors meeting, 13 January 1961.
26. Charles D. Strang Jr., interview by Jeffrey L. Rodengen, audio recording, 20 May 1987, Write Stuff Enterprises, LLC.
27. Meeting notes from an "Outdrive Program Meeting" held Saturday, 18 March 1961, conducted by Thomas B. King and sent to E.C. Kiekhaefer, 22 March 1961. Marked "Confidential."
28. In a report by Ralph E. Lambrecht, OMC Sterndrive division of Outboard Marine Corporation, July 1979.
29. Patent number 3,376,842, issued 9 April 1968 to J.R. Wynne for "Boat Propulsion Mechanism." Patents number 3,368,516 and 3,368,517 issued 13 February 1968 to C.E. MacDonald.
30. Harald Wiklund, interview by Jeffrey L. Rodengen, audio recording, 13 December 1990, Write Stuff Enterprises, LLC.

Chapter Nine

1. Handwritten notes concerning the history of relationships between Brunswick Corporation and Kiekhaefer Corporation by E.C. Kiekhaefer, produced in1963.
2. Memo to E.C. Kiekhaefer from Charles D. Strang, 9 September 1961.
3. Mercury line brochure, 1955.
4. Charles D. Strang Jr., interview by Jeffrey L. Rodengen, audio recording, 20 May 1987, Write Stuff Enterprises, LLC.
5. Letter to a Mercury owner quoted in a letter from Tom King to "All Mercury Dealers, Distributors, Branch Managers and Area Representatives," 27 April 1960.
6. Memo to "All Department Heads, Mail Clerks and Switchboard Operators," from E.C. Kiekhaefer, 5 January 1962.
7. Memo to various Brunswick staff members from B.E. "Ted" Bensinger, 9 February 1962.
8. Memo to Ted Bensinger from E.C. Kiekhaefer, 26 October 1962.
9. Memo from T.B. King to E.C. Kiekhaefer titled, "Review of Brunswick-Kiekhaefer Relationship During the 1962 Model Year," 26 October 1962.
10. Memo to Frederic Sammond and Marvin E. Klitsner of the legal firm of Foley, Sammond & Lardner from B.S. Kubale of the same firm, regarding "E.C. Kiekhaefer — Repurchase," 19 February 1963.
11. Letter to B.E. Bensinger, president of the Brunswick Corporation from E.C. Kiekhaefer, 29 January 1963.
12. In a draft of a letter never mailed to Howard F. Baer, chairman of Aloe, division of Brunswick in St. Louis, from

E.C. Kiekhaefer, 30 January 1963; revised 6 February 1963.
13. Rick Kogan, *Brunswick, The Story of an American Company from 1845 to 1985* (Brunswick Corporation, 1985).
14. Letter to J.L. Hanigan from E.C. Kiekhaefer, 17 September 1964.
15. Handwritten notes concerning the history of relationships between Brunswick Corporation and Kiekhaefer Corporation by E.C. Kiekhaefer, produced in 1963.
16. Charles D. Strang Jr., interview by Jeffrey L. Rodengen, audio recording, 26 January 1989, Write Stuff Enterprises, LLC.
17. *Ibid.*
18. *Ibid.*
19. Reconstructed from a detailed log of the conversation kept by Charles D. Strang, with further editing and additions following subsequent conversations with Carl Kiekhaefer.
20. From the transcribed dictabelt recording of the conversation between Charles D. Strang and Jack Hanigan, 29 May 1964.
21. Interview of C.W. "Doc" Jones, 13 December 1990.
22. Interview of James H. Jost, 14 December 1990.
23. From a speech titled, "These Are Wonderful Years: Why?" delivered by Carl Kiekhaefer on the 25th anniversary of the Kiekhaefer Corporation, 18 January 1964.
24. *Ibid.*
25. Excerpts from "A Request To All The Citizens Of Fond du Lac From The Kiekhaefer Corporation," a paid insertion advertisement prepared for the *Commonwealth Reporter*, February 1964.
26. *Commonwealth Reporter*, 26 April 1964.
27. Remarks prepared for the Brunswick Corporation board of directors meeting, and delivered by Carl Kiekhaefer at the Kiekhaefer Corporation's new assembly building auditorium, 1 June 1965.
28. *Fortune*, 15 July 1966.
29. "Heavy, Heavy ... is the load of debt and uncertainty still hanging over Brunswick Corp," *Forbes*, 15 August 1965.

Chapter Ten

1. Letter to Roger C. Hanks of Midland, Texas, from E.C. Kiekhaefer, 4 March 1972.
2. Letter never mailed to fellow Brunswick director Walter M. Heymann, drafted by E.C. Kiekhaefer, 22 January 1969.
3. In a transcribed telephone conversation between E.C. Kiekhaefer and Jack Hanigan, president of Brunswick Corporation, 22 July 1966.
4. *Ibid.*
5. Jim Schenk, interview by Alex Lieber, audio recording, 17 August 1998, Write Stuff Enterprises, LLC.
6. Letter from J.L. Hanigan to E.C. Kiekhaefer, 13 October 1969.
7. "Suggested Terms To Implement Mr. Hanigan's Latest Proposal" drafted by E.C. Kiekhaefer, 21 November 1969.
8. E.C. Kiekhaefer "Retirement Memorandum," drafted November 1969.

9. Transcripts of the 25 November 1969 management meeting.
10. *Milwaukee Sentinel*, 26 November 1969.
11. Transcripts of a management meeting, 25 November 1969.
12. Fred "Fritz" Shoenfeldt, interview by Jeffrey L. Rodengen, audio recording, 31 July 1987, Write Stuff Enterprises, LLC.
13. Clem Koehler, interview by Jeffrey L. Rodengen, audio recording, 18 August 1998, Write Stuff Enterprises, LLC.
14. Letter to J.L. Hanigan, president of Brunswick Corporation from E.C. Kiekhaefer, 30 December 1969, with copies indicated to "Board of Director Members" and "K.B. Abernathy."
15. Letter to Ray Waters from E.C. Kiekhaefer, 2 October 1970.
16. Letter to A.A. Hauser from E.C. Kiekhaefer, 24 March 1970.
17. Owen L. "Billy" Steele, interview by Jeffrey L. Rodengen, audio recording, 4 August 1987, Write Stuff Enterpries, LLC.
18. John C. Hull, interview by Jeffrey L. Rodengen, audio recording, 31 July 1988, Write Stuff Enterprises, LLC.
19. Fred Kiekhaefer, interview by Jeffrey L. Rodengen, audio recording, 16 August 1987, Write Stuff Enterprises, LLC.
20. *Ibid.*

Chapter Eleven

1. Jack F. Reichert, interview, 26 March 1987.
2. Roger Patterson, interview by Jeffrey L. Rodengen, audio recording, 18 August 1998, Write Stuff Enterprises, LLC.
3. *Ibid.*
4. Clem Koehler, interview by Jeffrey L. Rodengen, audio recording, 18 August 1998, Write Stuff Enterprises, LLC.
5. *Ibid.*
6. Roger Miller, interview by Alex Lieber, audio recording, 16 September 1998, Write Stuff Enterprises, LLC.
7. *Ibid.*
8. Roger Patterson, interview by Jeffrey L. Rodengen, audio recording, 18 August 1998, Write Stuff Enterprises, LLC.
9. Jim Schenk, interview by Alex Lieber, audio recording, 17 August 1998, Write Stuff Enterprises, LLC.
10. Rick Kogan, *Brunswick, The Story of an American Company from 1845 to 1985* (Brunswick Corporation, 1985).
11. Charles Alexander, interview by Jeffrey L. Rodengen, audio recording, 16 June 1998, Write Stuff Enterprises, LLC.
12. Jim Schenk, interview by Alex Lieber, audio recording, 17 August 1998, Write Stuff Enterprises, LLC.
13. Lois Cutburth, interview by Alex Lieber, audio recording, 20 August 1998, Write Stuff Enterprises, LLC.
14. Barry Eller, interview by Mike Koretzky, 16 June 1998.
15. Mercury Marine press release, 30 November 1974.
16. *Ibid.*
17. Dave Martin, interview by Alex Lieber, audio recording, 4 September 1998, Write Stuff Enterprises, LLC.
18. Mercury 1976 sales brochure, Brunswick Corporation, 1975.
20. Jack F. Reichert, interview, 26 March 1987.

21. Letter to Dave Craig from E.C. Kiekhaefer, 28 March 1977.
22. Letter to Jack F. Reichert from E.C. Kiekhaefer, 28 March 1977.
23. Letter to William Martin-Hurst from E.C. Kiekhaefer, 16 February 1978.
24. Jack F. Reichert, interview, 26 March 1987.

Chapter Eleven Sidebar: Acting Locally

1. *The World of Mercury Marine*, Mercury Marine Corporation, 1972.
2. Kiekhaefer Marine press release, 2 November 1969.
3. *Ibid.*
4. Mercury Marine press release, 2 November 1971.

Chapter Twelve

1. Rick Kogan, *Brunswick, The Story of an American Company from 1845 to 1985* (Brunswick Corporation, 1985).
2. Fred Hauenstein, interview by Jeffrey L. Rodengen, audio recording, 27 May 1998, Write Stuff Enterprises, LLC.
3. Charles Alexander, interview by Jeffrey L. Rodengen, audio recording, 29 June 1998, Write Stuff Enterprises, LLC.
4. Roger Patterson, interview by Alex Lieber, audio recording, 15 September 1998, Write Stuff Enterprises, LLC.
5. *Ibid.*
6. Denny Sheller, interview by Michael Koretzky, 22 June 1998.
7. Charles Alexander, interview by Jeffrey L. Rodengen, audio recording, 16 June 1998, Write Stuff Enterprises, LLC.
8. Rick Kogan, *Brunswick, The Story of an American Company: The First 100 Years* (Brunswick Corporation, 1995).
9. Michael Millenson, "Firm Basking in Good Fortune," *Chicago Tribune*, 2 January 1985.
10. Rick Kogan, *Brunswick, The Story of an American Company: The First 100 Years* (Brunswick Corporation, 1995).
11. Mercury Marine press release, 10 September 1982.
12. *Ibid.*
13. Roger Miller, interview by Alex Lieber, audio recording, 15 September 1998, Write Stuff Enterprises, LLC.
14. Mike Gyorog, interview by Jeffrey L. Rodengen, audio recording, 27 May 1998, Write Stuff Enterprises, LLC.
15. Rick Davis, interview by Michael Koretzky, 10 June 1998.
16. Mike Gyorog, interview by Jeffrey L. Rodengen, audio recording, 27 May 1998, Write Stuff Enterprises, LLC.
17. Brunswick Corporation press release, 12 April 1982.
18. Dennis Banks, interview by Jeffrey L. Rodengen, audio recording, 27 May 1998, Write Stuff Enterprises, LLC.
19. Summary of Mercury Marine's recent history by Jim Hubbard, 15 August 1998.
20. Tony Chamberlain, *The Boston Globe*, 4 January 1991.
21. Angus Phillips, "Boat Luxury Tax End Within Sight," *The Washington Post*, 20 May 1990.
22. "Boat Luxury Tax End Within Sight," *PR Newswire*, 25 June 1992.

23. Rick Kogan, *Brunswick, The Story of an American Company from 1845 to 1985*, (Brunswick Corporation, 1985).
24. "E.C. Kiekhaefer Medical History," prepared by Kiekhaefer, March 1983.
25. Letter to Richard J. Jordan from E.C. Kiekhaefer, 12 July 1983.
26. Letter to Charles D. Strang, from E.C. Kiekhaefer, 18 October 1977.

Chapter Twelve Sidebar: Reeling in the Market

1. Clem Koehler, interview by Jeffrey L. Rodengen, audio recording, 18 August 1998, Write Stuff Enterprises, LLC.
2. *Ibid.*
3. Jim Kalkofen, interview by Alex Lieber, audio recording, 14 September 1998, Write Stuff Enterprises, LLC.
4. Jim Kalkofen, interview by Alex Lieber, audio recording, 14 September 1998, Write Stuff Enterprises, LLC.

Chapter Thirteen

1. George Buckley, interview by Jeffrey L. Rodengen, audio recording, 16 June 1998, Write Stuff Enterprises, LLC.
2. Roger Patterson, interview by Jeffrey L. Rodengen, audio recording, 18 August 1998, Write Stuff Enterprises, LLC.
3. Rick Kogan, *Brunswick, The Story of an American Company, The First 150 Years* (Brunswick Corporation, 1995).
4. *Ibid.*
5. Roger Patterson, interview by Jeffrey L. Rodengen, audio recording, 18 August 1998, Write Stuff Enterprises, LLC.
6. Gerald Neisen, interview by Michael Koretzky, 27 May 1998.
7. Steve Prestegard, "Full Speed Ahead for Mercury Marine," *Marketplace Magazine*, 12 September 1995.
8. *The Reporter*, 14 September 1992.
9. "Meridian/MediCenter Announces agreement with Mercury Marine in Stillwater, Oklahoma," *PR Newswire*, 10 October 1997.
10. *Oshkosh Northwestern*, 17 October 1993.
11. Mike Dries, "HR and Maintaining the Art of Motor Making," *Milwaukee Business Journal*, 18 February 1995.
12. Denny Sheller, interview by Michael Koretzky, 22 June 1998.
13. Notes supplied by Jim Hubbard, chief of staff at Mercury.
14. MercuryCare brochure, Issue #1, August 1999.
15. Fred Kiekhaefer, interview by Jeffrey L. Rodengen, audio recording, 30 June 1998, Write Stuff Enterprises, LLC.
16. *Ibid.*
17. Tom Mielke, interview by Jeffrey L. Rodengen, audio recording, 27 May 1998, Write Stuff Enterprises, LLC.
18. Rick Davis, interview by Michael Koretzky, 10 June 1998.
19. Mercury Marine press release, September 1993.
20. Mercury Marine press release, 26 October 1992.
21. *Fond du Lac News Press*, 6 June 1993.
22. Mercury Marine press release, "Mercury Sport Jet all new for '96," 1995.
23. Barry Eller, interview by Jeffrey L. Rodengen, audio recording, 16 June 1998, Write Stuff Enterprises, LLC.

24. "Company to Present Plan for Creek Cleanup," *Milwaukee Journal*, 18 November 1993.
25. Johnny Morris, interview by Jeffrey L. Rodengen, audio recording, 5 October 1998, Write Stuff Enterprises, LLC.
26. Jim Schenk, interview by Alex Lieber, audio recording, 17 August 1998, Write Stuff Enterprises, LLC.
27. Joe Wisner, interview by Alex Lieber, audio recording, 13 September 1998, Write Stuff Enterprises, LLC.
28. *Ibid.*
29. Jim Hubbard, interview by Jeffrey L. Rodengen, audio recording, 21 September 1999, Write Stuff Enterprises, LLC.
30. *Ibid.*
31. George Buckley, interview by Jeffrey L. Rodengen, audio recording, 16 June 1998, Write Stuff Enterprises, LLC.
32. Barry Eller, interview by Jeffrey L. Rodengen, audio recording, 16 June 1998, Write Stuff Enterprises, LLC.
33. Fred Brightbill, interview by Jeffrey L. Rodengen, audio recording, Write Stuff Enterprises, LLC.
34. George Buckley, interview by Jeffrey L. Rodengen, audio recording, 16 June 1998, Write Stuff Enterprises, LLC.
35. *Ibid.*
36. Jim Hubbard, interview by Jeffrey L. Rodengen, audio recording, 21 September 1999, Write Stuff Enterprises, LLC.
37. George Buckley, interview by Jeffrey L. Rodengen, audio recording, 21 October 1999, Write Stuff Enterprises, LLC.
38. Dennis Banks, interview by Jeffrey L. Rodengen, audio recording, 27 May 1998, Write Stuff Enterprises, LLC.
39. George Buckley, interview by Jeffrey L. Rodengen, audio recording, 16 June 1998, Write Stuff Enterprises, LLC.

Chapter Fourteen

1. Patrick Mackey, interview by Jeffrey L. Rodengen, audio recording, 7 September 2007, Write Stuff Enterprises, LLC.
2. "Highlights of George Buckley's Address to Dealers, Orlando Business Meeting," Weekly Information Sheet, 30 November 1998–4 December 1998.
3. "Letter from George Buckley to Mercury Employees Regarding the Dealer Meeting," Weekly Information Sheet, 7 December 1998–11 December 1998.
4. Letter from George Buckley to Mercury Marine Employees, 13 March 1998.
5. Kris Hundley, "Going Full Throttle," *St. Petersburg Times*, 7 August 2000.
6. Jim Flasch, "Fond du Lac's Comebacks," *Marketplace Magazine*, 15 September 1998, 28.
7. Letter from George Buckley to Mercury Marine employees, 27 April 1998.
8. "Propulsion '99 Inboard and Outboard Engines," *Trailer Boats*, 1 February 1999.
9. Jim Hubbard, interview by Jeffrey L. Rodengen, audio recording, 7 August 2007, Write Stuff Enterprises, LLC.
10. Mark Rothfield, "Models of Efficiency; Weekend Boating," *Newcastle Herald*, 14 November 1998.
11. Jim Hubbard, interview by Jeffrey L. Rodengen, audio recording, 7 August 2007, Write Stuff Enterprises, LLC.
12. "Rick Davis, V.P. Engine Development & Chief Technology Officer," Weekly Information Sheet, 22 March 1999–26 March 1999.
13. "Propulsion '99 Inboard and Outboard Engines," *Trailer Boats*, 1 February 1999.
14. Caroline Ajootian, "New Technology in High Gear," *BoatUS: Magazine*, 1 May 1999.
15. Letter from William E. Seeley, Vice President, Sales, Service & Marketing, to the Mercury Marine Customer, 27 March 1998.
16. "Highlights of George Buckley's Address to Dealers, Orlando Business Meeting," Weekly Information Sheet, 30 November 1998–4 December 1998.
17. Darlene Brady, "Mercury Drops Force and Unifies Brand," *Boating Industry*, 1 February 1999.
18. Jim Hubbard, interview by Jeffrey L. Rodengen, audio recording, 7 August 2007, Write Stuff Enterprises, LLC.
19. "Highlights of George Buckley's Address to Dealers, Orlando Business Meeting," Weekly Information Sheet, 30 November 1998–4 December 1998.
20. Jim Hubbard, interview by Jeffrey L. Rodengen, audio recording, 7 August 2007, Write Stuff Enterprises, LLC.
21. "OptiMax—Power to Burn But Easy on Fuel," *Sunday Mail* (South Africa), 21 November 1999.
22. Fred Kiekhaefer, interview by Jeffrey L. Rodengen, audio recording, 7 August 2007, Write Stuff Enterprises, LLC.
23. Rick Mackie, interview by Jeffrey L. Rodengen, audio recording, 7 September 2007, Write Stuff Enterprises, LLC.
24. "Motorola Plays Vital Role in Mercury Racing's History-Making Power Boat Race," *PR Newswire*, 4 August 2000.
25. "Celebrating Success at MerCruiser," *Profile*, Spring 2000.
26. "Multinational Gets Savage," *The Age*, 11 November 1999.
27. "Savage Boats Joins the Mercury Family," *Profile*, Spring 2000.
28. "Mercury Marine Acquires St. Cast Marine," Weekly Information Sheet, 13 September 1999–17 September 1999.
29. Michael Verdon, "Brunswick Fights New Court Battle," *Marine Marketing*, January 1999.
30. "Brunswick's Favorable Decision in Antitrust Appeal Upheld by U.S. Supreme Court," press release, 6 November 2000.
31. *Ibid.*
32. "Buckley Named Chairman and CEO of Brunswick," press release, 27 June 2000.
33. "Mackey Named President of Mercury Marine," *PR Newswire*, 2 October 2000.
34. Patrick Mackey, interview by Jeffrey L. Rodengen, audio recording, 7 September 2007, Write Stuff Enterprises, LLC.
35. *Ibid.*
36. *Ibid.*
37. "Pat Mackey Mission: the Remaking of Merc," *Soundings Trade Only*, April 2006.
38. Mike Gyorog, interview by Jeffrey L. Rodengen, audio recording, 7 August 2007, Write Stuff Enterprises, LLC.
39. "Mercury Marine Realigns to a Customer-Centered Organization," Brunswick press release, 11 May 2001.
40. Bob Slaff, "Rough Waters for Engine Giant," *The Capital*, 21 January 2001.
41. Mercury Marine Company profile.
42. Letter from John W. S. Ward, Mercury Marine Vice President of Outboard Sales and Service, to Mercury Marine dealers, 22 December 2000.
43. Dale K. DuPont, "Hatteras Purchased for $80 Million," *Miami Herald*, 25 October 2001.
44. George Buckley, interview by Jeffrey L. Rodengen, audio recording, 11 January 2008, Write Stuff Enterprises, LLC.
45. "New Light Weight V-6 Cowls for 2002 Models," Weekly Information Sheet, 3 December 2001–7 December 2001.
46. Caroline Ajootian, "New Technology in High Gear," *BoatUS: Magazine*, 1 May 1999.
47. "Four-Stroke First for Mercury," *Townsville Bulletin/Townsville Sun*, 16 May 2001.
48. "Mercury OptiMax Again Flawlessly Powers World Cat Tam in 41-Hour Endurance Run," Weekly Information Sheet, 6 August 2001–10 August 2001.
49. *The Wave* 2002, Weekly Information Sheet, 21 January 2002–25 January 2002.
50. *The Wave* 2002, Weekly Information Sheet, 21 January 2002–25 January 2002.
51. "OEC—Presentations—by Chairman/CFO/CEO," *AAP Company News*, 25 October 2001.

Chapter Fourteen Sidebar:
MotoTron: A Vital Component

1. Patrick Mackey, interview by Jeffrey L. Rodengen, audio recording, 7 September 2007, Write Stuff Enterprises, LLC.
2. *Ibid.*

Chapter Fourteen Sidebar:
Casting the World

1. David Shuyler, "Mercury Marine Expands Foundry, Will Pursue Small-Engine Customers," *The Business Journal*, 13 October 2000.
2. "Mercury Castings Receives Award," *Messenger*, November/December Volume 1, Issue 6.
3. David Shuyler, "Mercury Marine Expands Foundry, Will Pursue Small-Engine Customers," *The Business Journal*, 13 October 2000.
4. "Mercury Marine," *Foundry Management & Technology*, 1 June 2001.
5. "Mercury Castings Receives Award," *Messenger*, November/December Volume 1, Issue 6.
6. David Shuyler, "Mercury Marine Expands Foundry, Will Pursue Small-Engine Customers," *The Business Journal*, 13 October 2000.
7. Jim Hubbard, interview by Jeffrey L. Rodengen, audio recording, 7 August 2007, Write Stuff Enterprises, LLC.

Chapter Fifteen

1. Patrick C. Mackey, "From the Helm," *Messenger*, April/May, Volume 4, Issue 1.
2. *The Wave* 2003 Weekly Information Sheet, 27 January 2003–31 January 2003.
3. *The Wave* 2004 Weekly Information Sheet, 26 January 2004–30 January 2004.
4. "Memos 2002–2004," Brunswick Corp. Internal Memo.
5. Pat Mackey Mission: the Remaking of Merc," *Soundings Trade Only*, April 2006.
6. "Mercury Becomes First ISO 9001:2000 Registered Marine-Engine Manufacturer," *Messenger*, September/October 2003, Volume 2, Issue 4.

7. Letter from Pat Mackey to All Mercury Employees, RE: Mercury Organizational Changes, 22 March 2004.
8. "Buckley on Dumping, Acquisition Strategy," interview transcript, Brunswick internal document, Spring 2005.
9. Thomas Content, "Motor Firms Make Deal; Mercury, Cummins Agree to Produce Diesel Marine Engines," *Milwaukee Journal Sentinel*, 15 February 2002.
10. Steve Cramer, interview by Jeffrey L. Rodengen, audio recording, 7 August 2007, Write Stuff Enterprises, LLC.
11. "Mercury Marine Acquires Teignbridge Propellers," *PR Newswire*, 14 February 2002.
12. *The Wave* 2003 Weekly Information Sheet, 17 February 2003–21 February 2003.
13. "Polaris Enters New Recreational Vehicle Category With Sport Boat Launch; Polaris Continues Product Diversification with Strategic Alliance with Baja and Mercury Marine," *Business Wire*, 23 January 2003.
14. "Brunswick Acquires Three Aluminum Boat Brands," *Messenger*, April/May 2004, Volume 3, Issue 1.
15. "Mercury Marine and Triton Boats Now Official and Exclusive Brands of B.A.S.S.," *Messenger*, April/May 2004, Volume 3, Issue 1.
16. Jim Hubbard, interview by Jeffrey L. Rodengen, audio recording, 7 August 2007, Write Stuff Enterprises, LLC.
17. "Claus Bruestlé Joins Mercury Marine as Vice President, Research & Development," *Messenger*, September/October 2002, Volume 1, Issue 5.
18. Clay Gaillard, "DTS: Experience the Future," *Messenger*, September/October 2003, Volume 2, Issue 4.
19. *Ibid.*
20. "Mercury Marine Developing Alternative Fuel Engines for US Military," *Messenger*, May/June 2003, Volume 2, Issue 3.
21. *Ibid.*
22. "Mercury MerCruiser: The Innovation Continues," Mercury MerCruiser product brochure, Summer 2004.
23. Claus Bruestlé, interview by Jeffrey L. Rodengen, audio recording, 2 November 2007, Write Stuff Enterprises, LLC.
24. "Mercury Marine Introduces New Line of Outboard Engines at Miami Boat Show," *Milwaukee Journal Sentinel*, 13 February 2004.
25. Tim Reid, interview by Jeffrey L. Rodengen, audio recording, 7 September 2007, Write Stuff Enterprises, LLC.
26. "Verado: The Revolution Begins, *Messenger*, April/May 2004, Volume 3, Issue 1.
27. "Latest DuPont Automotive Materials Technology 'Hits the Waves' in Breakthrough Mercury Marine Outboard Engine," press release, 12 March 2004.
28. *Ibid.*
29. Steve Fleming, "Verado Arrives," *Messenger*, April/May 2004, Volume 3, Issue 1.
30. Mitesh B. Sheth and Thomas J. Walczak, "Designing the World's Largest Injection Molded Nylon Part; A Cowling Assembly for a Mercury Marine Large Four-Stroke Outboard Engine," Mercury Marine report.
31. *Ibid.*
32. *Ibid.*

33. *Ibid.*
34. Steve Toloken, "Mercury Marine's Got Top Award 'Covered,'" *Plastics News*, http://www.plasticsnews.com, 5 April, 2004.
35. "X-Sightings," *Messenger*, November/December 2003, Volume 2, Issue 5.
36. *Ibid.*
37. Fred Kiekhaefer, interview by Jeffrey L. Rodengen, audio recording, 7 November 2007, Write Stuff Enterprises, LLC.
38. "X-Sightings," *Messenger*, November/December 2003, Volume 2, Issue 5.
39. Clay Gaillard, "Verado Tops Yamaha 300 HPDI," *Messenger*, June/July 2004, Volume 3, Issue 2.
40. "Mercury Verado Winds IBEX Innovation Award," *Messenger*, April/May 2005, Volume 4, Issue 1.
41. "Verado Named 'Best of the Best,' " *Field & Stream*, April/May 2005, Volume 4, Issue 1.
42. Steve Toloken, "Mercury Marine's Got Top Award 'Covered,'" *Plastics News*, http://www.plasticsnews.com.
43. Caroline Ajootian, "Engine Dumping or Chest Thumping?" *BoatUS: Magazine*, 2 November 2004.
44. "US Commerce Department Imposes 22.52 Percent Duty on Japanese Engine Manufacturers in 'Dumping' Case," *Messenger*, September/October 2004, Volume 3, Issue 3.
45. Brian Tumulty, "Mercury Marine Pleads for Permanent Duties on Japanese Outboards," *Gannett News Service*, 15 December 2004.
46. "Key Messages Regarding DOC's Dumping Decision," Mercury Marine internal document.
47. Renee DuFore Russell, "Mercury Ruling Won't Affect Any Jobs, President Says," *The Reporter*, 4 February 2005.
48. Joe Pomeroy, interview by Jeffrey L. Rodengen, audio recording, 7 September 2007, Write Stuff Enterprises, LLC.
49. Jim Hubbard, interview by Jeffrey L. Rodengen, audio recording, 7 August 2007, Write Stuff Enterprises, LLC.
50. Melanie Winters, "Mercury's Price Claims Stir up a Hornet's Nest," *Sounding Trade Only*, February 2004.
51. "Mercury Responds to Jacobs' Charges," *Boating Industry*, 12 August 2004.
52. Letter from Jack Malone, Mercury VP, Dealer and Retail Sales and Joan Hoagland, Mercury VP, OEM Sales and Marketing, to Mercury Customer/Partner, Re: Anti-Dumping Petition, 18 October 2004.
53. The Associated Press, "Judge Strikes Down Yamaha Price Increase to Mercury Marine," 20 October 2004.
54. Rick Barrett, "Indicators Bode Well for Boats," *Milwaukee Journal Sentinel*, 15 January 2005.
55. Patrick C. Mackey, "From the Helm," *Messenger*, April/May, Volume 4, Issue 1.

Chapter Fifteen Sidebar: An X-traordinary Site

1. "Mercury Announces New X-Site Test Facility," *Messenger*, April/May 2004, Volume 3, Issue 1.
2. *Ibid.*

3. *Ibid.*
4. *Ibid.*
5. Rich Barrett, "Fond du Lac, Wis., Firm Closes Boat Engine Testing Facility in Central Florida," *Milwaukee Journal Sentinel*, 27 March 2004.

Chapter Fifteen Sidebar: A Difference of Opinion

1. Melanie Winters, "Mercury's Price Claims Stir up a Hornet's Nest," *Sounding Trade Only*, February 2004.
2. Letter from Irwin L. Jacobs to All US Boat Manufacturers & Marine Dealers, 12 August 2004.
3. " 'Dumping' by Japanese Engine Makers Found, US Commerce Department Imposes 22.52 Percent Duty," Brunswick internal clip.
4. Melanie Winters, "Mercury's Price Claims Stir up a Hornet's Nest," *Sounding Trade Only*, February 2004.
5. Testimony of Rep. Thomas E. Petri, Submitted to the US International Trade Commission, 14 December 2004.
6. Testimony of Governor Jim Doyle, Submitted to the US International Trade Commission, 14 December 2004.

Chapter Sixteen

1. Patty Brandl, "Union President Blames China Plant for Mercury Layoffs," *The Reporter*, 3 February 2006.
2. *Ibid.*
3. "Execution the Key to 2006 Success," *The Wave*, 2 February 2006, Vol. 2, No. 52.
4. Patty Brandl, "Union President Blames China Plant for Mercury Layoffs," *The Reporter*, 3 February 2006.
5. Pat Mackey, interview by Jeffrey L. Rodengen, recording, 7 September 2007, Write Stuff Enterprises, LLC.
6. *Ibid.*
7. Scott Hoffman, interview by Jeffrey L. Rodengen, audio recording, 7 September 2007, Write Stuff Enterprises, LLC.
8. *Ibid.*
9. "May the Road Rise Up," *Boating Industry*, March 2008.
10. Rick Barrett, "Mercury Marine to Open Plant in China," *Milwaukee Journal Sentinel*, 18 February 2005.
11. "May the Road Rise Up," *Boating Industry*, March 2008.
12. John Pfeifer, interview by Jeffrey L. Rodengen, audio recording, 11 December 2007, Write Stuff Enterprises, LLC.
13. Rick Barrett, "China Offers Open Waters," *Milwaukee Journal Sentinel*, 4 February 2007.
14. "Despite Uncertainty, Mercury Contributes to Strong Brunswick Quarter," *The Wave*, 3 November 2005, Vol. 1, No. 43.
15. Mark Schwabero, interview by Jeffrey L. Rodengen, audio recording, 7 August 2007, Write Stuff Enterprises, LLC.
16. "Brunswick Corp.—Brunswick's 2nd Qtr. Results," Company News Feed, 27 July 2005.
17. "May the Road Rise Up," *Boating Industry*, March 2008.
18. Claus Bruestlé, interview by Jeffrey L. Rodengen, audio recording, 2 November 2007, Write Stuff Enterprises, LLC.
19. Clay Gaillard, "Mercury Verado Family Grows by Three," *Messenger*, April/May 2005.

20. "Mercury Turns up the Heat in Magic City," *Messenger*, Spring 2007.
21. "Mercury Introduces OptiMax 225 Pro XS Outboard," *Messenger*, April/May 2005.
22. "Mercury Launches New OptiMax 250 Pro XS," *Messenger*, August/September 2006.
23. "Mercury Launches Two New Engines in the Fuel-Efficient OptiMax Family," *Messenger*, Summer 2007.
24. Chris Petersen, "Speed on the Water: a Division of Mercury Marine, Mercury Racing Produces Marine Engines Influenced by the Technology of High-Performance Racing Boats," *US Business Review*, 1 July 2006.
25. Jacques Bronchart, interview by Jeffrey L. Rodengen, audio recording, 4 December 2007, Write Stuff Enterprises, LLC.
26. "Brunswick Corp.—Brunswick's 2nd Qtr. Results," Company News Feed, 27 July 2005.
27. "OptiMax on a Roll," *Sunday Times* (Perth, Australia), 21 January 2007.
28. "75 and 90 HP Mercury FourStrokes Go EFI," *Messenger*, April/May 2005.
29. Jim Barron, "BWB Propulsion Test: Middleweight Contender; Mercury's New 115 EFI Four Stroke Packs a Wallop," *Bass & Walleye Boats*, 1 October 2006.
30. "Mercury Turns up the Heat in Magic City," *Messenger*, Spring 2007.
31. "Mercury Marine Launches Revolutionary New Engines; Ranked Highest in Customer Satisfaction Again," *PR Newswire*, 15 February 2007.
32. "Mercury Wire Harnesses Opens for Business," *The Wave*, 20 October 2005, Vol. 1, No. 41.
33. "Field & Stream Names MotorGuide's Wireless Trolling Motors 'Best of the Best,'" *Messenger*, August/September 2006.
34. "MotorGuide's New Saltwater Wireless Motor," *The Wave*, 26 October 2006, Vol. 2, No. 41.
35. "Shadow Technology Is Answered Prayer for Triple-Engine Boaters," *Messenger*, April/May 2005.
36. *Ibid.*
37. Howard Wolinsky, "Making Waves in the Boating Business," *Chicago Sun Times*, 5 July 2006.
38. Jeff Bollier, "Introducing Project Zeus; Watercraft Go High-Tech with Mercury Marine," *Oshkosh Northwestern*, 7 October 2006.
39. Rick Davis, interview by Jeffrey L. Rodengen, audio recording, 7 August 2007, Write Stuff Enterprises, LLC.
40. "Miami Boat Show: A Mercury Showcase," *Messenger*, March/April 2006.
41. "Zeus Wins Motor Boating Magazine's 'Best of the Year' in Advanced Propulsion Category," *Messenger*, Spring 2007.
42. Hei di Garvin, "Honoring the Best in Manufacturing," Corporate Report Wisconsin, April 2006.
43. "Mercury Marine Named Wisconsin Manufacturer of the Year," *Messenger*, March/April 2006.
44. "Mercury Receives Wisconsin's Export Achievement Award," *The Wave*, 11 May 2006, Vol. 2, No. 18.
45. "Mercury Marine Named Wisconsin Manufacturer of the Year," *Messenger*, March/April 2006.
46. "J. D. Power and Associates Reports: PCM, Honda, Mercury and MerCruiser Rank Highest in Marine Engine Customer Satisfaction," *PR Newswire*, 16 February 2006.
47. *Ibid.*
48. "Mercury OptiMax, Mercury MerCruiser Ranked Highest in Customer Satisfaction," *Messenger*, March/April 2006.
49. "Mercury MerCruiser, Mercury OptiMax Again Ranked Highest in Customer Satisfaction by J. D. Power," *Messenger*, Spring 2007.
50. "Mercury OptiMax Ranked Highest In Customer Satisfaction for Third Consecutive Year," *PR Newswire*, 25 February 2008.
51. Jeff Van Asten, "Mercury Remanufacturing Now 'No. 1 on the Road,'" *Messenger*, August/September, 2005.
52. "Dealers Leave Impressed," *The Wave*, 30 June 2005, Vol. 1, No. 25.
53. "Brunswick Shares Dealer Advantage Details," *Boating Industry*, 23 March 2007.
54. "Calling All Customers," *The Wave*, 18 August 2005, Vol. 1, No. 32.
55. *Ibid.*
56. Reinhard Burk, interview by Jeffrey L. Rodengen, audio recording, 7 September 2007, Write Stuff Enterprises, LLC.
57. Mike Gyorog, interview by Jeffrey L. Rodengen, audio recording, 7 August 2007, Write Stuff Enterprises, LLC.
58. Jim Hubbard, interview by Jeffrey L. Rodengen, audio recording, 7 August 2007, Write Stuff Enterprises, LLC.
59. "Brunswick to Purchase N.C. Boat Factory From Oconto Yacht Builder KCS International," *M2 FinancialWire*, 3 July 2007.
60. "Brunswick Acquires Valiant," *The Wave*, 23 June 2005, Vol. 1, No. 24.
61. "Brunswick Buys Harris-Kayot Boat Company," *Milwaukee News Journal*, 16 September 2005.
62. Brunswick Buys Cabo Yachts," *Chicago Tribune*, 17 February 2006.
63. "Brunswick Taps New CEO," *The Reporter*, 8 December 2005.
64. "Dusty McCoy Elected Brunswick Chairman and CEO," *The Wave*, 8 December 2005, Vol. 1, No. 47.
65. "Brunswick Chairman Sets Course for Marine Businesses," *The Wave*, 9 March 2006, Vol. 2, No. 57.
66. Ken Krizner, "Mercury MerCruiser Chooses to Expand in Oklahoma," *Expansion Management*, 1 January 2006.
67. Stephen Cramer, interview by Jeffrey L. Rodengen, audio recording, 7 November 2007, Write Stuff Enterprises, LLC.
68. "Mercury Turns up the Heat in Magic City," *Messenger*, Spring 2007.
69. *Ibid.*
70. "Mercury Marine Launches Revolutionary New Engines; Ranked Highest in Customer Satisfaction Again," *PR Newswire*, 15 February 2007.
71. "Dealer Tips: How to Sell the MerCruiser SeaCore System," *Messenger*, Summer 2007.
72. "MerCruiser's Hot New Products for 2007," *Messenger*, Summer 2007.
73. Reinhard Burk, interview by Jeffrey L. Rodengen, audio recording, 7 September 2007, Write Stuff Enterprises, LLC.
74. "Mercury Axius Claims IBEX Innovation Award," *PR Newswire*, 12 October 2007.
75. Reinhard Burk, interview by Jeffrey L. Rodengen, audio recording, 7 September 2007, Write Stuff Enterprises, LLC.
76. Rick Barrett, "Clearing the Air; Mercury Unveils Prototype Exhaust System That Reduces Carbon Monoxide," *Milwaukee Journal Sentinel*, 20 February 2005.
77. Daniel Cusick, "Air Pollution: Small Engine Rule to Yield 95 Percent Emissions Cut—EPA," *E&E News*, 17 April 2007.

Chapter Sixteen Sidebar: A Racing Tradition

1. "Mercury Wins 24 Hours of Rouen—Powers Top 12 Finishers," *Messenger*, Summer 2007.
2. "Mercury Makes Big Screen Appearance in the Movie *Miami Vice*," *Messenger*, Fall 2006.

Chapter Sixteen Sidebar: Qualified and Capable: Helping Victims of Hurricane Katrina

1. Paul Gores, "Money's Not Only Way to Help, Businesses Find," *Milwaukee Journal Sentinel*, 11 September 2005.
2. "Brunswick Companies Answer Call for Hurricane Assistance," *Messenger*, August/September 2005.
3. "Officials, Agencies Offer Thanks for Hurricane Relief," *Messenger*, March/April 2006.
4. "Brunswick Companies Answer Call for Hurricane Assistance," *Messenger*, August/September 2005.
5. "Mercury Employees, Brunswick Aid Hurricane Relief," *Messenger*, August/September 2005.
6. *Ibid.*

Chapter Sixteen Sidebar: Safety in Numbers

1. "Safety, the Mercury Way," *The Wave*, 17 June 2005, Volume 1, No. 23.
2. "Mercury Creates Health, Safety and Environmental Council," *The Wave*, 8 December 2005, Vol. 1, No. 47.
3. "2005: Milestone Year for Mercury Marine," *The Wave*, 15 December 2005, Vol. 1, No. 48.
4. "Mercury Marine Celebrates 1 Million Accident-Free Hours at FdL's Plant," *The Reporter*, 21 June 2007.
5. "Plant 15 Reaches 2 Million Hours Without a Lost-Time Incident," *The Wave*, 10 November 2005, Vol. 1, No. 44.
6. "Mercury Marine Plant Reaches Safety Milestone," *The Reporter*, 11 March 2007.

Chapter Sixteen Sidebar: Lean Six Sigma: Not Just the Flavor of the Month

1. "May the Road Rise Up," *Boating Industry*, March 2008.
2. "Lean Six Sigma Training & Certification-Overview of Six Sigma," http://www.6sigma.us/six-sigma.php.
3. "Hourly Black Belt Positions Being Filled," *The Wave*, 28 July 2005, Vol. 1, No. 29.
4. "May the Road Rise Up," *Boating Industry*, March 2008.
5. "Mercury Crosses Continuous Improvement Milestone," *Messenger*, Fall 2006.

Chapter Seventeen

1. Allen Buechel, interview by Jeffrey L. Rodengen, audio recording, 13 September 2013, Write Stuff Enterprises, LLC.

2. Marty Bass, interview by Jeffrey L. Rodengen, audio recording, 8 July 2013, Write Stuff Enterprises, LLC.
3. Michael Crowley, "Outboard Update; New Models Introduced at Both Ends of the Power Spectrum," *Workboat*, 1 January 2008.
4. Stephen Cramer, interview by Jeffrey L. Rodengen, audio recording, 7 August 2007, Write Stuff Enterprises, LLC.
5. Charley Flores, interview by Jeffrey L. Rodengen, audio recording, 7 December 2007, Write Stuff Enterprises, LLC.
6. "Overseas Sales Drive Mercury Marine," *Milwaukee Business Journal*, 31 January, 2008.
7. Stephen Cramer, interview by Jeffrey L. Rodengen, audio recording, 7 August 2007, Write Stuff Enterprises, LLC.
8. "May the Road Rise Up," *Boating Industry*, March 2008.
9. John Schmid, "Brunswick Takes a Hit," *Milwaukee Journal Sentinel*, 21 July 2007.
10. Brett Rowland, "Merc Temporarily Shuts Down in Aim to Balance Output," *The Reporter*, 28 February 2008.
11. "Merc Leader Retires," *The Reporter*, 23 January 2008.
12. "Patrick C. Mackey to Retire from Brunswick's Mercury Marine Group," *PR Newswire*, 22 January 2008.
13. "Mercury Marine Execs Take on New Roles," *Milwaukee Business Journal*, 5 March 2008.
14. "May the Road Rise Up," Boating Industry, March 2008.
15. "Brunswick, Mercury Marine 1Q profits drop," *Milwaukee Business Journal*, 24 April 2008.
16. "Boat Brands Cut as Marine Industry Slumps," *The Reporter*, 18 May 2008.
17. "Mercury Marine Union Ratifies Contract," *The Reporter*, 29 June 2009.
18. "Merc Wins Consumer Digest Accolades," *The Reporter*, 27 June 2008.
19. Debbie Blossom, "Boat Sales Sputter; Gas Prices Fueling Slump That May Affect Mercury Marine," *The Oklahoman*, 9 July 2008.
20. Rick Barrett, "Marine Engine Sales Power Down: Downturn in Boating Industry Stalls Area Outboard Motor Manufacturers," *Milwaukee Journal Sentinel*, 21 September 2008.
21. "Brunswick, Mercury Marine Post Losses," *Milwaukee Business Journal*, 23 October 2008.
22. "New President Named for Mercury Marine," *The Reporter*, 7 November 2008.
23. Stephan Cloutier, interview by Jeffrey L. Rodengen, audio recording, 8 July 2013, Write Stuff Enterprises, LLC.
24. David Foulkes, interview by Jeffrey L. Rodengen, audio recording, 9 July 2013, Write Stuff Enterprises, LLC.
25. Ray Atchinson, interview by Jeffrey L. Rodengen, audio recording, 9 July 2013, Write Stuff Enterprises, LLC.
26. "More Layoffs Coming," *The Reporter*, 11 December 2008.
27. "Brunswick Reports 4Q Earnings Loss," *Milwaukee Business Journal*, 29 January 2009.
28. "Mercury Marine Confirms Job Losses," *The Reporter*, 15 February 2009.
29. "Mercury Marine Losses Continue," *The Reporter*, 1 May 2009.

30. Rick Barrett, "Brunswick Plan Covers Boat Payments If Job Lost," *Milwaukee Journal Sentinel*, 2 June 2009.
31. "Mercury Marine Sales Plunge 43 Percent," *Milwaukee Business Journal*, 30 July 2009.
32. "Low Demand for Products Cited by Merc Parent Company for 52% Sales Drop," *The Reporter*, 1 August 2009.
33. *Ibid.*
34. Mark Biznek, interview by Jeffrey L. Rodengen, audio recording, 9 July 2013, Write Stuff Enterprises, LLC.
35. Ray Atchinson, interview by Jeffrey L. Rodengen, audio recording, 9 July 2013, Write Stuff Enterprises, LLC.
36. Colleen Kottke and Sharon Roznik, "Mercury Accepts 'Yes' Vote on Contract Proposal," The Reporter, September 6, 2009.
37. Wayne Rollin, interview by Jeffrey L. Rodengen, audio recording, 13 September 2013, Write Stuff Enterprises, LLC.
38. Tom Herre, interview by Jeffrey L. Rodengen, audio recording, 13 September 2013, Write Stuff Enterprises, LLC.
39. Colleen Kottke and Sharon Roznik, "Mercury Accepts 'Yes' Vote on Contract Proposal," *The Reporter*, 6 September 2009.
40. Ray Atchinson, interview by Jeffrey L. Rodengen, audio recording, 9 July 2013, Write Stuff Enterprises, LLC.
41. Rick Barrett, "Petition Seeks 2nd Mercury Vote: Union Officials Say Revote Isn't Planned," *Milwaukee Journal Sentinel*, 28 August 2009.
42. *Ibid.*
43. *Ibid.*
44. *Ibid.*
45. Colleen Kottke and Michael Mentzer, "Mercury Marine, Union 'Talking' Again," *Green Bay Press-Gazette*, 1 September 2009.
46. Rick Barrett, "New Vote at Mercury Marine: Employees Will Take 3rd Ballot on Contract Concessions This Week," *Milwaukee Journal Sentinel*, 2 September 2009.
47. *Ibid.*
48. "Machinists Ink Seven-Year Deal With Mercury Marine," *PR Newswire*, 4 September 2009.
49. Rick Barrett, Mercury Workers Accept Concessions: Union Vote Keeps Jobs in Fond du Lac and Might Bring More," *Milwaukee Journal Sentinel*, 5 September 2009.
50. Colleen Kottke and Sharon Roznik, "Mercury Accepts 'Yes' Vote on Contract Proposal," *The Reporter*, 6 September 2009.
51. Steve Cramer, interview by Jeffrey L. Rodengen, audio recording, 8 July 2013, Write Stuff Enterprises, LLC.
52. Rick Barrett, Mercury Workers Accept Concessions: Union Vote Keeps Jobs in Fond du Lac and Might Bring More," *Milwaukee Journal Sentinel*, 5 September 2009.
53. *Ibid.*
54. Barry Adams, "Manufacturing Job Losses Cast Gloom On Labor Day," *Wisconsin State Journal*, 7 September 2009.
55. "Mercury Marine Incentive Package Explained," *The Reporter*, 9 September 2009.
56. Allen Buechel, interview by Jeffrey L. Rodengen, audio recording, 13 September 2013, Write Stuff Enterprises, LLC.
57. "Mercury Marine Loses $13.4 Million," *Milwaukee Business Journal*, 29 October 2009.

58. "Mercury Marine offered big incentive package," *Green Bay Press-Gazette*, 9 September 2009.
59. Sharon Roznik, "State Backs Mercury," *The Reporter*, 8 November 2009.
60. Rick Barrett, "Mercury Marine Parent Says It Will Build More Boats: Brunswick seeks to Replenish Inventories," *Milwaukee Journal Sentinel*, 30 October 2009.
61. Mark Rothfield, "Sunnier Outlook on Sales; On the Water With Mark Rothfield and Simon Walker," *Newcastle Herald*, 11 September 2009.
62. *Ibid.*
63. Heather Stanek, "Local Enterprises Look Forward to Merc's Future," *The Reporter*, 15 September 2009.
64. *Ibid.*
65. Mark Schwabero, interview by Jeffrey L. Rodengen, audio recording, 9 July 2013, Write Stuff Enterprises, LLC.
66. Steve Cramer, interview by Jeffrey L. Rodengen, audio recording, 8 July 2013, Write Stuff Enterprises, LLC.
67. Marty Bass, interview by Jeffrey L. Rodengen, audio recording, 8 July 2013, Write Stuff Enterprises, LLC.
68. Jeff Stueven, interview by Jeffrey L. Rodengen, audio recording, 9 July 2013, Write Stuff Enterprises, LLC.

Chapter Seventeen Sidebar: Stillwater: Still Standing

1. Silas Allen, "Stillwater Tech Center Provides Training for Mercury Marine Employees," *Stillwater NewsPress*, 5 September 2011.
2. Ray Atchinson, interview by Jeffrey L. Rodengen, audio recording, 9 July 2013, Write Stuff Enterprises, LLC.
3. Denise Devereaux, interview by Jeffrey L. Rodengen, audio recording, 8 July 2013, Write Stuff Enterprises, LLC.
4. "International Aerospace Company to Open Production Facility In Stillwater; Creates More Than 500 Jobs," *States News Service*, 11 July 2012.

Chapter Seventeen Sidebar: Aftermath

1. Condensed Consolidated Financial Statement, Brunswick archives.
2. Steve Cramer, interview by Jeffrey L. Rodengen, audio recording, 8 July 2013, Write Stuff Enterprises, LLC.
3. "Dealer Count," company archives, PowerPoint presentation.
4. "Mercury Customer Fountain Files Chapter 1," *Milwaukee Business Journal*, 25 August 2009.
5. Melanie Winters, "The Slimming Down of the Boat Business," *Soundings Trade Only*, July 2009.

Chapter Eighteen

1. "Mercury Marine Honored During State Senate Adjournment," *Boating Industry*, 30 January 2014.
2. Laurie Ritger, "Merc Marine Continues Consolidation," *Oshkosh Northwestern*, 11 January 2010.
3. Laurie Ritger, "Mercury Chief Shares Strategy in Downturn," *The Reporter*, 30 April 2010.
4. "Mercury Plans to Hire 150," *The Reporter*, 5 April 2011.

5. "Mercury Marine Job Fair Draws Hundreds," *The Reporter*, 23 July 2010.
6. "Results Show Mercury and Brunswick Doing Better," *The Reporter*, 29 October 2010.
7. "Governor Doyle Announces Mercury Marine to Bring 200 New Jobs to Fond du Lac," *Targeted News Service*, 17 August 2010.
8. "Move of MerCruiser Assembly Operations to FdL Could Bring 200 Jobs," *The Reporter*, 17 August 2010.
9. "Results Show Mercury and Brunswick Doing Better," *The Reporter*, 29 October 2010.
10. "FLW Outdoors and Mercury Marine Announce Major Partnership; MotorGuide, Brunswick Zone Complement Sponsorship Package," *PR Newswire*, 20 October 2010.
11. "Mercury Marine Sales Up 17%; Losses Down," *Milwaukee Business Journal*, 27 January 2011.
12. "Marine Market Helps Mercury, Brunswick," *Milwaukee Business Journal*, 28 April 2011.
13. Heather Stanek, "Sales Up at Mercury Marine," O*shkosh Northwestern*, 30 April 2011.
14. "Mercury Adding 150 Jobs," *The Reporter*, 13 July 2011.
15. Rick Barrett, "Mercury's Business Picks Up: Engine-Maker Sets Job Fair, Will Hire Another 150 Workers," *Milwaukee Journal Sentinel*, 13 July 2011.
16. Bruce Buls, "ACB Awarded $38 Million Coast Guard Contract; On The Ways; Aluminum Chambered Boats," *Workboat* 67, No. 7 (July 2010).
17. "New Hampshire Issues Solicitation for Mercury Marine Engines," *Targeted News Service*, 7 February 2011.
18. "Military Transom Assemblies Sought by Defense Department," *Targeted News Service*, 17 August 2011.
19. "Contract Notice: Department of Homeland Security (Maryland) Issues Solicitation for Mercury Marine Verado Outboard Engines," *US Fed News*, 1 September 2011.
20. "Military Outboard Engine Parts Sought by U.S. Navy," *Targeted News Service*, 13 September 2011.
21. "Contract Awards: Alabama Department of Finance Awards Solicitation for Boat Motor Parts to Mercury Marine–Div of Brunswick," *US Fed News*, 6 December 2011.
22. Sam Hudson, "Mercury 150 Pro XS; The Latest in Boats & Power," *Florida Sportsman* 42, No. 4 (April 2010).
23. "Every 2010 BASS Elite Winner Has Been Powered by Mercury Pro XS," *The Reporter*, 22 June 2010.
24. "Fishing Team Dominates," *The Reporter*, 5 August 2010.
25. "Merc Wins Three Readers Choice Awards," *The Reporter*, 2 August 2010.
26. Scott Coghlan, "Verado 250 Pro Is a Winner for Mercury," *The Sunday Times*, 16 January 2011.
27. "Robust Upgrade," *CARSguide*, 19 March 2011.
28. "Comfort and Compactness in Engine Revamp," *The New Zealand Herald*, 9 July 2011.
29. Jeff Stueven, interview by Jeffrey L. Rodengen, audio recording, 9 July 2013, Write Stuff Enterprises, LLC.

30. Steve Cramer, interview by Jeffrey L. Rodengen, audio recording, 8 July 2013, Write Stuff Enterprises, LLC.
31. "Merc Wins 'Green' Award," *The Reporter*, 26 February 2010.
32. *Ibid.*
33. "Gov. Doyle Awards $1.7 Million to Six Manufacturers to Invest in Energy Efficiency," *US State News*, 11 March 2010.
34. *Ibid.*
35. Peter A. Janssen, "The Green Revolution," *Motor Boating* 203, No. 4 (April 2010).
36. *Ibid.*
37. *Ibid.*
38. "Mercury 150 FourStroke Wins at IBEX," *ENP Newswire*, 21 October 2011.
39. Laurie Ritger, "Mercury Marine Starting to Repay $50 Million Loan," *The Reporter*, 8 January 2013.
40. Tim Reid, interview by Jeffrey L. Rodengen, audio recording, 9 July 2013, Write Stuff Enterprises, LLC.
41. *Ibid.*
42. Randy Poirier, interview by Jeffrey L. Rodengen, audio recording, 4 October 2013, Write Stuff Enterprises, LLC.
43. "Mercury 150 FourStroke Wins at IBEX," *ENP Newswire*, 21 October 2011.
44. "New Mercury 150 FourStroke Wins International Award," *The Reporter*, 22 October 2011.
45. John Pfiefer, interview by Jeffrey L. Rodengen, audio recording, 9 July 2013, Write Stuff Enterprises, LLC.
46. "Mercury 150 FourStroke Wins at IBEX," *ENP Newswire*, 21 October 2011.
47. Gary Smet, interview by Jeffrey L. Rodengen, audio recording, 8 July 2013, Write Stuff Enterprises, LLC.
48. Ben Duke, interview by Jeffrey L. Rodengen, audio recording, 9 July 2013, Write Stuff Enterprises, LLC.
49. Kevin Grodski, interview by Jeffrey L. Rodengen, audio recording, 13 September 2013, Write Stuff Enterprises, LLC.
50. "Consolidation Continues at FdL's Mercury Marine," *The Reporter*, 23 January 2010.
51. "Mercury Marine Expands Fond du Lac Plant," *The Reporter*, 11 November 2010.
52. Laurie Ritger, "Mercury Marine Set to Leave Oklahoma," *The Reporter*, 2 December 2011.
53. Laurie Ritger, "Mercury Marine Set to Leave Oklahoma," *The Reporter*, 2 December 2011.
54. John P. McDermott, "Boating Partnership to Break Up; Cummins, Mercury Changing Course," *The Post and Courier*, 6 December 2011.
55. *Ibid.*
56. "Cummins and Mercury Marine to Transit From CMD joint venture," *Datamonitor NewsWire*, 2 December 2011.
57. Laurie Ritger, "1,200 Hourly Mercury Marine Employees Will Get Bonus," *The Reporter*, 17 December 2011.
58. *Ibid.*
59. *Ibid.*
60. Laurie Ritger, "Mercury Marine Workers Receive Bonuses," *The Reporter*, 25 February 2012.
61. Rick Barrett, "Mercury Marine Pays Out Bonuses; Workers Rewarded After a Trying, Profitable Year," *Milwaukee Journal Sentinel*, 15 December 2011.

62. Tom Schuessler, interview by Jeffrey L. Rodengen, audio recording, 2 October 2013, Write Stuff Enterprises, LLC.
63. Chris Drees, interview by Jeffrey L. Rodengen, audio recording, 16 September 2013, Write Stuff Enterprises, LLC.
64. Laurie Ritger, "Mercury Marine Workers Receive Bonuses," *The Reporter*, 25 February 2012.
65. Heather Stanek, "Merc Engines Help in Oil Spill Cleanup," *The Reporter*, 7 July 2010.
66. "Mercury Marine Unveils the Spitfire Aluminum Propeller," *ENP Newswire*, 9 August 2011.
67. "Propeller Alert Prevents Injury," *The Sunday Times*, 8 April 2012.
68. "Mercury Adds Propellers to Popular Enertia, Revolution 4 Lineups," *ENP Newswire*, 31 October 2012.
69. "Mercury Marine Unveils New Line of Bravo Three Propellers for Diesel Engine," *ENP Newswire*, 5 February 2013.
70. "Quicksilver Launches Consumer Website," *M2 PressWIRE*, 18 July 2012.
71. "Mercury Marine Unveils Two New Vesselview Engine Displays," *ENP Newswire*, 14 February 2013.
72. "Mercury Marine to Introduce Joystick Piloting for Outboards," *ENP Newswire*, 14 February 2013
73. Mike Gyorog, interview by Jeffrey L. Rodengen, audio recording, 8 July 2013, Write Stuff Enterprises, LLC.
74. *Ibid.*
75. *Ibid.*
76. "Sales, Profits Increase at Mercury Marine," *Milwaukee Business Journal*, 27 July 2012.
77. "Mercury Marine Wins Three Consumer Digest 'Best Buy' Accolades," *ENP Newswire*, 25 June 2012.
78. "Mercury Marine Earns Three Customer Satisfaction Index Awards From NMMA," *M2 PressWIRE*, 13 September 2012.
79. Laurie Ritger, "$20 Million Expansion Under Way at Mercury Marine," *The Reporter*, August 28, 2012.
80. Laurie Ritger, "Ceremony Celebrates Mercury Marine $20 Million Expansion," *The Reporter*, 30 September 2012.
81. Jeff Engel, "Mercury Marine 3Q Profits Up on Higher Sales," *Milwaukee Business Journal*, October 25, 2012.
82. "Mercury Set to Hire 170," *The Reporter*, 13 November 2012.
83. Rick Barrett, "Mercury Marine Starts Expansion: Fond du Lac Project Should Be Finished in 2013," *Milwaukee Journal Sentinel*, August 28, 2012.
84. Rick Barrett, "A Workweek Fits Into a Weekend: New Mercury Marine Shift— 3 12-Hour Nights," *Milwaukee Journal Sentinel*, 14 November 2012.
85. "Mercury Marine Posts Growth in Sales, Earnings," *Milwaukee Business Journal*, 24 January 2013.
86. Rick Barrett, "Mercury Marine Head Says Work Is Revving Up: Q&A President Talks Jobs, Industry," *Milwaukee Journal Sentinel*, 7 May 2013.
87. "Mercury Marine to Hire 80 New Workers," *The Reporter*, 22 February 2013.
88. "Mercury Marine Reports Strong Gains," *The Reporter*, 27 January 2013.
89. "Fred Kiekhaefer will leave Mercury Marine," *The Reporter*, 6 December 2012.

90. Fred Kiekhaefer, interview by Jeffrey L. Rodengen, audio recording, 27 September 2013, Write Stuff Enterprises, LLC.

91. "Fred Kiekhaefer will leave Mercury Marine," *The Reporter*, 6 December 2012.

92. Erik Christiansen, interview by Jeffrey L. Rodengen, audio recording, 9 July 2013, Write Stuff Enterprises, LLC.

93. Laurie Ritger, "Mercury Invests $20M in Fond du Lac Plants," *The Reporter*, 11 July 2013.

94. Gart Smet, interview by Jeffrey L. Rodengen, audio recording, 9 July 2013, Write Stuff Enterprises, LLC.

95. Laurie Ritger, "Mercury Invests $20M in Fond du Lac Plants," *The Reporter*, 11 July 2013.

96. "Mercury Racing 520; High-Performance Sterndrive for the Masses," *M2 PressWIRE*, 23 August 2013.

97. "Mercury introduces Enertia ECO fuel-saving propeller," *ENP Newswire*, 19 September 2013.

98. *Ibid.*

99. Rick Barrett, "Mercury Marine Plans $30 Million Expansion," *Milwaukee Journal Sentinel*, 6 November 2013.

100. 2013 "Wisconsin Manufacturer of the Year" application, Mercury Marine archives.

101. "Brunswick Reports Fourth Quarter and Full-Year Results," Brunswick news release, 30 January 2014.

102. "Mercury Marine Earns 'Green Master' Honors for Third Year," *ENP Newswire*, 20 November 2013.

103. *Ibid.*

104. Kevin Grodzki, interview by Jeffrey L. Rodengen, audio recording, 30 September 2013, Write Stuff Enterprises, LLC.

105. Mark Schwabero, "Mercury Marine celebrates 75th anniversary," company press release, 20 January 2014.

106. *Appleton Post Crescent*, online, "Mercury Marine opens museum celebrating company's history," Sharon Hanuszczak-Froberg, 3 April 2014.

107. Mercury Marine, online, "Lake X marks the spot," Mercury Marine, accessed April 5, 2014.

108. *Appleton Post Crescent*, online, "Mercury Marine opens museum celebrating company's history," Sharon Hanuszczak-Froberg, 3 April 2014.

109. *Ibid.*

110. Rick Barrett, "Mercury Marine Plans $30 Million Expansion," *Milwaukee Journal Sentinel*, 6 November 2013.

111. *Ibid.*

112. Gary Smet, interview by Jeffrey L. Rodengen, audio recording, 8 July 2013, Write Stuff Enterprises, LLC.

113. Chris Landry, "Mercury and Volvo Discuss the Future of Sterndrive Propulsion," *Soundings Trade Only* website, http://www.tradeonlytoday.com/2013/11/video-mercury-volvo-talk-sterndrive-propulsion/.

114. Randy Poirier, interview by Jeffrey L. Rodengen, audio recording, 4 October 2013, Write Stuff Enterprises, LLC.

115. John Pfiefer, interview by Jeffrey L. Rodengen, audio recording, 9 July 2013, Write Stuff Enterprises, LLC.

116. Georges Jalbert, interview by Jeffrey L. Rodengen, audio recording, 13 September 2013, Write Stuff Enterprises, LLC.

117. Stuart Halley, audio interview by Jeffrey L. Rodengen, recording, 9 July 2013, Write Stuff Enterprises, LLC.

118. Tim Reid, interview by Jeffrey L. Rodengen, audio recording, 9 July 2013, Write Stuff Enterprises, LLC.

119. Denise Devereaux, interview by Jeffrey L. Rodengen, audio recording, 8 July 2013, Write Stuff Enterprises, LLC.

120. *Milwaukee Journal Sentinel*, online, "Consumers Return to Buying New Rather Than Used," Rick Barrett, 7 June 2014.

121. *Ibid.*

122. *Ibid.*

Chapter Eighteen Sidebar:
A New Deal: Taking Care of Dealers

1. "Dealer Count," company archives, PowerPoint presentation.

2. Randy Caruana, interview by Jeffrey L. Rodengen, audio recording, 8 July 2013, Write Stuff Enterprises, LLC.

3. "Brunswick Expands Dealer-Advantage Program," *Soundings Trade Only* website, http://www.tradeonlytoday.com/2011/07/brunswick-expands-dealer-advantage-program/.

4. "Mercury Dealers Top the Boating Industry 'Top 100'," Mercury Marine press release, 26 December 2013.

Chapter Eighteen Sidebar:
Fond du Lac: Paying Back, Giving Back

1. Laurie Ritger, "Mercury Marine Starting to Repay $50 Million Loan," *The Reporter*, 8 January 2013.

2. "Merc Wins 'Green' Award," *The Reporter*, 26 February 2010.

3. "Mercury Marine and STEM School Share Partnership," *The Reporter*, 9 September 2012.

4. *Ibid.*

5. 2013 "Wisconsin Manufacturer of the Year" application, Mercury Marine archives.

Chapter Eighteen Sidebar:
Safety: Always First

1. "Mercury Racing Receives Brunswick Safety Award," *The Reporter*, 6 November 2012.

2. "Brunswick Corporation: Brunswick Facilities Worldwide Achieve Safety Recognition," Comtex News Network, Inc., 14 March 2013.

3. "Merc Workers Honored for Safety," *The Reporter*, 23 April 2010.

4. "Director of Safety at Mercury Marine Receives Safety Award," *Targeted News Service*, 7 March 2013.

5. 2013 "Wisconsin Manufacturer of the Year" application, Mercury Marine archives.

Chapter Eighteen Sidebar:
Helping Our Vets

1. "Mercury Marine and U.S. Army Partner in Recruiting Program," M2 PressWIRE, 6 September 2013.

2. *Ibid.*

Chapter Eighteen Sidebar:
The International Market

1. William Gress, interview by Jeffrey L. Rodengen, audio recording, 15 October 2013, Write Stuff Enterprises, LLC.

2. John Temple, interview by Jeffrey L. Rodengen, audio recording, 16 September 2013, Write Stuff Enterprises, LLC.

3. Georges Jalbert, interview by Jeffrey L. Rodengen, audio recording, 13 September 2013, Write Stuff Enterprises, LLC.

4. Ray Atchinson, interview by Jeffrey L. Rodengen, audio recording, 9 July 2013, Write Stuff Enterprises, LLC.

5. *Ibid.*

6. John Pfeifer, interview by Jeffrey L. Rodengen, audio recording, 9 July 2013, Write Stuff Enterprises, LLC.

7. Bill McEarthron, interview by Jeffrey L. Rodengen, audio recording, 15 August 2013, Write Stuff Enterprises, LLC.

8. William Gress, interview by Jeffrey L. Rodengen, audio recording, 15 October 2013, Write Stuff Enterprises, LLC.

9. John Pfeifer, interview by Jeffrey L. Rodengen, audio recording, 9 July 2013, Write Stuff Enterprises, LLC.

10. William Gress, interview by Jeffrey L. Rodengen, audio recording, 15 October 2013, Write Stuff Enterprises, LLC.

INDEX

Page numbers in italics indicate photographs.